BRITISH FLOWERING PLANTS
EVOLUTION AND CLASSIFICATION

J.H.

BRITISH FLOWERING PLANTS

Evolution and Classification of Families and
Genera, with Notes on their Distribution

by

JOHN HUTCHINSON

LL.D., F.R.S., F.L.S., V.M.H.
Keeper of Museums of Botany, Royal
Botanic Gardens, Kew

With 174 black and white illustrations and 22 colour plates by the author

and an account of the GRAMINEAE by
C. E. HUBBARD, F.L.S.

P. R. GAWTHORN LTD.
55 RUSSELL SQUARE
LONDON, W.C.1
1948

First Published 1948

PRINTED IN GREAT BRITAIN BY RICHARD CLAY AND COMPANY, LTD
BUNGAY, SUFFOLK.

PREFACE

TOWARDS the end of the third year of the Second World War, when I had nearly finished preparing the MS. and drawings for the present book, a visit was paid to one of the largest second-hand bookshops in London, which usually stocks a goodly supply of botanical works. By that time the study of pure botany was naturally at a low ebb, and there was an accumulation of second-hand copies, new editions, and reprints of standard works on the subject. At first sight it seemed unlikely that there would be room for yet another, though this impression soon passed away when they were searched through in vain for even a short chapter on the *phylogeny* and *classification* of flowering plants, with which this book deals. Except for my own two volumes, *The Families of Flowering Plants*, the subject seemed to have been scarcely brought to the notice of British students.

The absence of such a work is perhaps readily understood. Phylogeny cannot be studied very adequately except in a large herbarium of dried plants from all parts of the world, and with the aid of a comprehensive library, such as those at Kew and the British Museum (Natural History). And at Kew there is the additional advantage of the living collections. The subject, therefore, is not one likely to be taken up by the average British botanist or University professor, who has not such facilities constantly at hand. It is true that my detailed knowledge of our native plants was not, to begin with, very great, though since increased,[1] but, then, " What do they know of England who only England know " is also true of the British flora !

Phylogeny, like other branches of botany, can never become static, because every new flower dissected, every fresh anatomical section cut, may either modify, or even cancel, conclusions previously arrived at. So it has been, at any rate in my own studies. Much water has flowed under Kew Bridge since I published my new system of classification in 1926 (Dicotyledons) and 1934

[1] See Hutchinson, *Common Wild Flowers* (Penguin Book Co., Ltd., 1945).

(Monocotyledons), and now in this small book on the British flora some important modifications are introduced. These are, especially, the amalgamation of the *Archichlamydeae* (*Polypetalae* + *Apetalae*) and the *Metachlamydeae* (*Gamopetalae* or *Sympetalae*), the complete separation of the *Lignosae* from the *Herbaceae* in the linear sequence, and some improvements (I trust) in the arrangement of certain families in these groups.

The separation on broad lines of the *Trees and Shrubs* from the *Herbs* may at first seem a crude procedure, indeed almost harking back to Biblical times, when plants were referred to in this way. And I am fully aware that I cannot hope to carry all botanists with me in this, though I do claim that the resulting classification is no less natural than any existing, and that related families formerly widely separated are brought much nearer together.

Some of the line drawings have been taken from my *Families of Flowering Plants* (1926, 1934) and Pelican book of *Common Wild Flowers* (1945); the remainder are new and original. For the coloured illustrations, however, I have here and there made use of the lovely plates by S. Rivier in H. Correvon's *Fleurs des Champs et des Bois des Haies et des Murs* (Geneva, 1911).

I have again had the good fortune to obtain the collaboration of my colleague, Mr. C. E. Hubbard, F.L.S., who has provided a very valuable and original account of the *Gramineae*, including the drawings showing structural details. I am also indebted to Mr. V. S. Summerhayes, B.Sc., for helping me with the key to the genera of *Orchidaceae* and notes on the phylogeny of the British members of that family, and to Dr. C. R. Metcalfe for checking the anatomical notes wherever they occur. Dr. George Taylor, British Museum (Natural History), has very kindly read the proofs.

One reviewer said of my first volume of *The Families of Flowering Plants* that, like the curate, I had made my meaning very clear. I hope the same may be said of the present work.

Hanover House, Kew, 1947.

CONTENTS

COLOURED ILLUSTRATIONS

Frontispiece

INTRODUCTION

In nearly every general handbook of the British flora, the families of Angiospermous flowering plants are classified under headings such as *Dicotyledones* and *Monocotyledones*, *Polypetalae*, *Gamopetalae*, and *Apetalae* (*Monochlamydeae*), with the *Polypetalae* subdivided into *Thalamiflorae*, *Disciflorae*, and *Calyciflorae*. The names of these groups are self-evident, though it may be convenient to explain them for the benefit of some readers. *Dicotyledones* embrace all those plants with two seed-leaves and the vascular bundles arranged in a circle, *Monocotyledones* those with only one seed-leaf and closed, scattered, vascular bundles. *Polypetalae* contained those Dicotyledonous families with separate petals, *Gamopetalae* those with the petals more or less united, and *Apetalae* (or *Monochlamydeae*) those without petals. *Thalamiflorae* included the families with a hypogynous type of flower—i.e., the sepals, petals, and stamens inserted below the gynoecium, and with no disk—*Disciflorae* those with a disk, and *Calyciflorae* those with perigynous or epigynous flowers—i.e., with the sepals, petals, and stamens inserted around or above the gynoecium respectively. With reference to the British flora, the characters mentioned are fairly constant for these groups, though the student encounters many exceptions when he becomes acquainted with the flora of other parts of the world.

These groups were used as the basis of classification in Bentham's *British Flora*, Hooker's *Students' Flora*, and in Bentham and Hooker's classical *Genera Plantarum* (*Genera of Plants*). They were acquired by them from the De Candolle system published in their great *Prodromus* (1824–1873), which in turn adopted some from the system of Jussieu, published in 1789. Jussieu's system was about the first to associate plants into families (at first called " natural orders ") more or less as we know

1

them to-day, and it replaced the artificial system of Linnaeus, which held the field during the second half of the eighteenth century.

Subsequently, however, many continental Floras followed the German system of Engler and Prantl, which appeared in their great work *Die natürliche Pflanzenfamilien*, published from 1887 to 1909. In this system the Flowering Plants are arranged quite differently. The *Monocotyledones* are given first place (after the *Gymnospermae*),[1] and the *Dicotyledones* are subdivided primarily into two main groups only—the *Archichlamydeae* and the *Metachlamydeae*. Here, it will be noted, Greek terms are employed instead of Latin, the *Archichlamydeae* embracing both the *Polypetalae* and the *Apetalae* of the Bentham and Hooker system, *Metachlamydeae* being just another name for the *Gamopetalae* (sometimes also called *Sympetalae*). Engler and Prantl's system was based on the earlier German system of Eichler, of which there have been several other modifications, such as that of Wettstein (1901–1908).

In the Englerian system plants without petals, such as the genus *Betula* and other catkin-bearers, were usually regarded as representing a more primitive type than those with well-developed petals, like Magnolias and Buttercups.

In 1913, about a year before the outbreak of the First World War, a small book was published in this country entitled *Genera of British Plants*,[2] arranged according to Engler's system as elaborated in his *Syllabus der Pflanzenfamilien*. In the preface it was stated :—

"What is known as Engler's System of the Classification of Plants embodied in the *Natürliche Pflanzenfamilien* and in the successive editions of the *Syllabus der Pflanzenfamilien*, in the opinion of many modern systematic botanists, represents, as a whole,

[1] The *Gymnospermae* (*Pinaceae*, *Taxaceae*, etc.) are not regarded as true flowering plants, only the *Angiospermae* being discussed here.
[2] H. G. Carter, *Genera of British Plants*, Cambridge University Press, 1913.

the nearest approach to a natural system that we possess."

Who the modern systematic botanists were, was not stated. Indeed, there were few, at least in Britain, or even outside Britain, who had the requisite knowledge of the whole world of plants, and of flowering plants in particular, to express such an opinion with any degree of authority. Lindley lived too early, Bentham had gone many years before, and Hooker had just passed away— all widely experienced taxonomists whose views on the subject would have carried great weight. The opinions of botanists living at the time, such as Dr. Otto Stapf and Dr. N. E. Brown of Kew, and Mr. Spencer Moore of the British Museum, would have been important, for they knew plants as few will probably ever do again. So far as I am aware—and I was intimately acquainted with them all— they never said anything so sweeping about the Engler system. Hooker [1] once remarked about it, however, that it was neither better nor worse in the abstract than De Candolle's (so called), and that it was far more troublesome to apply for practical purposes.

Indeed, even students with very little knowledge of botany may wonder why, in the Englerian system, a Saxifrage or a Stonecrop should be placed in the same order (*Rosales*) as a Cherry or an Apple, what there is in common between a *Geranium* and a *Euphorbia*, why the Touch-me-not (*Impatiens*) should rub shoulders with the Horse Chestnut, and, finally, why the Cucumber family (*Cucurbitaceae*) should be classed in the *Sympetalae* next to the group containing the *Compositae*.

As may be inferred, the author of the present book does not share this eulogy of the Engler system, because his own studies [2] of the flora of a considerable part of the world have led him to agree with the opinions of Hallier, Bessey, Arber, and Parkin, and others, that the earliest Flowering Plants were furnished with quite large and

---

[1] See L. Huxley, *Life and Letters of Sir Joseph D. Hooker*, 2 : 22.
[2] See Hutchinson, *The Families of Flowering Plants*, I (1926); II (1934) (Macmillan and Co., London).

conspicuous sepals and petals, and that the absence of these organs from certain families is due to reduction, because other associated features are clearly not primitive. Students who wish to do so, however, may follow up this subject by reading the papers of the botanists just mentioned, whose principal works are set out below.[1]

Jussieu's system, as elaborated by De Candolle and by Bentham and Hooker, was somewhat artificial, because it sometimes widely separated families which are really closely related, particularly through undue stress being laid on the presence or absence of petals. This was largely remedied by Engler and Prantl, who amalgamated the *Polypetalae* and *Apetalae* into one group—the *Archichlamydeae*—and arranged them on a phylogenetic basis, founded, as already noted, on the assumption that in Flowering Plants the absence of a perianth indicated greater antiquity than its presence.

The writer of the present book, after several years' special study of the subject, took up the crusade against the Engler system in his *Families of Flowering Plants*, the volume on Dicotyledons being published in 1926, and that on the Monocotyledons eight years later. In contrast with Engler and Prantl, the *Dicotyledones* were placed before *Monocotyledones*, and began, not with achlamydeous or apetalous groups, but with petaliferous families such as *Magnoliaceae* and *Ranunculaceae*, these being regarded as representing the most primitive living examples of true Flowering Plants. Most British local floras have continued to follow the older system of De Candolle as modified by Bentham and Hooker. This is fortunate, because it would have been regrettable if a system had been blindly adopted which is based on principles probably not in accordance with what may have taken place during the course of evolution.

Engler's system is built up on the assumption that the

[1] H. Hallier, " Provisional Scheme of the Natural (Phylogenetic) System of Flowering Plants," *New Phytologist*, 4 (1905), and other papers. C. E. Bessey, " Phylogenetic Taxonomy ", *Ann. Missouri Botanic Garden*, 2 : 112 (1915). Arber and Parkin, " The Origin of Angiosperms ", *Journ. Linn. Soc. Bot.*, 38 : 29–80 (1907).

perianth (of calyx and corolla, but especially corolla) was not present in the earliest flowering plants, and that, as Arber and Parkin said, it has been evolved *de novo* and is an organ *sui generis*. Accordingly, to put the matter simply, Engler began with Monocotyledons and ended with Dicotyledons; in the Monocotyledons he placed first those families without a perianth, such as *Typhaceae* and *Sparganiaceae*; these are followed by *Alismatales*, then the Grasses and Aroids, and finally the petaloid families such as *Liliaceae* and *Orchidaceae*. No one will quarrel with the position of the last-mentioned family.

In the Dicotyledons the same principle is followed. Those families without a calyx or corolla, or with neither, take precedence, such as the Willows, the Oaks and the Nettles, gradually leading up to families with petals. As soon as the petaliferous families are reached, however, the system does not differ very much from that of De Candolle + Bentham and Hooker, though students may wonder why *Crassulaceae* (*Sedum*) and *Platanaceae* (Plane Tree) should be associated in the same group (Reihe).

Nearly all systematists are agreed that such families as *Umbelliferae*, *Compositae*, *Asclepiadaceae*, and *Labiatae*, amongst the *Dicotyledones*, are very highly evolved, though opinions have differed regarding the position of the grasses, but not with respect to orchids, in the *Monocotyledones*.

Perhaps at this stage it may be as well to state the reason for regarding certain groups as being the most ancient living Angiosperms. It is based on the theory that the various parts of a flower are nothing more than modified leaves, for which assumption there is ample evidence from examples of reversion.[1] As most Gymnosperms (*Pinaceae*, etc.) have spirally arranged parts, it seems probable that the more primitive Angiospermous families would show a similar arrangement, and that the degree of cohesion and adhesion in these would be much less than in those mentioned above (*Umbelliferae*, etc.),

[1] Common examples of floral parts reverting to leaves are given by Masters in his book on *Vegetable Teratology* (1869).

in which it is very marked. Thus families with flowers made up of sepals, petals, stamens, and carpels, free amongst themselves and from each other, would be more ancient phylogenetically than those with flowers showing a high degree of cohesion or adhesion or both. If the structure of all the families of Angiosperms be examined from this standpoint, therefore, it will be found that only two show the greatest number of these more primitive features —viz., *Magnoliaceae* and *Ranunculaceae*. The gap between these and the higher families already mentioned has therefore to be bridged in order to arrive at a probable phylogenetic system of classification, and the student with only a very elementary knowledge of mathematics knows that the 340 or so families could be set out in linear sequence in an almost infinite number of ways. The present author ventured to propose a new arrangement in his *Families of Flowering Plants*, already mentioned, and the principal object of the present book is to arrange the *British* families and genera according to that work, in the hope that it may instil in the mind of the student the idea of phylogeny.

Even when he published his first volume of the *Families of Flowering Plants* in 1926, the writer had not sufficiently divested himself of the beliefs and prejudices assimilated from his early training in botany during the late nineties. At that time much emphasis was still laid on the importance of *hypogyny*, *perigyny*, and *epigyny*, and even more so on *polypetaly*, *gamopetaly*, and *apetaly*. That he had shaken off a considerable amount, however, is proved by the following passage :—

" With the exception of the primary division into Dicotyledons and Monocotyledons large groups are usually artifical, especially if the characteristic fixed upon to distinguish them is a general tendency and founded on a single character. Examples are the De Candollean artificial groups *Thalamiflorae, Disciflorae, Calyciflorae, Inferae,* and to a less extent the *Parietales, Centrospermae,* and *Amentiferae.* The special characteristics indicated by the names of some of these groups are general tendencies in many families of flowering plants.   Although it is still very convenient to recognise two main groups of Dicotyledons as *Archichlamydeae* (*Polypetalae* + *Monochlamydeae*) and *Metachlamydeae* (*Gamopetalae, Sympetalae,* etc.), *a phylogenetic classification would be better attained if the gamopetalous character were regarded in its true light,* i.e., *as a general tendency, for gamopetaly is quite a common feature is many so-called polypetalous families.*"

With fuller knowledge and experience the writer's opinions and convictions have naturally not remained static.   The time seems opportune, therefore, to make the change foreshadowed in the italicised second part of the quotation, and to distribute the sympetalous families amongst their true relations in the *Archichlamydeae.*

In addition, he now has the courage of his convictions with respect to the recognition of two main phyla in the Dicotyledons, the one *fundamentally and predominantly woody*, the other *fundamentally and predominantly herbaceous*, and the families have been rearranged in accordance with this view, in the belief that they have in nature developed on parallel lines.   This point was put forward rather timidly in his previous work, but he is now more and more convinced that it is a very probable hypothesis, and that some cases of similarities in floral structure which were formerly considered to indicate relationships are due to *convergent evolution* or *parallelism.*   Consequently some groups previously associated in one family or one order (Reihe) are now found far apart.

For these alterations no apology is offered, and indeed support has been found in a quite unexpected quarter. For example, in the *Report of the Marlborough College Natural History Society* for 1896, p. 43, the late E. Meyrick, F.R.S., wrote :—

" A system of classification is in effect a summary of knowledge, and, when effectively mastered, serves as a kind of index or mental aid to memory, without which the mass of detail acquired in scientific study cannot be properly grasped, or the relative bearing of the different facts understood. Hence it is of the first importance that this system should embody the latest improvements, and a student who wishes to keep on progressing must not be averse to alter his system from time to time as occasion requires.

" Unfortunately there is always in science, as in other pursuits, a large body of conservative opinion which is disposed to cry out, like Alexander's soldiers, against this interminable marching to the front, and to protest that there is no use or enjoyment of our conquests, if we are to abandon them immediately for fresh ones. This tendency to crystallisation can best be counteracted by continued movement; if a halt is called, the longer we stop, the less we are inclined to move on again, and reluctance soon passes into inability.

" The root of modern classification lies in the recognition of the principle of evolution or development, and all systems which are not clearly based on this are obsolete . . ."

This summarises for the student of British botany the viewpoint necessary to study these pages. The book has been prepared to introduce a phylogenetic system for the families and genera of our native Flowering Plants as an aid to a better understanding of them. This involves no criticism of the other systems of classification already mentioned, for, as the same writer continues :—

" Of course this implies no discredit to the older systematists, who could not anticipate the progress of knowledge, and made the most skilful use of their materials that the knowledge of their age permitted."

In Britain we have been using for over three-quarters of a century the system of Bentham and Hooker, which, in reality, as already pointed out, is a modification of the older De Candolle system. And, as also stated, if we chose we could trace the origin of the latter system farther back still, through that of Jussieu until we arrive at the system of Linnaeus, published about the middle of the eighteenth century. In a way, therefore, all new systems are modifications of one or all of the earlier systems, no matter how antiquated.

Because the system of Bentham and Hooker is partly artificial, and because its successor on the Continent— that of Engler and Prantl—is not considered to be based on logical phylogenetic principles, a new arrangement seems to be called for. As Meyrick also says :—

> " There is always a large body of conservative opinion which is not disposed to move with the times."

This was particularly so with taxonomic botanists up to the end of last century. In spite of the advent of Darwin's theory of descent, artificial systems persisted, and still persist, and a great deal of existing classification dates back to Linnaeus (*circa* 1753). This has largely been due to the necessity of supplying an easy means for ascertaining the *names* of plants. Keys were usually provided for this purpose, and to be really useful, they must be somewhat artificial, and the system generally followed the lines of the keys. But now that most species of plants, at least of Flowering Plants, have been discovered and named, a more phylogenetic classification is needed, based on the theory of descent, such as has been available for a long time in the kindred science of Zoology.

For this purpose the plants themselves have to be studied, from either living or dried specimens. We cannot in our short lives see and compare very many living species, so we have to rely mainly on a herbarium of dried plants, or *hortus siccus*, as it used to be called. If species are related, they must have a common origin, as must genera also, and the same applies to families. There are naturally many gaps among them, but it should be possible to piece what is left roughly into a " family tree ". Thus some species are quite isolated, and are the sole representatives of genera—for example, the remark-

B

able African genus *Welwitschia,* which has probably no living relatives.[1]

Some botanists are inclined to ridicule the " family tree ", and even to sneer at phylogeny. *Damnunt quod non intelligunt!* But there is evidence in many recent taxonomic papers that phylogeny is being more and more emphasised, and eventually more phylogenetic classifications of species and genera will be forthcoming. This should be of great advantage to the science of botany in general, especially in ecological and phytogeographical studies. As Parkin [2] has written :—

" Taxonomy without phylogeny may be likened to bones without flesh."

This book is intended to supply for the student of British botany a little " flesh ", and thus add to the interest of our fascinating, though somewhat meagre flora.

*   *   *   *   *

In his first scheme the present writer pointed out the desirability of separating the *Magnoliaceae* and other woody allied families from the herbaceous *Ranales,* because he could discover no real affinity between them, and regarded the close approximation in floral structure as due to *parallelism.* Another example is the old conception of *Saxifragaceae,* which in Bentham and Hooker's system embraced also such widely different groups as the *Escalloniaceae,* the *Cunoniaceae,* the *Greyiaceae,* the *Hydrangeaceae,* and the *Grossulariaceae.* If this view be logical, then it seems equally logical to keep the two phyla separate throughout. This he has now attempted to do. Students are warned, however, and even learned critics, against taking the view that he has reverted to the old practice of putting all the woody plants into one group and all the herbaceous plants into

[1] Although *Welwitschia* has usually been classed with *Gnetum* and *Ephedra* in the *Gnetaceae,* the present writer does not consider it to be related to these two genera, the only character in common being the exposed ovule and seed.

[2] *Nature,* cxxxiv, 553 (1934).

another. He has not done anything quite so elementary. What has been done is to put all those families which are *predominantly woody*, and the more *primitive* genera of which are *woody*, into the woody phylum, and conversely the same has been done with the *herbaceous* families.

In other words, the *woody* division consists of *trees and shrubs plus herbs which are related to trees and shrubs*, and the *herbaceous* division consists of *herbs plus some clearly related woody plants*.

The result may not appear to be as convincing as it might be, because the present work deals only with the British flora, which, when compared with that of the whole world, is naturally but a small sample. In Great Britain and Eire there are only 116 families represented out of a world total of about 340, and about 700 genera out of something like 14,000. Over 200 of these genera are represented by only a single species. In order to make the phylogenetic sequence more intelligible, however, the names of those families which are important connecting links, but which are not represented in Britain, are included where necessary, and are inserted in square brackets [   ] in the family " trees " and in the linear arrangement on p. 25. Naturalised genera are marked with an *. The families have been arranged in as logical a sequence as possible, beginning with those showing the more primitive types of flowers, and ending with the most advanced.

No one, however ardent an evolutionist, would dream of trying to prove that mankind is still being evolved from different tribes of monkeys, however strong his belief that they are closely related. It is the same with the families of Flowering Plants. Many are so obviously related that they must have had a common origin from more primitive ancestral stocks, and this can be made clear only by reference to less advanced families. For example, *Cruciferae* are clearly descended from the same stock as the *Papaveraceae*, the latter showing more primitive characters, such as numerous stamens and a larger number of united carpels. And *Papaveraceae* can be traced back, *by those who have eyes to see,* to the more primitive group *Ranunculaceae,* which exhibits still more ancient features—i.e., numerous free stamens and numerous free carpels.   But *Cruciferae* have not descended from the *present-day Papaveraceae,* and neither have *Papaveraceae* been derived from *existing Ranunculaceae.*   This point should be kept in mind throughout, and it is shown clearly in the diagram at the end of the book.

*   *   *   *   *

Although it is possible that the first evolved Angiospermous flowering plants had no perianth, it does not follow that they were related to or resembled those flowers devoid of a perianth which exist at the present day.[1]   In the one case the perianth had not as yet been evolved, in the other it has been dispensed with or become very much reduced.

The various parts of flowers—such as those of a buttercup, for example—are probably nothing but highly modified leaves.   In position they are borne towards the end of an axis in regular acropetal order : below, a *calyx* (of sepals, normally green); above that, a *corolla* (of petals, often coloured), then the *androecium* (of stamens, often yellow), and, finally, the *gynoecium* (carpels, or ovary, often green).

In the primitive flower, no doubt, a few of the upper leaves were crude structures bearing a great quantity of male sporangia, and above them other leaves with female sporangia either on the nerves or infolded margins or on both.   As there were perhaps few insects, the pollen may even have been blown by the wind directly on to the ovules.   There may have been no style, for the style is but the barren tip of the midrib of the carpellary leaf, which would in due course function as a stigma when the carpel became a closed structure.   *But no such plants are*

[1] Eames in *Proc. Intern. Congr. Pl. Sci. Ithaca,* 1926, 1 : 426 (1929), says : " In the *Salicaceae* it is clear from the vascular structure that the flower formerly possessed a highly developed perianth, doubtless of two whorls.   The nectaries of *Salix* represent morphologically some of the lost perianth parts."

living to-day. Those early flowers were probably unstable experimental structures which persisted only sufficiently long to produce more efficient and specialised
types. This could best be attained by cross-pollination;
hence the upper leaves immediately below the sporophylls
gradually became coloured to attract the insects necessary

Fig. 1.—Vertical section of hypothetical proangiospermous
flower, with the male (A) and female (B), sporophylls
little modified from the ordinary foliage leaves.

for the purpose, and became the *corolla* as we know it
today. Later, or perhaps simultaneously—to cover the
vital reproductive organs—the internodes of the next series
of foliage leaves were suppressed, and these upper leaves
took on the function of protection necessary during the
bud-stage, and formed the *calyx*. I give a rough drawing
of this hypothetical flower. Amongst existing plants

it approximates most closely to that of a *Magnolia*, which many botanists now consider to be one of the most ancient of living flowering plants. It is therefore from this primitive Dicotyledonous family, *Magnoliaceae*, and its parallel family, *Ranunculaceae*, that this phylogenetic system is built up, for this hypothetical flower also resembles, though rather remotely, that of a Paeony in the

Fig. 2.—The Himalayan *Magnolia pterocarpa* Roxb. (Magnoliaceae) is perhaps the most ancient type of living angiospermous flowering plant; note the gradual reduction of the leaves towards the flower.

A, the same in fruit.   B, separate carpel with seed.

latter family. Indeed, the so-called "Tree Paeony", *P. suffruticosa* Andrews (*P. moutan* Sims) Linn., may represent an ancestral type indicating a connection between the two families, though there is rather a wide gap between a *Magnolia* and a *Paeonia*. At any rate they do not appear to me to have, as we say in human affairs, a very close "blood relationship".

In Britain the more primitive types of woody plants,

apart from the Gymnosperms, no longer exist except in a fossil state, for they were no doubt destroyed by successive ice ages. In the complete system for the whole world, therefore, the linear sequence begins with *Magnoliaceae*, and is followed by *Annonaceae* and *Dilleniaceae*, all with free carpels, and it is not until *Rosaceae* is reached that there are any British representatives.

Although the more primitive families of woody plants are not now found in Britain, those of the herbaceous subphylum are well represented—for example, *Ranunculaceae* and the families immediately derived from it. On the whole, herbs are better adapted to our climate than trees and shrubs, as most of them pass the winter in the seed stage in the soil, or by means of underground rhizomes.

Closely connected with phylogeny is plant distribution. The geographical relationships of the British flora have been fairly fully investigated since the pioneer work of Edward Forbes in 1846,[1] and the student has now the advantage of recent papers on the subject by O. Stapf,[2] E. J. Salisbury,[3] and J. R. Matthews.[4] For the general affinities of the flora with those of neighbouring regions, therefore, the student should read these highly interesting accounts. Although this subject is intimately connected with it, the present book is mainly concerned with the general phylogeny of the flora, and attention is called only to the more important genera and species whose geographical distribution is of outstanding interest. The late Professor Sir Albert Seward, in his charming little book *Links with the Past in the Plant World*[5] (p. 19), says:—

" Confining our attention to the dominant group

[1] E. Forbes, " On the connexion between the distribution of the existing fauna and flora of the British Isles and the geological changes which have affected their area ", *Mem. Geol. Surv. U.K.*, 1 : 336–432 (1846).

[2] O. Stapf, " The Southern Element in the British Flora ", *Engl. Bot. Jahrb., Engler Festband* (1914).

[3] E. J. Salisbury, " The East Anglian Flora ", *Trans. Norfolk and Norwich Naturalists' Soc.*, 13 : 191–263 (1932).

[4] J. R. Matthews, " Geographical Relationships of the British Flora ", *Journ. of Ecology*, 25 : 1–90 (1937).

[5] *Cambridge Manuals of Science and Literature*, 1911.

of plants in the British flora, namely the Flowering Plants, we may profitably consider the question, though we cannot satisfactorily answer it—which members of this group are entitled to be regarded as the most ancient inhabitants? The past history of our native plants, and their geographical range, not only in the British Isles but on the Continent of Europe, are subjects well worthy of the attention of field botanists, whose interests are apt to be confined within too narrow bounds. There are numerous problems relating to the composition of the present vegetation of Britain which might be discussed in reference to the relative antiquity of plants, but in a single chapter it is impossible to do more than call attention to certain considerations which are frequently overlooked by students of British species."

In general, the bulk of the flora of the British Isles is naturally much the same as that of the maritime countries of western Europe—that is to say, of France, Belgium, Holland, Denmark, and Norway. A large percentage of the flora of these countries is, in turn, widely spread through Central, Northern, and Southern Europe, and into Western Asia. There are nearly 500 such species in the British flora.

Then about 200 of our species are widely distributed right across the North Temperate Zone, whilst 130 or so belong almost exclusively to Europe itself, a few of these occurring also in Northern Africa. Under these three categories fall therefore nearly two-thirds of our indigenous plants, leaving out of account the large number of microforms of such genera as *Rubus*, *Rosa*, *Hieracium*, *Taraxacum*, and *Euphrasia*.

The distribution of the remaining third of our species naturally claims our greatest interest. Matthews arranges them under twelve different headings. He computes there are thirty-eight species with a Mediterranean distribution. Two of the most interesting of these are *Arbutus unedo* L. (*Ericaceae*), the " Strawberry Tree ", which in our islands occurs only in South-west Eire, and *Neotinea intacta* Reichb. f. (*Habenaria intacta* Benth.) (*Orchidaceae*), which is found in the same area. About 80% of this Mediterranean element occurs in West Cornwall, and only five species reach Scotland.

The Lusitanian element in the south-west of England is also of considerable interest, particularly such well-known examples as the three species of *Trifolium*, which are restricted to the coastal districts of Cornwall. These are *T. bocconei* Savi, *T. strictum* Linn., and *T. molineri* Balb. The first is found also in Madeira, the Canary Islands, and in North Africa.

Of particular importance to those interested in the Wegener hypothesis of drifting continents are those species which are common to the western parts of our islands and to North America. These, curiously, are all Monocotyledons : *Eriocaulon septangulare* With. (*Eriocaulaceae*), *Sisyrinchium angustifolium* Mill. (*Iridaceae*), and *Spiranthes romanzoffiana* Cham. (*Orchidaceae*). They are probably relics of a flora which stretched across the North Atlantic by a continuous or subcontinuous land-surface and have survived through the various glacial periods.

It would carry me too far to indicate more than these few intriguing points regarding the distribution of British plants, and enough have probably been mentioned to induce the student himself to pursue the matter farther by reading the available literature, references to which he will find in the papers quoted at the foot of p. 15.

PRINCIPLES OF CLASSIFICATION ADOPTED IN THIS NEW SYSTEM

The present system for the Flowering Plants is based on the following general principles, and the arrangement of the families, and of the genera within the families, is governed by them so far as practicable :—

GENERAL PRINCIPLES FOLLOWED IN THE CLASSIFICATION OF BRITISH FLOWERING PLANTS

Other things being equal, it may be stated that :—

1. Evolution is both upwards and downwards, the former tending towards the preservation and further specialisation of characters already evolved, the latter to their reduction or suppression; examples of the former in the family *Ranunculaceae* are the highly modified petals of *Aquilegia*, and of the latter their complete reduction in *Anemone*.

2. Evolution does not necessarily involve all organs at the same time; one set of organs may be changing whilst the remainder are stationary; example, the retention of numerous stamens in the otherwise advanced flowers of the family *Malvaceae*.

Relating to the General Habit of Plants

3. Broadly speaking, trees and shrubs are more primitive than herbs in any one family or genus—for example, herbaceous members of the *Rosaceae* and *Papilionaceae* are more advanced phylogenetically than the woody members; this is reversed in *Clematis* in the *Ranunculaceae*.

4. Trees and shrubs are older than climbers in any one family or genus.

5. Perennials are older than biennials and annuals; good examples are found in the family *Ranunculaceae* (see p. 130).

18

6. Aquatic flowering plants are derived from terrestrial ancestors, and epiphytes, saprophytes, and parasites are more recent than plants of more normal habit; examples of the former are the terrestrial species (more primitive) of *Ranunculus*, and the aquatic species (more advanced); of the latter type see especially *Scrophulariaceae* (p. 225).

Relating to the General Structure of Flowering Plants

7. Plants with vascular bundles arranged in a cylinder (Dicotyledons) are more primitive in origin than those with scattered bundles (Monocotyledons), though the latter split off from the former very early.

8. The spiral arrangement of leaves on the stem and of floral leaves (sepals and petals) precedes that of the opposite and whorled type.

9. As a rule simple leaves are older than compound leaves—for example, the unlobed-leaved species of *Sorbus* are more ancient than those with pinnate leaves.

Relating to the Flowers and Fruits of Plants

10. Bisexual flowers are older than unisexual; dioecious plants are more recent than monoecious.

11. The solitary flower is more primitive than the inflorescence—for example, *Delphinium*, with its raceme, is much more advanced than *Trollius*.

12. Contorted (1), imbricate (2), and valvate (3) floral parts (sepals and petals) have been evolved in this sequence.

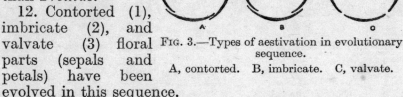

FIG. 3.—Types of aestivation in evolutionary sequence.
A, contorted.   B, imbricate.   C, valvate.

13. Flowers with petals are generally of a more primitive type than those without petals; examples *Ranunculus* (petals) and *Clematis* (without petals).

14. Free petals are more primitive than connate petals; examples *Ranunculus* (petals free) and *Campanula* (petals connate).

15. Actinomorphic (" regular ") flowers are an earlier type than zygomorphic (" irregular ") flowers; examples *Caltha* and *Delphinium* respectively.

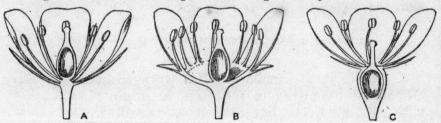

FIG. 4.—Types of flowers in evolutionary sequence.

A, hypogynous—*i.e.*, ovary superior; sepals, petals and stamens below the ovary.   B, perigynous—*i.e.*, ovary superior; sepals, petals and stamens around the ovary.   C, epigynous—*i.e.*, ovary inferior; sepals, petals and stamens above the ovary.

16. Hypogyny is in general most primitive, then comes perigyny, and finally epigyny; examples *Ranunculus*, *Potentilla*, and *Galium*, respectively.

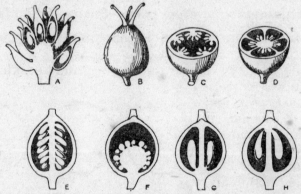

FIG. 5.—Types of carpels and placentation in evolutionary sequence.

A, apocarpous pistil.   B, syncarpous pistil.   C, parietal placentation.   D, axile placentation.   E, free-central placentation.   F, free-basal placentation.   G, basal erect ovules.   H, apical pendulous ovules.

17. Free carpels are more primitive than connate carpels; examples *Ranunculus* (free) and *Nigella* (con-

nate); parietal placentation is more primitive than axile.

18. Many carpels preceded few carpels.

19. Seeds with endosperm and small embryo are older than seeds without endosperm and a large embryo; examples *Ranunculaceae* and *Rosaceae* respectively.

20. In general, flowers with numerous stamens are more primitive than those with few, though numerous stamens may be retained up to the end of a group, as in *Malvaceae*.

21. Separate stamens and (or) anthers precede united stamens or anthers; examples *Tiliaceae* (free stamens) and *Malvaceae* (united stamens), *Campanulaceae* (free anthers) and *Lobeliaceae* or *Compositae* (united anthers).

22. Aggregate fruits are more highly evolved than single fruits; as a rule the capsule precedes the berry or drupe.

The result of the application of these principles to the British flora is summarised in the diagram on the next page, which, for the sake of clarity, includes only the names of the principal series or orders of families (cohorts), with the chief representative family belonging to each.

The linear sequence of all the families begins on p. 25, each page of which should be read from below upwards— a method adopted to keep constantly in the mind of the student the evolutionary sequence, starting with the most primitive and ending with the most advanced. Thus the gap is bridged between the ROSALES and the VERBENALES in column 1, between the RANALES and LAMIALES in column 2, and between the BUTOMALES and GRAMINALES in column 3. The group names in square brackets are not represented in the indigenous flora of Britain, but are inserted because they are necessary links in the chain.

DIAGRAM OF SYSTEM

* * * *
VERBENALES (*Verbenaceae*)

* * * *
RUBIALES (*Rubiaceae*)
APOCYNALES (*Apocynaceae*)
LOGANIALES (*Oleaceae*)

* * * *
SAPINDALES (*Aceraceae*)
RHAMNALES (*Rhamnaceae*)
SANTALALES (*Santalaceae*)
CELASTRALES (*Celastraceae*)

GUTTIFERALES (*Hyperica-ceae*)

* * * *
ERICALES (*Ericaceae*)
[THEALES (*Theaceae*)]

* * * *
EUPHORBIALES (*Euphorbia-ceae*)
MALPIGHIALES (*Linaceae*)

* * * *
MALVALES (*Malvaceae*)
TILIALES (*Tiliaceae*)

* * * *
CUCURBITALES (*Cucurbita-ceae*)
[PASSIFLORALES (*Passi-floraceae*)]

* * * *
POLYGALALES (*Polygala-ceae*)
TAMARICALES (*Tamarica-ceae*)
VIOLALES (*Violaceae*)

* * * *
THYMELAEALES(*Thymelaea-ceae*)
BIXALES (*Cistaceae*)

* * * *
URTICALES (*Urticaceae*)
FAGALES (*Fagaceae*)
MYRICALES (*Myricaceae*)
SALICALES (*Salicaceae*)
HAMAMELIDALES (*Buxa-ceae*)
ARALIALES (*Araliaceae*)
CUNONIALES (*Grossularia-ceae*)

* * * *
LEGUMINOSAE (*Papiliona-ceae*)
ROSALES (*Rosaceae*)
[DILLENIALES (*Dillenia-ceae*)]
[MAGNOLIALES (*Magnolia-ceae*)]

LIGNOSAE

* * * *
LAMIALES (*Labiatae*)
BORAGINALES (*Boragina-ceae*)
POLEMONIALES (*Polemonia-ceae*)
GERANIALES (*Geraniaceae*)

* * * *
PERSONALES (*Scrophularia-ceae*)
SOLANALES (*Solanaceae*)

* * * *
ASTERALES (*Compositae*)
CAMPANULALES (*Campanu-laceae*)

* * * *
VALERIANALES (*Valeriana-ceae*)

* * * *
UMBELLALES (*Umbelliferae*)
SARRACENIALES (*Drosera-ceae*)
SAXIFRAGALES (*Saxifraga-ceae*)

* * * *
PLANTAGINALES (*Planta-ginaceae*)
PRIMULALES (*Primulaceae*)
GENTIANALES (*Gentiana-ceae*)

* * * *
LYTHRALES (*Lythraceae*)

* * * *
CHENOPODIALES (*Cheno-podiaceae*)
POLYGONALES (*Polygona-ceae*)
CARYOPHYLLALES (*Caryo-phyllaceae*)

* * * *
RESEDALES (*Resedaceae*)
CRUCIALES (*Cruciferae*)
RHOEADALES (*Papavera-ceae*)

* * * *
ARISTOLOCHIALES (*Aristo-lochiaceae*)
BERBERIDALES (*Berberida-ceae*)
RANALES (*Ranunculaceae*)

HERBACEAE

GRAMINALES (*Gramineae*)
CYPERALES (*Cyperaceae*)
JUNCALES (*Juncaceae*)

GLUMIFLORAE

ORCHIDALES (*Orchidaceae*)
[HAEMODORALES (*Haemo-doraceae*)]

* * * *
IRIDALES (*Iridaceae*)
AMARYLLIDALES (*Amaryl-lidaceae*)

* * * *
TYPHALES (*Typhaceae*)
ARALES (*Araceae*)

* * * *
DIOSCOREALES (*Dioscorea-ceae*)
LILIALES (*Liliaceae*)

COROLLIFERAE

* * * *
ERIOCAULALES (*Eriocaula-ceae*)
[COMMELINALES (*Commeli-naceae*)]

* * * *
NAJADALES (*Najadaceae*)
POTAMOGETONALES (*Pota-mogetonaceae*)
JUNCAGINALES (*Juncagina-ceae*)
[APONOGETONALES (*Apono-getonaceae*)]
ALISMATALES (*Alismata-ceae*)
BUTOMALES (*Butomaceae*)

CALYCIFERAE

DICOTYLEDONES

MONOCOTYLEDONES

HYPOTHETICAL PROANGIOSPERMS

" Bird's-Eye View " of the arrangement of the principal groups (Orders) of Flowering Plants and chief family of each represented in the British flora. (Important non-British linking groups are shown in square brackets, and a row of * indicates a climax group.)—To be read from below upwards.

22

PRINCIPAL GROUPS OF SEED-PLANTS REPRESENTED IN THE INDIGENOUS FLORA OF BRITAIN

We are not concerned here with the evolution of the lower plants, such as Algae, Fungi, Mosses, Liverworts, and Ferns, but only the higher or seed-bearing plants, the *Spermaphyta*, which include the Gymnosperms and Angiosperms.

In this phylogenetic system of living seed-plants relatively few large groups are recognised. These are as follows :—

Phylum I. **Gymnospermae** (Gymnosperms).—Ovules naked, not enclosed by an ovary, wind-pollinated and receiving the pollen-grains directly on the micropyle; wood with no true vessels. Trees and shrubs with usually evergreen xerophilous needle-like foliage and unisexual " flowers " mostly arranged in cones (strobili); usually called " Conifers ", providing valuable soft-wood timbers. See p. 35.

Phylum II. **Angiospermae** (Angiosperms).—Ovules enclosed in separate carpels or in an ovary of one or more united carpels crowned by a style and/or stigma, the latter receiving the pollen-grains mainly through the agency of insects or by close approximation, or by wind-pollination (being secondary); wood, when present, consisting of true vessels. A more advanced phylum than I, and evolved independently, constituting the bulk of the present world vegetation, and from which are obtained practically all food, forage, medicine, and the hardest woods. See p. 36.

Subphylum 1. Dicotyledones (Dicotyledons).—Young (embryonic) plant with 2 seed-leaves (cotyledons); vascular bundles of the stem usually arranged in a circle (with a few exceptions); leaves typically net-veined, alternate or opposite or whorled, often stipulate; flowers usually 5- or 4-parted (pentamerous or tetramerous). See p. 36.

    I. *Lignosae.*—More or less woody plants, or, if herbaceous, then obviously derived from woody ancestors. See p. 36.

    II. *Herbaceae.*—Herbaceous, or, if softly woody, then obviously derived from herbaceous ancestors. See p. 40.

Subphylum 2. Monocotyledones (Monocotyledons).—Young (embryonic) plant with only 1 seed-leaf (cotyledon); vascular bundles of the stem closed and scattered; leaves typically parallel-nerved, alternate, very rarely stipulate; flowers usually 3-parted (trimerous). See p. 42.

I. *Calyciferae.*—Perianth-parts in two distinct series or whorls, and usually dissimilar, often the outer green and *calyx-like*. See p. 43.

II. *Corolliferae.*—Perianth-parts more mostly or less in one whorl and usually all *petaloid*. See p. 43.

III. *Glumiflorae.*—Perianth small and *scale-like* or completely reduced and replaced by scaly bracts (glumes). See p. 44.

These subdivisions of the Dicotyledons and Monocotyledons are further split up into series or groups of families, which was partially done in the classification of Bentham and Hooker, and more elaborately carried out in that of Engler and Prantl. In the former these smaller groups were called " Cohorts " and in the latter " Reihen " (series). In English botanical books the " Reihen " of the Germans have been called " Orders "; rather unfortunately, because the smaller units, now called *families*, were formerly known as " Natural Orders ". The name of the Order is usually taken from that of the principal or most typical family, and ends in " ales ", such as *Magnoliales* (after *Magnoliaceae*), and *Ranales* (after *Ranunculaceae*), etc. With a few exceptions, sanctioned by the International Rules of Botanical Nomenclature, the family names end in " aceae ".

PHYLOGENETIC SEQUENCE OF THE ORDERS AND FAMILIES OF BRITISH SEED-PLANTS (SPERMAPHYTA).

(Rows of asterisks mark climax families.)

(To be read from below upwards.)

Habit.   *Derivation.*

* * * * * * *

8. **Araliaceae** (p. 68)

7. **Cornaceae** (p. 66)

Woody to rarely herbaceous . . (6) ARALIALES . from *Cunoniales* (5)

6. **Grossulariaceae** (p. 65)

Woody . . . . . (5) CUNONIALES . . from *Rosales* (3)

* * * * * * * *

5. **Papilionaceae** (p. 58)

Woody to herbaceous . . (4) LEGUMINOSAE . . from *Rosales* (3)

4. **Rosaceae** (p. 51)

Woody to herbaceous . . (3) ROSALES . from *Dilleniales* (2)

[Dilleniaceae]

Woody . . . . . (2) [DILLENIALES] . from *Magnoliales* (1)

[Magnoliaceae]

Woody . . . . . (1) [MAGNOLIALES] from hypothetical *Proangiospermae*

I. Lignosae.—Fundamentally and predominantly woody (to p. 28)

Subphylum I. DICOTYLEDONES (p. 51)

Phylum II. ANGIOSPERMAE (p. 51)

* * * * * * *

3. **Cupressaceae** (p. 48)

2. **Pinaceae** (p. 45)

1. **Taxaceae** (p. 45)

Woody . Phylum I. GYMNOSPERMAE (p. 45)

C   25

BRITISH FLOWERING PLANTS

(To be read from below upwards.)

Habit.   *Derivation.*

* * * * * * *

23. Polygalaceae (p. 93)

Woody to
  herbaceous . . (16) POLYGALALES . from *Bixales* (12)

22. Tamaricaceae (p. 91)
21. Frankeniaceae (p. 91)

Woody . . . . . (15) TAMARICALES . . from *Bixales* (12)

20. Violaceae (p. 88)

Woody to
  herbaceous . . (14) VIOLALES . . from *Bixales* (12)

* * * * * * *

19. Thymelaeaceae (p. 86)

Woody . . . . (13) THYMELAEALES . from *Bixales* (12)

18. Cistaceae (p. 84)

Woody to
  subherbaceous . (12) BIXALES . from *Dilleniales* (2)

* * * * * * *

17. Cannabinaceae (p. 83)
16. Urticaceae (p. 82)
15. Ulmaceae (p. 81)

Woody to herbaceous
  (fibrous) . . . (11) URTICALES from *Hamamelidales* (7)

14. Fagaceae (p. 78)
13. Corylaceae (p. 77)
12. Betulaceae (p. 75)

Woody . . . . . (10) FAGALES . from *Rosales* (3)

* * * * * * *

11. Myricaceae (p. 74)

Woody . . . . . (9) MYRICALES . . from *Rosales* (3)

10. Salicaceae (p. 72)

Woody to
  subherbaceous . (8) SALICALES . from *Hamamelidales* (7)

9. Buxaceae (p. 71)

Woody . . . . (7) HAMAMELIDALES . from *Rosales* (3)

(To be read from below upwards.)

Habit.   *Derivation.*

* * * * * * *

33. **Hypericaceae** (p. 112)

Woody to
  herbaceous   .   (25) GUTTIFERALES   . from *Theales* (23)

* * * * * * *

32. **Monotropaceae** (p. 111)

31. **Pyrolaceae** (p. 111)

30. **Vacciniaceae** (p. 109)

29. **Ericaceae** (p. 105)

Woody to
  herbaceous   .   .   (24) ERICALES   .   . from *Theales* (23)

[**Theaceae**, etc.]

Woody .   .   .   .   .   (23) [THEALES]   .   . from *Bixales* (12)

* * * * * * *

28. **Euphorbiaceae** (p. 100)

Woody to   .   (22) EUPHORBIALES   .   Probably from
  herbaceous   *Tiliales* (19), *Malvales* (20),
                                       and *Celastrales* (26)

27. **Linaceae** (p. 98)

Woody to
  herbaceous   .   (21) MALPIGHIALES   . from *Tiliales* (19)

* * * * * * *

26. **Malvaceae** (p. 96)

Woody to herbace-
  ous (fibrous) .   .   (20 MALVALES   .   . from *Tiliales* (19)

25. **Tiliaceae** (p. 93)

Woody .   .   .   .   .   (19) TILIALES   .   from *Bixales* (12)
                                       and *Dilleniales* (2)

* * * * * * *

24. **Cucurbitaceae** (p. 93)

Herbaceous   .   .   (18) CUCURBITALES   .   from *Passi-*
                                       florales (17)

[**Passifloraceae**]

Woody to
  herbaceous   .   (17) [PASSIFLORALES]   . from *Bixales* (12)

(To be read from below upwards.)

Habit.   *Derivation.*

*   *   *   *   *   *   *

46. **Verbenaceae** (p. 129)

Woody to
    herbaceous   .   . (33) Verbenales . from *Loganiales* (30)

*   *   *   *   *   *   *

45. **Caprifoliaceae** (p. 125)

44. **Rubiaceae** (p. 124)

Woody to
    herbaceous   .   . (32) Rubiales . from *Loganiales* (30)

43. **Apocynaceae** (p. 122)

Woody to sub-
    herbaceous   .   . (31) Apocynales . from *Loganiales* (30)

42. **Oleaceae** (p. 121)

Woody .   .   .   . (30) Loganiales . from *Celastrales* (26)

41. **Aceraceae** (p. 120)

Woody .   .   .   . (29) Sapindales . from *Celastrales* (26)

*   *   *   *   *   *   *

40. **Elaeagnaceae** (p. 119)

39. **Rhamnaceae** (p. 117)

Woody .   .   .   . (28) Rhamnales . from *Celastrales* (26)

*   *   *   *   *   *   *

38. **Santalaceae** (p. 117)

37. **Loranthaceae** (p. 116)

Woody .   .   .   . (27) Santalales . from *Celastrales* (26)

36. **Celastraceae** (p. 115)

35. **Empetraceae** (p. 114)

34. **Aquifoliaceae** (p. 113)

Woody .   .   .   . (26) Celastrales . . from *Theales* (23)

(To be read from below upwards.)

Habit.   *Derivation.*

62. **Plumbaginaceae** (p. 171)

61. **Primulaceae** (p. 168)

Herbaceous   .   .   . (42) Primulales   .   .   .   from *Caryo-*
phyllales (40)

60. **Menyanthaceae** (p. 168)

59. **Gentianaceae** (p. 166)

Herbaceous   .   .   . (41) Gentianales   .   .   .   from *Caryo-*
phyllales (40)

58. **Portulacaceae** (p. 163)

57. **Caryophyllaceae** (p. 159)

56. **Elatinaceae** (p. 158)

Herbaceous   .   . (40) Caryophyllales   . from *Ranales* (34)

* * * * * * * *

55. **Resedaceae** (p. 156)

Herbaceous to
subwoody.   .   . (39) Resedales   . from *Rhoeadales* (37)

54. **Cruciferae** (p. 151)

Herbaceous   .   . (38) Cruciferales   from *Rhoeadales* (37)

53. **Fumariaceae** (p. 150)

52. **Papaveraceae** (p. 147)

Herbaceous   .   .   . (37) Rhoeadales .   . from *Ranales* (34)

* * * * * * * *

51. **Aristolochiaceae** (p. 143)

Herbaceous to
softly woody . (36) Aristolochiales from *Berberidales* (35)

50. **Berberidaceae** (p. 141)

Herbaceous to
woody   .   . (35) Berberidales   . from *Ranales* (34)

49. **Nymphaeaceae** (p. 140)

48. **Ceratophyllaceae** (p. 140)

47. **Ranunculaceae** (p. 130)

Herbaceous to
softly woody .   . (34) Ranales   .   from hypothetical
Proangiospermae

II. **Herbaceae.**—Fundamentally and predominantly
herbaceous (to p. 31).

(To be read from below upwards.)

Habit.   *Derivation.*

79. **Lobeliaceae** (p. 209)

78. **Campanulaceae** (p. 206)

Herbaceous . .   (51) Campanulales   from *Gentianales* (41)

* * * * * * *

77. **Dipsacaceae** (p. 205)

76. **Valerianaceae** (p. 204)

Herbaceous . .   (50) Valerianales   from *Saxifragales* (47)

* * * * * * *

75. **Umbelliferae** (p. 192)

Herbaceous . .   (49) Umbellales   from *Saxifragales* (47)

* * * * * * *

74. **Droseraceae** (p. 191)

Herbaceous . .   (48) Sarraceniales   from *Saxifragales* (47)

73. **Adoxaceae** (p. 190)

72. **Saxifragaceae** (p. 186)

71. **Crassulaceae** (p. 184)

Herbaceous . .   (47) Saxifragales   . from *Ranales* (34)

                                      and *Caryophyllales* (40)

* * * * * * *

70. **Callitrichaceae** (p. 184)

69. **Halorrhagaceae** (p. 182)

68. **Onagraceae** (p. 180)

67. **Lythraceae** (p. 178)

Herbaceous . . .   (46) Lythrales from *Caryophyllales* (40)

* * * * * * *

66a. [Amaranthaceae] (p. 178)

66. **Chenopodiaceae** (p. 177)

Herbaceous . .   (45) Chenopodiales   .   from *Caryo-*

                                          phyllales (40)

65. **Illecebraceae** (p. 175)

64. **Polygonaceae** (p. 173)

Herbaceous . .   (44) Polygonales   .   from *Caryo-*

                                          phyllales (40)

* * * * * * *

63. **Plantaginaceae** (p. 172)

Herbaceous . .   (43) Plantaginales from *Gentianales* (41)

(To be read from below upwards.)

Habit.   *Derivation.*

* * * * * * *

91. **Labiatae** (p. 237)

Herbaceous   . . .   (58) LAMIALES   from *Boraginales* (57)

90. **Boraginaceae** (p. 236)

Herbaceous   . .   (57) BORAGINALES †   from *Geraniales* (55)

89. **Polemoniaceae** (p. 235)

Herbaceous   . .   (56) POLEMONIALES   . from *Geraniales*
                                (55) and *Caryophyllales* (40)

* * * * * * *

88. **Balsaminaceae** (p. 234)

87. **Oxalidaceae** (p. 234)

86. **Geraniaceae** (p. 231)

Herbaceous   . . .   (55) GERANIALES . . .   from *Caryo-*
                                                phyllales (40)

* * * * * * *

85. **Lentibulariaceae** (p. 230)

84. **Orobanchaceae** (p. 229)

83. **Scrophulariaceae** (p. 225)

Herbaceous   . . .   (54) PERSONALES   from *Saxifragales* (47)

82. **Convolvulaceae** (p. 223)

81. **Solanaceae** (p. 221)

Herbaceous to
   subwoody   . .   (53) SOLANALES   from *Saxifragales* (47)

* * * * * * *

80. **Compositae** (p. 209)

Herbaceous   . . .   (52) ASTERALES   from *Campanulales* (51)

---

† Excluding *Ehretiaceae*, a tropical woody group, which I now consider to be distinct from *Boraginaceae*.

(To be read from below upwards.)

Habit.   *Derivation.*

Herbaceous throughout
(except *Ruscaceae*)

         105. **Ruscaceae** (p. 260)
         104. **Liliaceae** (p. 254)
         103. **Trilliaceae** (p. 253)
              (66) LILIALES . From *Butomales* (59)

         Corolliferae.

            * * * * * * *

         102. **Eriocaulaceae** (p. 252)
              (65) ERIOCAULALES .

         101. **Najadaceae** (p. 251)
         100. **Zannichelliaceae** (p. 251)
              (64) NAJADALES .

         99. **Ruppiaceae** (p. 251)
         98. **Potamogetonaceae** (p. 250)   from   *Alis*
              (63) POTAMOGETONALES   *matales* (60)

         97. **Juncaginaceae** (p. 250)
              (62) JUNCAGINALES .

             (96a) [Commelinaceae]
             (61a. [COMMELINALES]

         96. **Zosteraceae** (p. 250)
              (61) APONOGETONALES .

         95. **Scheuchzeriaceae** (p. 249)
         94. **Alismataceae** (p. 248)
              (60) ALISMATALES . . . from achenial
                                      Ranales (34)
         93. **Hydrocharitaceae** (p. 246)
         92. **Butomaceae** (p. 246)
              (59) BUTOMALES . .   from follicular
                                        Ranales (34)

         Calyciferae.

Subphylum II. MONOCOTYLEDONES.

(To be read from below upwards.)

Habit.   *Derivation.*

Herbaceous throughout.

* * * * * * *

113. Orchidaceae (p. 272)

(73) ORCHIDALES Of tropical origin, derived from *Haemo-
dorales : Apostasia-
ceae, Haemodoraceae,*
[Apostasiaceae]   etc., not represented
[Haemodoraceae]   in Britain.

(72) [Haemodorales]

112. Iridaceae (p. 270)

(71) IRIDALES   . from *Liliales* (66) independently of the
Amaryllidaceae.

111. Amaryllidaceae (p. 267)

(70) AMARYLLIDALES from *Liliaceae,* with
more advanced
type (umbellate)
of inflorescence.

* * * * * * *

110. Typhaceae (p. 267)

109. Sparganiaceae (p. 266)

(69) TYPHALES   . from *Liliales* (66),
more or less par-
allel with *Araceae.*

* * * * * * *

108. Lemnaceae (p. 264)

107. Araceae (p. 261)

(68) ARALES   . from *Liliaceae,*
through tribe
Aspidistreae.

106. Dioscoreaceae (p. 261)

(67) DIOSCOREALES climbing *Liliaceae*
with baccate
fruits.

(To be read from below upwards.)

Habit.   *Derivation.*

Herbaceous throughout
 (except some *Bambuseae*)

* * * * * * *

116. **Gramineae** (p. 284)

(76) Graminales   from   *Liliales* (66)
                  with great reduc-
                  tion (lodicules) to
                  complete suppres-
                  sion   of   the
                  perianth.

115. **Cyperaceae** (p. 282)

(75) Cyperales . from *Liliales* (66)
                  with gradual sup-
                  pression of the
                  perianth.

114. **Juncaceae** (p. 281)

(74) Juncales . from *Liliales* (66), re-
                  taining a small
                  glumaceous peri-
                  anth.

Glumiflorae.

BRIEF REVIEW OF THE SYSTEM AS REPRE-SENTED IN BRITAIN

Phylum I. **Gymnospermae** (Gymnosperms).

IT is universally admitted that the most ancient *living* seed-plants are the Gymnosperms (*Gymnospermae*), in which the ovule is not enclosed in a carpel or ovary. Consequently there is no true fruit, though the cone of a Cycad or Conifer serves a similar purpose. The Cycads are connected with Ferns because they have motile sperma-tozoids — a feature common to all Ferns. A like character occurs in the Maidenhair Tree, *Ginkgo biloba* Linn. (*Ginkgoaceae*), aptly termed a "liv-ing fossil", because it has nowhere been found wild, but has been preserved as a sacred tree by the religious and super-stitious Chinese. The *Adiantum*-like leaves indicated by the popu-lar name also give colour to the relationship.

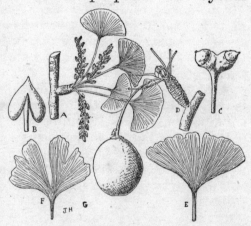

FIG. 6.—The Maidenhair Tree, *Ginkgo biloba* Linn., a very ancient race of trees dating back as far as the carboniferous period, and closely related to the Yew.

A, short shoot of male. B, anther. C, female " flower ". D, short shoot of female, with fruit. E, typical leaf. F, divided leaf.

Otherwise the Cycads and *Ginkgo* are, of course, very much more advanced than Ferns, for they have seeds but not true flowers. They are more closely related to the extinct *Pteridosperms* (seed-ferns).

Though *Ginkgoaceae* is now regarded as a distinct family, it possesses much in common with *Taxaceae*—the Yew-tree family—in which, indeed, it was formerly included. Sometimes in abnormal shoots of *Ginkgo*, the ovules, and therefore also the seeds, are borne on the margins of the leaves, indicating a reversion to an ancestral type such as *Cycas*.

In *Taxaceae*, which comes next in the scale, the ovules are borne more or less singly on the branchlets, and not in cones, as in the *Pinaceae*. The aril of the Yew seed is interesting, for an aril is probably a very ancient structure, being an early means of attraction for birds and other animals, thus assisting in the wider distribution of the seed. It seems significant that an aril is often found in the more primitive families of Dicotyledons—i.e., in *Magnoliaceae* and *Dilleniaceae*—but it rarely occurs in more advanced families, the seeds of which are distributed in many other different ways, either by contrivances in the fruit itself, such as colour and, or, succulence, or by wings, etc.

A higher expression of evolution in the Gymnosperms is to be found in the *Pinaceae*, which are the true cone-bearing plants, "Coniferae". They are all wind-pollinated, this being a primitive character; wind-pollination in Dicotyledons is not primitive, but is due to reversion. The leaves and cone-scales in *Pinaceae* are spirally arranged, the spiral arrangement being also very primitive.

In the more advanced *Cupressaceae* the leaves are opposite or in whorls, indicating suppression of some of the internodes, a condition extending to the cone-scales themselves, which do not overlap, but are *valvate*. In the common Juniper, *Juniperus communis* Linn., this has been carried even farther, for the valvate scales are concrescent into a fleshy berry. This marks the Juniper as being a very highly evolved type of Gymnosperm.

Phylum II. Angiospermae (Angiosperms).

Subphylum I. Dicotyledones (Dicotyledons).

Division I. *Lignosae* (fundamentally woody Dicotyledons).

An attempt will now be made to explain to the student the intricacies of this phylogenetic system for the Angiosperms, using for illustration in this chapter only the *orders* (mentioning the principal family of each of them) shown on the folded diagram at the end. The elementary student is advised to keep this in view whilst reading the next few paragraphs. And it should be noted that those orders enclosed in square brackets [ ] in the diagram are not represented in the British flora, but are inserted because they provide links between some of the groups.

Magnoliales (*Magnoliaceae*, etc.) are common in our gardens, and are considered in this system to be the most primitive of Flowering Plants. They are followed by *Dilleniales* (*Dilleniaceae*), which are found only in the tropics. These are regarded as the basic group for *Rosales* (*Rosaceae*). For this family the student is not likely to think only of *Rosa*, because he knows also the Strawberry, the Blackberry, the Hawthorn, the Rowan, and the Apple, Plum, and many others. *Rosaceae* show several primitive features; there are many with free carpels, as in *Ranunculaceae*, but the floral axis ("receptacle") is often hollowed out or expanded, and there is no endosperm in the seeds, such as is found in the Buttercups.

From *Rosales* are probably derived the *Leguminosae*, represented in Britain only by the completely climax family *Papilionaceae*, which contains several important economic plants. It is an interesting fact that most of the really important food and medicinal plants belong mainly to the highest evolved families—for example, Wheat, Barley, Oats, and Maize to the *Gramineae*; Coffee, Quinine, etc., to *Rubiaceae*, to mention only a few.

From *Rosaceae* it is not a far cry to *Araliales* (*Cornaceae* and *Araliaceae*) and to *Hamamelidales*, which in Britain are represented only by the Box trees, *Buxus*, now regarded as a distinct family, *Buxaceae*, and by *Hamamelis* and *Parrotia* in cultivation. And more and more reduced families which have descended from the same stock are the Willows and Poplars, *Salicales* (*Salicaceae*), the Bog-Myrtles, *Myricales* (*Myricaceae*), and the still more climax group *Fagales* (*Betulaceae*, *Corylaceae*, and *Faga-*

ceae), and finally *Urticales* (*Ulmaceae* and *Urticaceae*). It is claimed later on (p. 75) that these families are highly evolved and not primitive, as they are regarded in the German system of Engler and Prantl.

The next group is, of course, quite unrelated to the last-mentioned families. This is *Bixales*, of which only one family, *Cistaceae*, is represented in Britain. Though our native species are reduced almost to herbs (*Helianthemum*), most other members of the family are woody. In *Bixales* the ovary has *parietal* placentas. Probably derived from the *Bixales* (mainly tropical) are the *Violales* (*Violaceae*), the exotic members of which are also largely woody. The student is, therefore, warned (p. 88) against thinking of this family only in terms of *Viola*, of which he may know only the herbaceous species. Perhaps out of the *Bixales* stock we may also trace *Tamaricales* (*Tamaricaceae* and *Frankeniaceae*), and finally by way of the increasingly herbaceous *Passiflorales* (*Passifloraceae*, not represented in the British flora) follow through to the more climax and almost completely herbaceous though scandent *Cucurbitales* (*Cucurbitaceae*). In the last-mentioned *sympetaly* is quite common. And probably also derived from the *Bixales* are *Thymelaeales* (*Thymelaeaceae*), which have mainly lost their petals, but compensate for that with a petaloid calyx. It seems probable that the distinct and peculiar family *Proteaceae*, almost confined to the Southern Hemisphere, has a common origin with *Thymelaeaceae*, which are equally numerous in that region.

Then we come to a really woody group, the *Tiliales* (*Tiliaceae*). They are closely related to, and derived from, the tropical families *Dilleniaceae* and *Flacourtiaceae*. And derived from *Tiliaceae* are *Malvales* (*Malvaceae*), which, though largely herbaceous, have often tough fibrous stems, indicating that they have descended from a woody ancestral stock.

Parts of *Euphorbiales* (*Euphorbiaceae*) are closely related to *Tiliaceae*, and particularly its derived family *Sterculiaceae*, but the family *Euphorbiaceae* is regarded as something of a " rubbish heap " of apetalous groups, and the student is warned not to think of it only in terms of *Euphorbia* (see p. 100).

Taking a step down again we may find in the Tea family group *Theales* (*Theaceae*) some indication of the origin of the most primitive type of sympetalous group *Ericales* (*Ericaceae*), together with its higher representatives, *Vacciniaceae*, *Pyrolaceae*, and *Monotropaceae*. An author adopting this system might prefer to merge the *Vacciniaceae* in the *Ericaceae*, and I should not object very much, though *Vacciniaceae* are a little more than just inferior-ovaried *Ericaceae* (see p. 109). Therefore I prefer for the present to keep them as separate families.

We have now to deal with an isolated fragment which has perhaps also been derived from *Theaceae*—i.e., the *Guttiferales*, represented in our flora only by *Hypericaceae*, with opposite gland-dotted leaves, and the stamens united into bundles (phalanges). Trees and shrubs predominate in this family, though again most of the British species are herbs.

Each time we have to climb down our " tree " (see folder) a little and build up further from groups which seem to be centres of evolution for others. The next starting point is *Celastrales*, represented very meagrely in our flora by the Holly (*Aquifoliaceae*), by *Empetrum* (*Empetraceae*), and by *Euonymus* (*Celastraceae*). We trace the whole of this group from the *Theaceae*, which are not represented in the wild flora of Britain, but to which the familiar *Camellia* belongs. Further developments of this group are *Santaláles* (*Loranthaceae* and *Santalaceae*), *Rhamnales* (*Rhamnaceae* and *Elaeagnaceae*); and perhaps finally in this direction the *Sapindales*, represented only by native *Aceraceae*, but familiar also in the introduced horse-chestnut (*Aesculus*).

Loganiales grow mostly in the tropics and subtropics, and we have only *Oleaceae* to consider in Britain. They also may be derived from the Celastrales stock, the stamens usually being reduced to two, whilst *Apocynales* (*Apocynaceae*) and *Rubiales* (*Rubiaceae* and *Caprifoliaceae*) continue another branch of the same phylogenetic

" limb ", which attains its highest evolution in *Verbenales* (*Verbenaceae*).   And so we arrive at the top of the woody Dicotyledonous " tree ", and must begin again right from the " root " with the parallel subphylum, comprising the *herbaceous* Dicotyledons, and starting with *Ranunculaceae*.

It should be noted that in this *ligneous* division *poly-petaly* predominates, sympetaly is comparatively rare, whilst apetaly is nearly confined to derivatives of the *Rosales*—i.e., in the old group known as " Amentiferae ". This is in striking contrast with the herbaceous division, wherein only two groups have reached a climax and remained polypetalous—those ending in *Cruciferae* and *Umbellales*.   Another feature worthy of note is the rarity of zygomorphous flowers in the sympetalous *Lignosae*, the *Verbenales* providing the main exception.

Division II. *Herbaceae* (fundamentally herbaceous Dicotyledons).

As already stated, we begin our system of the herbaceous Dicotyledons with *Ranales* (*Ranunculaceae*), branches from which soon run out into the climax group *Aristolochiales* (*Aristolochiaceae*) through the herbaceous stock of *Berberidales* (*Berberidaceae*).   On p. 141 the student is reminded that most of the exotic genera of *Berberidaceae* are herbaceous, and bear little general resemblance to *Berberis*.

The next important stock whence further groups have found their origin is *Rhoeadales*, embracing the Poppy family, *Papaveraceae*, with its derivative families, *Fumariaceae* and *Cruciferae*, and probably *Resedaceae*, the *Cruciferae* being a completely climax group.

Next we must climb down our " tree " a little to another important basic stock, the *Caryophyllales* (*Caryophyllaceae* and allied families).   In these the embryo is often curved, and reduced apetalous derived groups are *Polygonales* (*Polygonaceae*) and *Chenopodiales* (*Chenopodiaceae*).

Another development of the Caryophyllaceous stock

may be the *Lythrales* (*Lythraceae*, *Onagraceae*, etc.), which have become perigynous, but have retained their petals.

One branch has probably developed into the *Gentianales* (*Gentianaceae*), *Primulales* (*Primulaceae*), and *Plantaginales* (*Plantaginaceae*), all of which are sympetalous, and the ovary in later stages has *free basal* placentation, the dividing walls between the original carpels having been completely or partially reduced.

We now arrive at a very important group, the *Saxifragales*, from which several groups may be traced. I feel that this is the proper place for the herbaceous family *Umbelliferae*, regarding it as a parallelism with *Araliaceae*, and not as a near relation (see p. 192). Botanists with rather fixed ideas may find this something of a bitter pill, as the author himself would have done in his younger days.

It is somewhat conjectural, perhaps, to place the *Campanulales* and *Asterales* as being derived from the *Saxifragales*, though *Campanulaceae* seem to be the only basic stock for the *Compositae*, a climax group, and one of the most homogeneous families of Flowering Plants, and mainly herbaceous.

From Saxifragales may also have been developed the *Valerianales* and *Solanales* (*Solanaceae* and *Convolvulaceae*), and finally the more climax families of the *Personales* such as *Scrophulariaceae*, *Orobanchaceae* and *Lentibulariaceae*, the last mentioned being a very advanced climax family both as regards floral structure, habit of growth, and even habitat.

There remain only the *Geraniales* (*Geraniaceae* and allied families), which have a local climax in the Balsams, *Balsaminaceae*, and soon become sympetalous in *Polemoniales* (*Polemoniaceae*) and *Boraginales* (*Boraginaceae*), and the completely climax *Lamiales* (*Labiatae*). It is pointed out (p. 236) that the gynobasic style so characteristic of the last two families, already occurs in *Limnanthaceae* (*Geraniales*), which has retained free petals. I am not quite on such sure ground with regard to the origin of *Boraginaceae* and *Labiatae*, but perhaps I shall learn from some critical reviewer where they really should go !

D

In the diagram at the end of the book I have shown the *Geraniales* as being derived through the Caryophyllaceous stock, but they might equally well have come directly from the *Ranales*.

It may be observed that only two of these groups of the herbaceous division reach their climax in apetalous forms, namely (1) *Ranales* to *Aristolochiales* and (4) *Caryophyllales* to *Chenopodiales*; two groups remain polypetalous, (2) *Ranales* to *Resedales*, and (7) *Ranales* to *Umbellales*; whilst the remainder find their climax families completely sympetalous with zygomorphy dominant.

Subphylum II. MONOCOTYLEDONES (Monocotyledons).

One might imagine from the name of this group that it depended entirely on the number of seed-leaves. This is not the case, however, and there are several associated characters; but the single cotyledon is the most important and quite constant feature. Although in the Dicotyledons there are a few exceptions which have only one seed-leaf, there are no plants amongst Monocotyledons which have two seed-leaves.

Associated with the single seed-leaf is the usually parallel nervation of the leaves, and these are nearly always alternate, the vascular bundles of the stem are closed and scattered, and the flowers are mostly trimerous.

The importance of the Monocotyledonous character was first recognised by the English botanist John Ray in 1686, and he made a very simple division of the group into two sections, (1) those with bulbs, and (2) those without bulbs, and he maintained a separate group for the grasses.

Subsequent authors, until about 1763, recognised the Monocotyledons as a distinct group, but nearly all of them first divided Flowering Plants into trees and herbs, and Monocotyledons appeared in both. Haller in 1742 stressed the importance of the superior and inferior ovary, and he was thus responsible for introducing a character which has led to much artificial classification. He was followed by Jussieu, who divided Monocotyledons into three sections, the first with hypogynous, the second with perigynous, and the third with epigynous stamens.

Various other authors arranged the families of Mono-cotyledons in many different ways; some started with the grasses, some ended with them, and some placed the Palms and Orchids in a similar way.

In Bentham and Hooker's classification the presence or absence of endosperm was considered important, and great prominence was also given to the relative position of the ovary and perianth. Although they began with a highly advanced family, *Orchidaceae*, they fortunately ended with the *Gramineae* (Grasses).

As already stated (p. 4), Engler and Prantl's system has been much challenged in its fundamental principles. Engler and Prantl placed first those families that are apetalous, so their arrangement began with the *Typhaceae* (Reedmaces), *Pandanaceae* (Screw-Pines), and *Spar-ganiaceae*; and the *Gramineae* (Grasses) follow soon after, all families which in this book are considered to be very advanced, and the grasses the most advanced of all. Engler even placed Monocotyledons *before* Dicotyledons.

As in Dicotyledons (see p. 5) we shall here regard the hypogynous, apocarpous flower as being the most primitive type. Hence we begin with the apocarpous groups *Butomales* (*Butomaceae*) and *Alismatales* (*Alismataceae*), and it happens that they much resemble *Ranunculaceae*.

The first evolved Monocotyledons probably grew in swamps in the tropics and several of the more primitive families have remained in this environment, some having even invaded salt water.[1]

The group containing the most primitive families has a calyx and corolla, just as in *Ranunculaceae*. I have called it Group I, **Calyciferae** (calyx-bearers), and it seems to be a link with the Dicotyledons. Later the two whorls become similar and petaloid, as in *Liliaceae* and *Amaryllidaceae*. I have called this Group II, **Corolliferae** (corolla-bearers), and these are the " petaloid Monocotyledons ". A third group has become very

[1] *Zosteraceae.*

much reduced in its floral structure and largely anemophilous. This is Group III, **Glumiflorae.**

In this new system the character of the superior and
inferior ovary formerly employed to separate the *Liliaceae*
and *Amaryllidaceae* has been discarded, and instead the
umbellate inflorescence has been taken as the distinguishing feature of the latter family. This involves the trans-
ference of the Onions (tribe *Allieae*) and two other exotic
tribes from the *Liliaceae* to the *Amaryllidaceae*.

The old and delightfully simple formula separating the
Liliaceae, Amaryllidaceae, and *Iridaceae,* is therefore no
longer considered to be tenable :—

Ovary superior; stamens 6	.	. .	*Liliaceae.*
Ovary inferior; stamens 6	.	. .	*Amaryllidaceae.*
Ovary inferior; stamens 3	.	. .	*Iridaceae.*

No doubt most of us as students received full marks for
giving correctly the characters of these three families.
But the evolutionary ramifications of nature are not to
be expressed so simply, and *formulae* such as these have
been stumbling blocks to a more natural system for nearly
two hundred years.

To sum up briefly, therefore, these new concepts of
Amaryllidaceae and *Liliaceae,* the appreciation of the
importance of the distinct calyx and corolla as a primitive
character, and of the *Gramineae* as the climax of Monocotyledonous evolution, are the principal points in this
classification of the Monocotyledons.

With this short sketch [1] the student may now be able
to understand the arrangement of the orders shown on
the folder and of the families in their linear sequence
on p. 32. Genera considered to be introduced and
more or less naturalised are marked in the keys with an *.

[1] For a fuller account of Monocotyledons see Hutchinson, *Families
of Flowering Plants,* vol. 2 (Macmillan and Co., 1934).

GYMNOSPERMAE.

1. TAXACEAE. 2. PINACEAE. 3. CUPRESSACEAE.

THE common Yew, *Taxus baccata* Linn., is the only member of the **Taxaceae** in Britain. This small family was formerly included in the larger group known as "Coniferae". It is very ancient phylogenetically, the female sporophylls not being collected into cones as in *Pinaceae*.

The Yew is found wild in most countries of Europe, in Algeria, Asia Minor, Caucasus, North Persia, and through the Himalayas to Sumatra, Celebes, and the Philippine Islands and through China to Japan, and is very variable in its foliage. In the Himalayas it ascends to 11,000 feet. In England the Yew occurs naturally on many of the chalky downs from Sussex to Wilts. It is very plentiful in the Wye Valley, Monmouthshire, and in Scotland it is found as far north as Aberdeen.

Yews are usually dioecious, and the male and female sporophylls are produced in early spring. A drop of mucilage is secreted by the micropyle of the ovule, and to this the pollen-grains are borne by the wind. It is an interesting fact that Yew seeds rarely germinate where they fall from the parent tree, but birds are attracted by the bright red fleshy aril which they devour with the seed. The latter is not affected by digestion, being voided and perhaps rendered fitter for germination.

Taxaceae are a little more advanced in a phylogenetic sense than *Ginkgoaceae*, the Maidenhair-tree family, which has close affinity with Cycads. *Ginkgoaceae* are probably second to *Cycadaceae* amongst seed-plants in being the most ancient. Although *Ginkgo* is found in a fossil state in Britain, it is now met with only in cultivation.

It seems rather curious that of the three families of Gymnosperms there is only one species of each of them indigenous in Britain. The Scots Pine, *Pinus sylvestris* Linn., represents **Pinaceae**. This species is distributed

45

over nearly the whole of Europe and most of Northern Asia as far as Manchuria, whilst it ranges south to North Persia and Spain. In Scotland it is still a wild tree, but in England it is considered to be planted, though it was plentiful in former times, as is evidenced by the occurrence of remains of logs, stumps of trees, and cones in peat mosses and submerged forests [1]. It is naturalised on many of the peat commons in southern England—for example, on the Bagshot Heath. When growing in a

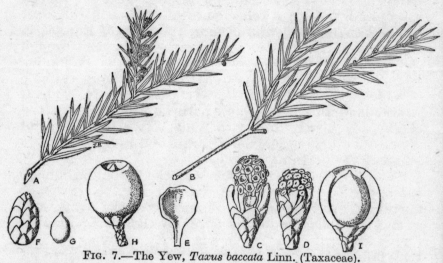

FIG. 7.—The Yew, *Taxus baccata* Linn. (Taxaceae).

A, male branch. B, female branch. C, D, male sporophylls. E, inner petal-like scale below males. F, female. G, ovule. H, ripe seed surrounded by fleshy aril. I, vertical section of same.

wild state and not crowded, the Scots pine adds great beauty to the landscape.

The leaves of the Scots pine are two in each short shoot and they persist about three years. The male strobili are borne in dense clusters towards the base of the annual shoots, and the female is usually solitary, at first erect but becoming pendulous after pollination. The cones open in the following spring and the seeds escape, spinning away in the wind. The empty cones usually hang on the

[1] Elwes and Henry, *Trees of Great Britain and Ireland*, 3 : 576.

FIG. 8.—The Scots Fir or Scots Pine, *Pinus sylvestris* L.
A, male or staminate cones. B, young, C, one year old female cones.
D, cone-scale bearing the two inverted ovules. E, seed.

47

tree until the following autumn, but their fall is sometimes hastened by drought.

As in the Juniper, there are several varieties and forms of the Scots pine.

Pinaceae is the largest family of Gymnosperms. Probably the most primitive living genera are to be found in the tribe *Abieteae*, which contains the Spruces (*Picea*) and Silver Firs (*Abies*) (largely planted in Britain), in which the leaves and cone-scales are spirally arranged, and the ovuliferous scale is free from the subtending bract. There is a parallel group, the *Araucarieae*, found almost entirely in the southern hemisphere, and they may have been evolved independently, their distribution corresponding with the *Podocarpeae* in the *Taxaceae*. The "Monkey Puzzle", *Araucaria araucana* K. Koch, is an example. In tribe *Pineae*, of which *Pinus* is the typical genus, the ovuliferous scale is completely adnate to the subtending bract.

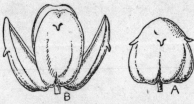

FIG. 9.—Related to the Juniper is the North African *Tetraclinis articulata* Mast.; it has only four cone-scales and they are *valvate*; these characters mark it as one of the most highly evolved of the genera of *Cupressaceae*, though somewhat less advanced than the Juniper.— A, young, B, mature cone.

The Juniper, *Juniperus communis* Linn., belongs to the family **Cupressaceae**, also formerly included in the "Coniferae" (now *Pinaceae*). In *Cupressaceae* the cone-scales are *valvate* and not overlapping as in *Pinaceae*, and in this character they are of a more advanced type. As regards its cones the genus *Tetraclinis* is one of the most advanced and reduced (fig. 9), there being only four scales. It is a native of North Africa. *Juniperus*, having a baccate "fruit", is even more advanced.

In *Juniperus communis* Linn., the "flowers" are usually dioecious and are formed in autumn in the axils of the lower leaves on the new shoots, and they open in the following spring. The male "flowers" are solitary and consist of five or six whorls of stamens, three in each whorl with ovate acute connectives. The female "flowers" are also solitary, the scales in several whorls, three in each whorl, the uppermost three small and alternating with three fleshy tubular ovules which become the seeds in the second or third year. When mature the seeds are blue-black and covered with bloom like that of a grape; the seeds are immersed in a soft, mealy sweet pulp; the seedling has two cotyledons.

Juniperus communis and its several geographical forms is the most widely distributed ligneous plant in

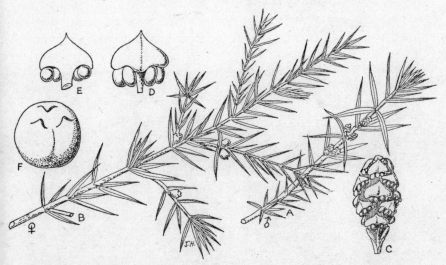

FIG. 10.—The Common Juniper, *Juniperus communis* Linn. (Cupressaceae), is a very advanced type of Gymnosperm with baccate "fruit".

A, male shoot. B, female shoot. C, male strobilus. D, and E, male sporophylls. F, berry.

the northern hemisphere, occurring right across the temperate zone. In its southern habitats it is found up to 12,000 feet altitude in the Himalayas. In the British Isles it occurs most abundantly in chalk and limestone districts, and it is sometimes a conspicuous feature of the downs in southern England. A dwarf montane kind, var. *montana* Ait., with a procumbent stem, grows wild in Scotland and Eire [1], in the Arctic, and in the Alps.

[1] For a discussion as to the status of this see Elwes and Henry, *Trees of Great Britain and Ireland*, 6 : 1401.

The families of British Gymnosperms and the more primitive families not represented may be arranged phylogenetically as under :—

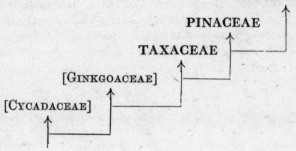

ANGIOSPERMAE
Dicotyledones—*Lignosae*
ROSALES and LEGUMINOSAE
4. Rosaceae. 5. Papilionaceae.

A FAMILY of exceptional interest from a phylogenetic point of view is **Rosaceae,** which is considered here to be the most primitive native woody group represented in Britain. With regard to its floral structure, it resembles *Ranunculaceae* very closely. But as the *Ranunculaceae* are nearly all herbs (except some species of *Clematis*) I do not consider they can be looked upon as the direct ancestors of *Rosaceae. Rosaceae* differ essentially from *Ranunculaceae* in the absence of endosperm, and in being fundamentally and predominantly woody (when all world members are considered).

Anatomical characters do not help very much for recognising the family *Rosaceae* as a whole, but some are characteristic of certain tribes. For example, in nearly all the exotic tribe *Chrysobalaneae* the stomata are accompanied by two or more subsidiary cells parallel to the pore, whilst in other *Rosaceae* they are surrounded by ordinary epidermal cells. The clothing hairs are unicellular and simple, or these may be bunched together like stellate hairs, or they may be glandular.

The more primitive tribes of *Rosaceae* are entirely [1] ligneous groups. These are the *Pruneae* and *Chrysobalaneae,* the second of these being almost wholly tropical, and allied to the more primitive family *Dilleniaceae. Pruneae* occur mostly in temperate regions.

The tendency nowadays among progressive taxonomists is to take a more restricted concept of genera, and to sort out very distinct groups of species as separate units. This has been done for *Pyrus,* which is now

[1] Some African species of *Parinari* (*Parinarium*) are reduced to subshrubs.

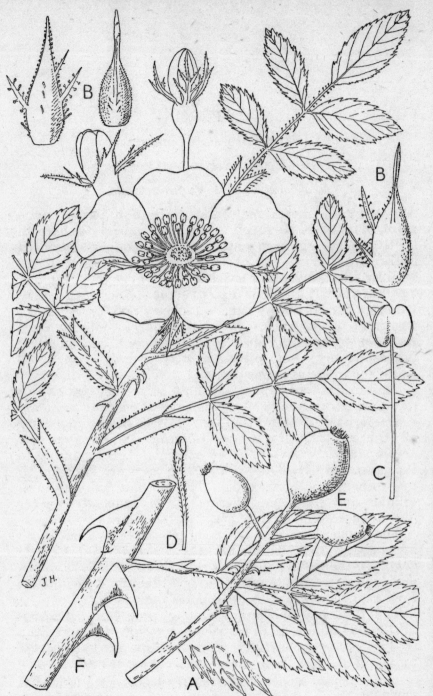

FIG. 11.—The common form of the Dog Rose, *Rosa canina* L. (Rosaceae), one of our most beautiful hedgerow plants.

A, enlarged teeth of the leaf. B, calyx-lobes. C, stamen. D, style.
E, fruits. F, prickles on vigorous shoot.

divided into several genera, of which we have only *Pyrus*
itself and *Sorbus* in Britain. A parallel case is the genus
Prunus, and some botanists, including the present author,
favour dividing it up in a similar way.

Consequently in this work *Padus* and *Cerasus* are
separated from *Prunus*
proper. The British
species involved in this
question are the Bird
Cherry, *Padus racemosa*
Lam. (*Prunus padus*
Linn.), the Gean,
Cerasus nigra Mill.
(*Prunus avium* Linn.),
the Dwarf Cherry,
Cerasus vulgaris Mill.
(*Prunus cerasus* Linn.),
the Blackthorn or Sloe,
Prunus spinosa Linn.,
and the " Bullace ",
Prunus insititia Linn.
The generic differences
are shown in the key.
On these lines the
Cherry Laurel (*Lauro-
cerasus*), and the Peach
and Almond (*Amygda-
lus*) are also separable
as distinct genera.

There is no true
Spiraea native of
Britain, but *S. salici-
folia* Linn. is natura-
lised. *Filipendula* is

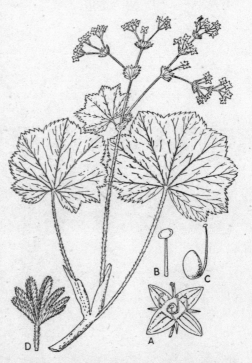

FIG. 12.—Lady's Mantle, *Alchemilla vulgaris* L. (Rosaceae), so named because
the leaves resemble a lady's mantle of
olden time, has much reduced inconspicuous flowers tending to become
unisexual.

A, flower. B, stamen. C, pistil. D,
young unfolding leaf.

now usually separated,
and is represented in our flora by *F. ulmaria* (L.)
Maxim. (syn. *Spiraea ulmaria* L.), the Meadow
Sweet, and *F. hexapetala* Gilib. (*Spiraea filipendula*
L.), the Dropwort. These should not be confused
with the " Spiraea " of greenhouses, which is not a

Spiraea but an *Astilbe,* belonging to the family *Saxifragaceae.*

Several other genera in Britain are herbaceous or subherbaceous; these are *Geum, Dryas, Potentilla, Alchemilla, Fragaria, Agrimonia, Sanguisorba,* and *Poterium.* But some are subwoody or have woody

Fig. 13.—*Rubus chamaemorus* Linn., a highly advanced
type of Rosaceae, reduced in habit to a single leaf
and flower, and with dioecious flowers.
A, whole plant.   B, fruit.

relations, and though their carpels greatly resemble those of certain *Ranunculaceae,* this likeness is considered to be due to parallel evolution.

Both *Rosa* and *Rubus* are highly advanced woody genera which are still in a state of flux and showing great instability. *Rubus chamaemorus* Linn., the " Cloud-

berry ", found at high altitudes in northern Britain, is an
exception and a striking example of a herb derived from
shrubs (see Fig. 13). And it is further advanced because
its flowers are dioecious. A parallel example is the dwarf

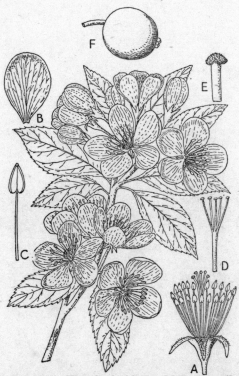

FIG. 14.—The Crab-Apple, *Malus pumila*
Mill. (Rosaceae) is beautiful either in
flower or fruit, though the flowers reserve
their sweetest odour for the night time.
A, flower with petals removed. B, petal.
C, stamen. D, style. E, stigma. F, fruit.

Cornel, *Chamaepericylmenum suecica* (Linn.) Aschers.
and Graebn. (see p. 23, Fig. 67). The small creeping
species of *Potentilla*, for example, should be compared with
P. fruticosa Linn., shrubby like most other exotic species.
The remaining woody genera, *Crataegus, Cotoneaster,
Pyrus, Malus, Mespilus,* and *Sorbus* are each represented

by only one or very few species, which are outliers from large groups spread over the north temperate zone.

The following diagram shows the origin of *Rosaceae*, and the key the phylogenetic sequence of the genera.

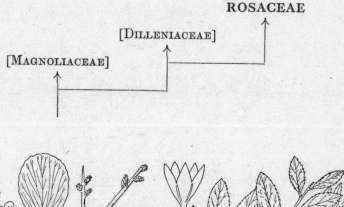

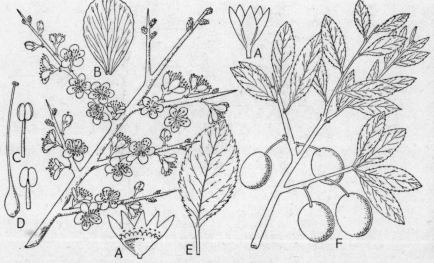

FIG. 15.—The Sloe, *Prunus spinosa* L. (Rosaceae), is one of the first to flower in spring before the leaves appear.

A, calyx closed and laid open. B, petal. C, stamens. D, pistil. E, leaf. F, fruits.

Rosaceae include many plants of considerable economic importance, such as the Apple (*Malus pumila* Mill.), Pear (*Pyrus communis* Linn.), Plum (*Prunus domestica*

Linn.), Prune (*Prunus domestica* Linn. var. *juliana* DC.), Peach (*Amagydalus persica* Linn.), (*Prunus persica* (Linn.) Batsch), Apricot (*Amagydalus armeniaca* Dum. (*Prunus armeniaca* Linn., and Almond (*Amagydalus amygdalina* Oken ex M. Roem.) (*Prunus amygdalus* Batsch), the Strawberry (*Fragaria vesca* Linn.), Blackberries and Raspberries (species of *Rubus*), Loquat (*Eriobotrya japonica* Lindl.), etc.

Finally, with regard to *Rosaceae*, it appears to show the path of evolution to another highly interesting family, the *Hamamelidaceae*, represented in gardens by the " Witch Hazels ", and other trees and shrubs. A close relation of the *Hamamelidaceae* is the family *Buxaceae*, formerly included in *Euphorbiaceae*, and an account of this family is given after *Papilionaceae*, because in this system families with more specialised flowers are as a rule placed before those characterised by reduction.

Key to the genera of *Rosaceae*.

Hard-wooded trees or shrubs; carpels not more than 5, more or less united; fruit fleshy or drupaceous :

Ovary superior; calyx deciduous; fruit a drupe, 1-seeded :

Flowers in racemes terminating the young leafy shoots . . PADUS

Flowers solitary or in umbel-like clusters or very short racemes separate from the leaves :

Terminal bud absent; axillary bud solitary; leaves convolute in bud; flowers single or 2–3 together . . . . PRUNUS

Terminal bud present; leaves conduplicate in bud; flowers in umbel-like clusters or very short racemes . . . CERASUS

Ovary inferior; calyx usually persistent :

Carpels bony when mature; fruit with 1–5 nutlets :

Leaves entire; branches unarmed :

Flowers small, with small calyx-lobes . . . COTONEASTER

Flowers rather large, with long foliaceous calyx-lobes MESPILUS

Leaves dentate or lobed; branches usually spiny; flowers in corymbose cymes . . . . CRATAEGUS

Carpels with leathery or papery walls when mature; fruit a 1–5-locular pome, each loculus with 1 or more seeds :

Flowers in simple umbels; leaves neither lobed nor pinnate :

Styles free; fruit pear-shaped . . . . PYRUS

Styles connate at the base; fruit apple-shaped . . . MALUS

Flowers in much-branched cymes; leaves toothed, lobed or pinnate . . . . SORBUS

E

Herbaceous plants, or if rather woody (*Rosa, Rubus*) then prickly and the carpels numerous and free or sometimes enclosed by the receptacle :
Ripe carpels not enclosed by the receptacle :
Epicalyx not present :
Fruit a follicle; carpels less than 15; stems and leaves not prickly
.... FILIPENDULA
Fruit a bunch of small drupes forming a " berry "; stems and leaves usually prickly . . . . RUBUS
Epicalyx present :
Style much elongating after flowering :
Leaves simple but coarsely toothed; scape 1-flowered; style plumose . . . . DRYAS
Leaves pinnately divided; style often hooked at the apex   GEUM
Style not elongating after flowering :
Achenes inserted on a dry or spongy receptacle . . POTENTILLA
(incl. *Comarum* and *Sibbaldia*)
Achenes on a large fleshy receptacle . . . . . FRAGARIA
Ripe carpels enclosed by the receptacle :
Carpels numerous, the fruit composed of many achenes enclosed by the fleshy receptacle . . . . ROSA
Carpels 1–3; achenes enclosed by the small but not fleshy receptacle :
Petals present; flowers in loose slender spikes; calyx covered with hooked bristles . . . . AGRIMONIA
Petals absent :
Epicalyx not present :
Heads purplish; flowers bisexual; stamens 4 (or 3–6)
.... SANGUISORBA
Heads green or tinged with red; flowers unisexual, dioecious, the males with numerous stamens with long filaments   POTERIUM
Epicalyx present; leaves palmately lobed or divided; flowers small and green . . . . ALCHEMILLA

It has been generally recognised that the group usually known as *Leguminosae* has been derived from the *Rosaceae*. In my general system I treated the three main subfamilies as families, only one of which is represented in our flora. These three families are *Caesalpiniaceae*, *Mimosaceae*, and *Papilionaceae*, the last-mentioned having numerous indigenous species in Britain.

The recognition of these as separate families is supported also on the anatomical side. For example, the ordinary clothing hairs of the *Papilionaceae* consist of simple or branched uniseriate hairs, which possess one or several short basal cells and a long terminal cell (Fig. 16). Such hairs have not been observed in the other two families (except in a few *Caesalpiniaceae*), which have ordinary unicellular hairs, a type that appears to be absent from the *Papilionaceae*. The type of stoma is variable in the family.

FIG. 16.—Types of hairs in the *Papilionaceae* (after Solereder).

The first mentioned two families are largely tropical and subtropical, whilst the *Papilionaceae* are very numerous in more temperate regions. We have thus a general derivation of temperate from tropical groups, which has probably been the usual course of events in the evolution of present-day flowering plants. It must again be impressed on the student that these points can only be appreciated by studying the tropical genera in a large herbarium or in the field.

Caesalpiniaceae are the most closely related to the *Rosaceae*. In *Caesalpiniaceae* the stamens are free from one another, and the aestivation of the petals is usually of the ordinary imbricate type. In *Papilionaceae*, however, the stamens are more or less

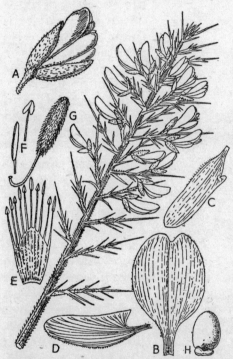

FIG. 17.—The Gorse, *Ulex europaeus* L. (Papilionaceae), is not content to produce its golden yellow flowers only in Spring but often gives another crop in Autumn.

A, flower. B, standard petal. C, wing-petal. D, keel-petal. E, staminal sheath opened out showing F, the two types of anthers. G, pistil. H, seed with its large fleshy aril.

united (monadelphous or diadelphous), and the corolla is zygomorphic.

The most primitive types of **Papilionaceae** are found mainly in the southern hemisphere, especially in South Africa and Australia, and this family may have been developed from the Caesalpiniaceous stock somewhere far south of the equator, perhaps on an antarctic continent, which also gave birth to the *Proteaceae* and other peculiar families now found mainly in South Africa and Australia.

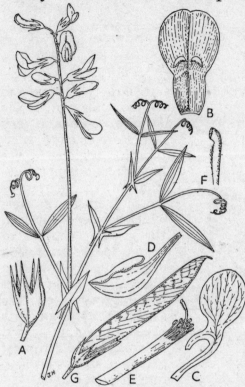

In order to find out which are the relatively primitive and the more advanced genera of *Papilionaceae* represented in Britain, the leaves and fruits will have to be studied on broad lines. With respect to the leaves it seems evident, taking Flowering Plants as a whole, that compound leaves have been de-

FIG. 18.—The Meadow Pea, *Lathyrus pratensis* L. (Papilionaceae), has bright yellow flowers, and its leaves are reduced to a single pair of leaflets and simple or branched tendrils.

A, calyx. B, standard petal. C, wing-petal. D, keel-petal. E, stamens united in a sheath. F, stigma. G, fruit.

rived from, and are therefore more recent than, simple leaves. For example, the primitive families *Magnoliaceae*[1] and *Annonaceae* have simple leaves which are not even toothed. It seems clear also that simple leaves may

[1] Except *Liriodendron* (*Magnoliaceae*), which has lobulate leaves.

have persisted right to the end of a large phylum, as in *Rubiaceae*, where they are always simple and rarely, if ever, toothed.

And it seems further logical to suppose that in pinnate leaves those with a terminal leaflet are on the whole more primitive than those without. In the tribe *Vicieae* the terminal leaflet is present or there is evidence showing its modification or almost entire reduction to a tendril or to a barren tip.

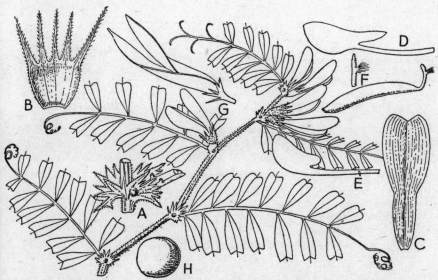

FIG. 19.—The Common Vetch, *Vicia sativa* L. (Papilionaceae), has long been cultivated as fodder and is widely distributed; flowers reddish purple; the stipules, A, have a dark spot in the middle. B, calyx laid open. C, standard-petal. D, wing-petal. E, keel-petal. F, stigma. G, fruit. H, seed.

Genera in Britain with simple leaves are *Ulex*, the " Gorse ", and *Genista*, and both are woody. These two genera are therefore probably the most primitive representatives of the family *Papilionaceae* in our islands, though the simple leaves may be due to reduction.

As trifoliolate leaves have probably been derived by reduction from pinnate types, those with pinnate leaves should come next in our papilionaceous " tree ". Of these, three genera belong to the tribe *Hedysareae*, which has a very specialised type of fruit, each seed being separated into one-seeded segments. These are *Ornithopus* and *Hippocrepis*, whilst the third, *Onobrychis*, has a one-seeded indehiscent fruit, being a very reduced type. On our family " tree " this tribe occupies a place very near the top.

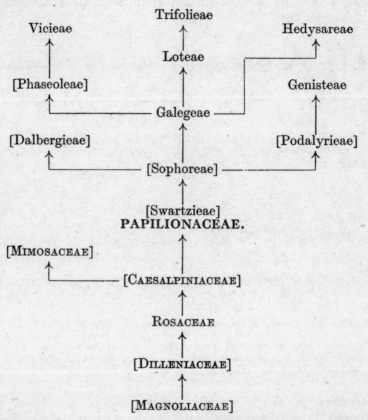

This diagram is given to show the origin of the order *Leguminosae* and the British tribes of the family *Papilionaceae*, some exotic families and tribes being included in square brackets.

Papilionaceae provide many valuable commodities, the most familiar to us in Britain being the Garden Pea (*Pisum sativum* L.), Broad Bean (*Vicia faba* L.), Pea

Nuts or Ground Nuts (*Arachis hypogaea* L.), Soy Beans (*Glycine max* Merrill), Clover (*Trifolium* spp.), Liquorice (*Glycyrrhiza glabra* L.), and there are many valuable exotic timbers. *Laburnum vulgare* L., *Wisteria sinensis*, *Lupinus* spp., and *Clianthus*, etc., are outstanding ornamental plants.

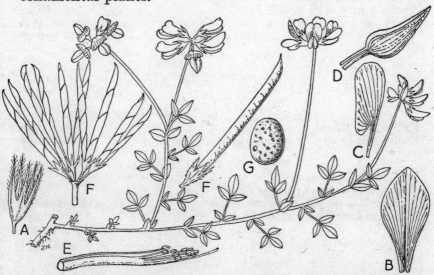

FIG. 20.—Bird's-foot Trefoil, *Lotus corniculatus* L. (Papilionaceae), with its red and yellow flowers, brings to mind warm summer days, and the buzz of the Bumble Bee.

A, calyx. B, standard-petal. C, wing-petal. D, keel-petals. E, stamens and style. F, fruits before and after releasing the seeds (G).

Key to the tribes and genera of *Papilionaceae*.

*Leaves simple (unifoliolate) . . . . GENISTEAE
**Leaves pinnate, with more than 3 leaflets :
   Leaf-rhachis without tendrils or barren point :
   Fruit dehiscent :
     Fruits without a longitudinal septum . . . . . LOTEAE
     Fruits divided by a longitudinal septum . . . GALEGEAE
     Fruits not dehiscent, composed of one or more than one 1-seeded
      joints . . . . HEDYSAREAE
   Leaf-rhachis ending in a tendril or barren point . . VICIEAE
***Leaves trifoliolate :
   Leaves digitately trifoliolate ; shrubs or herbs ; anthers alternately
    long and short. . . . . GENISTEAE
   Leaves pinnately trifoliolate ; mostly herbs ; anthers equal . .
                           TRIFOLIEAE

Tribe I.   GENISTEAE.

Calyx shortly 2-lipped :
  Calyx-lips deeply toothed . . . .   GENISTA
  Calyx-lips minutely toothed . . . .   CYTISUS
                                                    (*Saroth-
                                                    amnus*)
Calyx deeply 2-lipped :
  Spiny shrubs, with yellow flowers . . . .   ULEX
  Herb, with digitate leaves and 7–8 leaflets; flowers racemose, blue
    mixed with purple and white or yellow . . . .   LUPINUS*

Tribe II.   LOTEAE.

Calyx inflated and at length enclosing the fruit . . .   ANTHYLLIS
Calyx not inflated, pod exserted . . . .   LOTUS

Tribe III.   GALEGEAE.

Keel-petals obtuse . . . .   ASTRAGALUS
Keel-petals beaked or with an incurved apex . . . .   OXYTROPIS

Tribe IV.   HEDYSAREAE.

Fruit several-seeded :
  Fruit more or less cylindric; keel obtuse :
    Flower-cluster subtended by a leaf . . . . . .   ORNITHOPUS
    Flower-cluster not subtended by a leaf . . . . .   CORONILLA*
  Fruit flat, curved; keel beaked . . . .   HIPPOCREPIS
Fruit 1-seeded; keel obtuse . . . .   ONOBRYCHIS

Tribe V.   VICIEAE.

Wing-petals adherent to the keel; style filiform . . . .   VICIA
Wing-petals free or only slightly adherent to the keel; style flattened,
  longitudinally bearded . . . .   LATHYRUS

Tribe VI.   TRIFOLIEAE.

Filaments all united; flowers subracemose . . . . .   ONONIS
Filaments not all united :
  Inflorescence racemose :
    Racemes long . . . .   MELILOTUS
    Racemes short :
      Pod straight or curved, linear, mostly beaked. . .   TRIGONELLA
      Pod usually spirally twisted or broad and bent . .   MEDICAGO
  Inflorescence more or less capitate or shortly spicate .   TRIFOLIUM

CUNONIALES to URTICALES.

6. Grossulariaceae.   7. Cornaceae.   8. Araliaceae.   9.
Buxaceae.   10. Salicaceae.   11. Myricaceae.   12.
Betulaceae.   13. Corylaceae.   14. Fagaceae.   15.
Ulmaceae.   16. Urticaceae.   17. Cannabinaceae.

The Order *Cunoniales* is very sparsely represented in Britain by the genus *Ribes*, which includes the " Goose- berry" (*Ribes grossularia* L.), and the "Currants", Black (*R. nigrum* L.), Red, and White (forms of *R.*

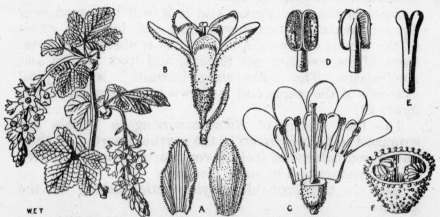

FIG. 21.—*Ribes sanguineum* L. (Grossulariaceae).

A, sepals. B, flower. C, same opened. D, front and back views of anther. E, stigma. F, cross section of ovary. (From Hutchinson, Families of Flowering Plants).

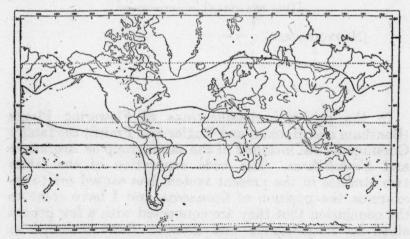

FIG. 22.—Range of the genus *Ribes* (Grossulariaceae); an interesting example of an advanced type of genus, widely spread in the Northern Hemisphere, which has penetrated far south by means of the Andes; note its absence from other parts of the Southern Hemisphere.

CORNACEAE AND ARALIACEAE

This illustration shows only two rather highly evolved families, CORNACEAE and ARALIACEAE. In most other systems both of these are placed close to the family UMBELLIFERAE, but in this classification their resemblance to this family is considered to be the result of parallel evolution. In consequence, in the diagram at the end of the book CORNACEAE and ARALIACEAE are shown to be descended from woody ancestors, whilst UMBELLIFERAE are considered to be derived from the *Saxifragaceous* stock. This may be regarded as purely hypothetical, of course, but who can say ?

That the families shown on this page are considerably advanced in the evolutionary scale is clear from the types of inflorescence. *Cornus*, shown at the bottom, has a *bractless* corymb. Derived from the same stock, but quite herbaceous, is *Chamaepericlymenum*, in which the upper leaves are in whorls of four and transformed into white petaloid bracts, which largely compensate for the small bunch of greatly reduced flowers. The berries of both are conspicuous. And it is probably through the same stock that the distinct and homogeneous family ARALIACEAE has been evolved, but not, as here contended, from the same stock as the UMBELLIFERAE (see p. 68).

The plants illustrated in the coloured plate are : Bottom, Cornus sanguinea *Linn.* Middle, Chamaepericlymenum suecicum (*Linn.*) *Aschers.* and *Graebn.* Top, Hedera helix *Linn.*

To face p. 66.

on anatomical structure (largely compiled from Solereder's work), and he has pointed out that there is a close resemblance in the wood structure of the *Cornaceae* and *Philadelphaceae*. And in whatever position *Cornaceae* are placed, *Araliaceae* should accompany them.

There are only two genera of *Cornaceae* in Britain, each represented by one species. *Cornus sanguinea* Linn., the common Dogwood, is a shrub up to six feet or so, with flowers in terminal cymes and without bracts or bracteoles. The other genus is *Chamaepericlymenum suecicum* (Linn.) Aschers and Graebn.[1], the Dwarf Cornel, with a slender creeping rhizome, short annual herbaceous stems, and the flowers crowded into a terminal cluster surrounded by an involucre of four large white petal-like bracts (modified upper leaves). The indumentum on the upper surface of the leaves is composed of unicellular T-shaped hairs.

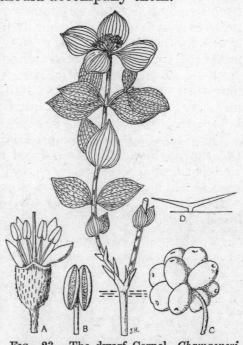

FIG. 23.—The dwarf Cornel, *Chamaepericylmenum suecicum* (Linn.) Aschers. & Graebn. (Cornaceae), a highly advanced herb descended from woody ancestors. Four of the upper leaves are modified to form an involucre which surrounds about twenty small and inconspicuous flowers. The hairs are unicellular and T-shaped, and occur only on the upper surface of the leaves.

A, single flower. B, anther. C, fruit. D, hair.

The petals are very small and dark purple, and the drupes are red. This delightful dwarf species occurs only in North-eastern England and on the Scottish

[1] See Hutchinson, *Annals of Botany*, n. ser. **6** : 83 (1942).

mountains, and nearly all around the Arctic Circle. If the student will study it for a while (see Fig. 23), he will realise that here is a species with a long phylogenetic history, a herb with a rhizome which has descended from shrubs and trees, whose flowers have become small and less attractive, and for which a compensating character has been evolved in the form of an involucre composed of the four upper leaves. There is a very similar species in Canada, *C. canadense* (Linn.) Aschers. and Graebn., with the upper leaves in a whorl like those of " Herb Paris ". These two species were formerly included in *Cornus*, but I agree with the German botanists in regarding them as a distinct genus.

There are no special subsidiary cells accompanying the guard cells of the stomata of the leaves of *Cornaceae*. The axis is characterised by scalariform perforations of the vessels which often have numerous bars.

Here is the hypothetical phylogenetic history of the family :—

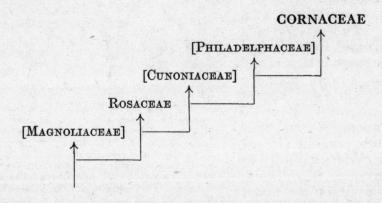

The common Ivy, *Hedera helix* Linn., belongs to the family **Araliaceae**, which presents a pretty problem to the phylogenist. It has nearly always been classified alongside *Umbelliferae*, but this position is now questioned.

Although there is a very considerable resemblance, I do not believe this to be due to real relationship, and it seems probable that the two families have had quite a different phylogenetic history. *Araliaceae* are almost invariably *woody*, the umbels are simple, or the flowers may even be arranged in spikes, racemes, or panicles; the leaves are stipulate, the stipules often *intra-petiolar*, and the ovary is usually composed of more than two carpels (sometimes nearly a hundred, as in *Tupidanthus*, from the Eastern Himalayas), and the fruit is a berry or drupe, whilst in several genera the endosperm is ruminate as in *Annonaceae* and *Myristicaceae*.

In contrast, *Umbelliferae* are *herbaceous*, with one or two slight exceptions; there are no real stipules, the umbels are frequently compound, the ovary is constantly two-locular, and the fruit is quite different from *Araliaceae*, separating into two one-seeded indehiscent carpels (mericarps), within the pericarps of which are often longitudinal canals (vittae), filled with oil or resin; and the endosperm is not ruminate.

It seems to the writer, therefore, that the resemblance between the two families is superficial and due to parallelism, that *Araliaceae* have descended from woody ancestors, such as *Rosales* and *Cunoniales*, which usually have stipules, and that *Umbelliferae* have been evolved from the same stock as the *Saxifragaceae*, which agree in having no stipules and which frequently have a bicarpellate ovary.

I might add another argument for the consideration of those who believe that all herbs have been derived from woody plants and those, if any, who believe the contrary. To the former, who would derive the *Umbelliferae* from the *Araliaceae*, I would point out that in *Umbelliferae* the petals are mostly *imbricate* in bud, whilst in *Araliaceae* they are *valvate*. Evolution with respect to this character has usually been considered to have been the converse of this. To those who would derive *Araliaceae* from *Umbelliferae* I would draw attention to the ovary of the former, which is composed usually of more than two carpels, whilst in *Umbelliferae* they are constantly two. And a berry or drupe could scarcely be expected to have been derived from the peculiar mericarpic fruit of the *Umbelliferae*.

In looking at the common Ivy (Fig. 24), therefore, the student may like to ponder the question of its origin, and realise that it is easy to be led astray by superficial resemblances. A peculiar habit of the common Ivy is its late flowering, usually not before September, when the faint almost putrefactive odour attracts various kinds of flies, besides *Hymenoptera*, which effect cross-pollination. The nectar is secreted in a disk surrounding the styles.

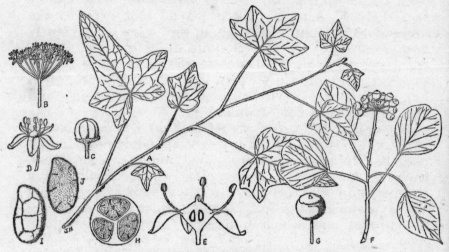

FIG. 24.—The Ivy, *Hedera helix* Linn. (Araliaceae).

A, barren young shoot. B, inflorescence. C, flower. D, flower. E, vertical section of flower. F, fruiting shoot. G, fruit. H, cross-section of fruit. I, seed. J, longitudinal section of seed.

The indumentum of young Ivy stems is composed of stellate hairs.

A remarkable exotic genus is *Helwingia* (Himalaya to Japan), with its dioecious flowers apparently springing from the middle of the leaf-blade, due to the peduncle being adnate to the midrib of the leaf.

Placed side by side below are tables showing the separate origin and subsequent parallel development of *Araliaceae* and *Umbelliferae*, to make clear to the student the points raised.

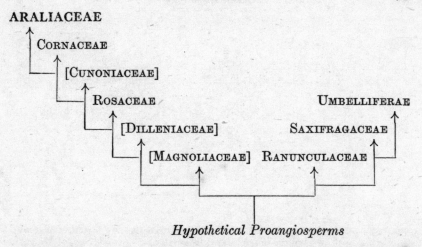

ARALIACEAE

↑
    CORNACEAE
        ↑
    [CUNONIACEAE]
    ↑
        ROSACEAE   UMBELLIFERAE
            ↑   ↑
        [DILLENIACEAE]   SAXIFRAGACEAE
        ↑   ↑
            [MAGNOLIACEAE] RANUNCULACEAE
                ↑   ↑

Hypothetical Proangiosperms

From *Cornaceae* and *Araliaceae* we pass on to a very
different family, **Buxaceae**, which, as noted on p. 37,
has probably been derived from *Hamamelidaceae,* and is
not related to *Euphorbiaceae* in which it is included in
Bentham and Hooker's system.   The common Box, *Buxus
sempervirens* Linn., grows wild in limestone districts,
namely, in the Chiltern Hills and on Box Hill in
Surrey.   Boxwood is a valuable timber, but is now very
scarce.

The distribution of *Buxaceae* over various parts of the
world suggests that like *Magnoliaceae* they are only
remnants of a stock which is fast dying out.   *Buxus* is
the largest genus and is the most widely spread.   It
occurs in Europe, North Asia, including Indo-China and
the Philippines, in the Azores, West Indies, and in isolated
places in East and South Africa and in Madagascar.
It is absent from the Eastern United States, where so
many of these older families are represented, but it is
found in the West Indies, not far away.

Anatomical characters common to the family are the
wood-prosenchyma and the vessels in contact with the
parenchyma with bordered pits.   The vessels usually
have scalariform perforations.   There are no external
glands, and the stomata in *Buxus* are surrounded by a
fairly well-defined rosette of subsidiary cells.

FIG. 25.—Box, *Buxus sempervirens* Linn. (Buxaceae), is familiar in a wild
state only in chalky districts and in gardens as an edging to the path.
Shoot with young fruit.

A, leaf.   B, male flower.   C, female flower.   D, cross-section of ovary.
E, vertical section of ovary.   F, fruit.   G, seed.   H, longitudinal section
of seed.

The origin of the family may be more readily understood by reference to the diagram below.

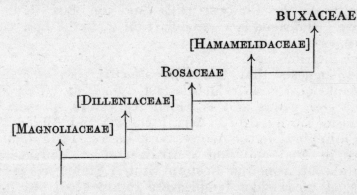

After the Box trees come the Willows, **Salicaceae.**
At one time we were taught (following the German
system of Engler and Prantl) that this family was primitive.   Now few botanists would be prepared to uphold
this view, and most would recognise it as being relatively
very advanced.   To start with, the flowers are *dioecious,*
they are borne in *highly specialised catkins,* the perianth is

entirely *reduced*, the stamens often *reduced to two*, and the ovary is composed of *two united carpels* with *parietal* placentas. Not one of these characters, either singly or in combination with the others, can be regarded as primitive.

Another feature pointing to recent origin of the group is the instability of the species of *Salix*, which are still in a state of flux, a condition usually the reverse of primitive and observable in advanced genera of nearly every large family, such as *Rubus* and *Crataegus* (Rosaceae), *Hieracium* (Compositae), etc. It is interesting to note that the less prolific genus *Populus* has wind-pollinated (anemophilous) flowers, whilst the more virile stock, *Salix*, has insect-pollinated (entomophilous) flowers.

Solereder gives several anatomical

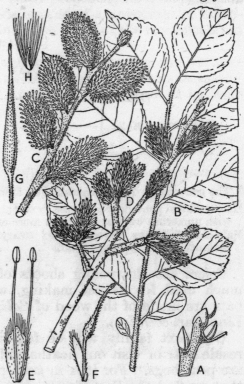

FIG. 26.—The Great Sallow Willow, *Salix caprea* L. (Salicaceae), is common in woods and copses and in waste places in many parts of the country.

A, winter buds. B, leafy shoot. C, male, D, female catkins. E, male bract and stamens. F, pistil. G, fruit. H, seed.

characters common to the family. The stomata tend towards the Rubiaceous type, with subsidiary cells parallel to the pore. There are no glandular hairs and internal secretory organs are also present. A very interesting character of the *Salicaceae* is the structure of the petiole of *Populus*, which has one or more superimposed rings of xylem and phloem.

F

Northern Europe across Asia and North America, and is also found in the mountains of Central Europe. The leaves are small and orbicular. The common Birches provide very good firewood, the wood throwing out much heat, and the timber is valuable, especially for plywood.

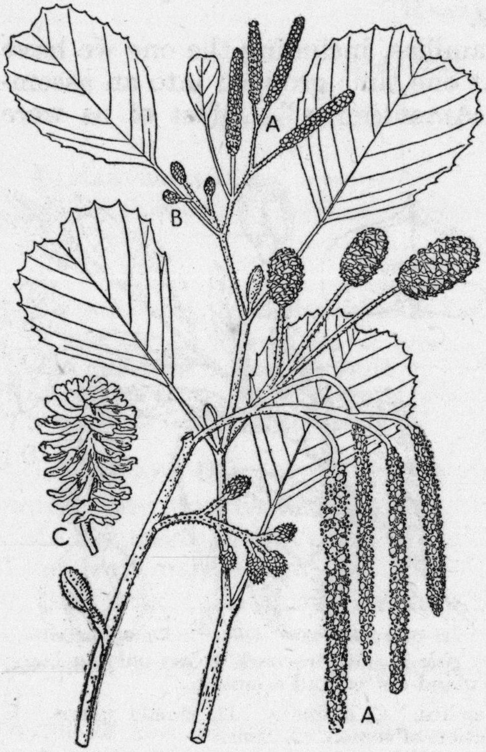

Alnus, the Alder, is represented in Britain by only one species, *A. glutinosa* Gaertn. It grows in rather wet places and usually by streams. The female fruiting catkin resembles a cone and is ellipsoid. The flowers are sub-precocious and appear in early spring, the catkins having been formed in the previous autumn.

The behaviour of the seeds of Alder is interesting.[1] The nutlets are shaken out of the " cones " by the wind during the autumn and winter. Their shells are provided with small air-tight

Fig. 28.—The Alder, *Alnus glutinosa* Gaertn. (Betulaceae), grows in wet borders of streams and low-lying fields, and ranges far into Siberia and North Africa.

A, male catkins. B, young female catkins. C, old fruiting catkin (" cone ").

cavities which enable them to float in water, and they secrete an oil which protects them from being wetted. If they fall into the water, which usually happens, they float undamaged during winter, and they germinate in the water in early spring, the young seedlings at length

[1] See Elwes and Henry, *Trees of Great Britain and Ireland*, 4 : 938.

drifting to the banks and establishing themselves in a suitable place.

The common Alder is very widely spread, through nearly all Europe, Siberia, Western Asia, and in Algeria and Morocco, and is in consequence very variable, about a dozen varieties being recognised.

The genus has also a wide distribution, with about twenty-five species, inhabiting, besides the regions mentioned above, extratropical Asia, North and Central America, and along the Andes of South America as far as the Argentine.

The two genera of *Betulaceae* may be distinguished as follows :—

Stamens 6–12 to each scale of the catkin; female catkins cylindric in fruit, the scales 3-lobed and falling off with the fruits, which are surrounded by a thin wing . . . . *Betula*
Stamens 4 in each of the three flowers under each scale of the catkin; female catkins ellipsoid in fruit, cone-like, the scales persisting on the axis; fruits not winged . . . . *Alnus*

The clothing hairs of *Betulaceae* are simple, unicellular, or uniseriate, and there is no special type of stoma. A distinguishing feature is the very characteristic perforations of the vessels with very thin numerous bars.

The diagram below shows the origin of *Betulaceae* more clearly :—

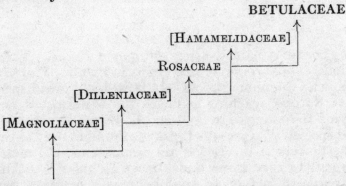

From the Birches and Alders it is not a great step to the Nut-bushes and Hornbeams, **Corylaceae.** The Hornbeam, *Carpinus betulus* Linn., is a small tree, largely planted, but native in Wales and central and southern England. The clusters of fruits are very conspicuous with their large leafy three-lobed bracts, and the fruit is enveloped by the calyx. This species is widely distributed in Europe, reaching the Caucasus, Asia Minor, and Persia, but is absent from the Iberian Peninsula.

In *Corylus* the male flowers are in pendulous catkins, and the female flowers are solitary or clustered as seen in fruit, each within a jagged leafy involucre containing the familiar " nuts ". The indumentum of the leaves of *Corylaceae* consists of unicellular and uniseriate hairs and of club-shaped glands. The stomata are confined to the lower surface and surrounded by ordinary epidermal cells.

Here is a diagram to show the probable origin of the family :—

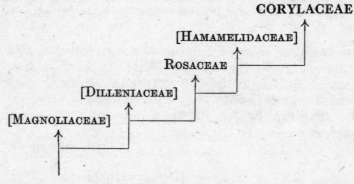

Fagaceae is named after the genus *Fagus*. There is one indigenous species of this genus in Britain, *F. sylvatica* Linn., the Common Beech. It is widely spread in temperate Europe, reaching as far as the Crimea, but is not believed to be native in Scotland or Eire. A very closely allied species, *F. orientalis* Lipski, is found in the Caucasus.

The flowers of the Beech are monoecious, the males in pedunculate very short and almost globular " catkins ". The perianth is four to six-lobed, with eight to twelve stamens, the filaments slender, and with small two-locular anthers. The female flowers are in a globular almost sessile cluster, only two or three flowers in the

ROSACEAE TO FAGACEAE

The gap between a Rose and an Oak may seem a wide one, though there are many connecting links. The Rose family, ROSACEAE (*Rosa* and *Cerasus* drawn), is closely related to the large group of plants known as LEGUMINOSAE, of which three families are now often recognised. Only one, PAPILIONACEAE (*Lathyrus* shown), is represented in the British flora, the more closely related tribes being found in other parts of the world, especially in the tropics. The Box tree belongs to a group which links up with the trees with catkins. It is related to the Witch Hazel family, HAMAMELIDACEAE, which points to the origin of the catkin-bearing trees, such as *Corylus* (shown), the Birches, Beeches and Oaks (shown). The catkin is not here regarded as a primitive structure. On the contrary it is looked upon as a very highly specialised type of inflorescence, and a complete climax in development with much reduced and often unisexual flowers.

The plants illustrated in the coloured plate are : Bottom, left, Rosa wilsonii *Borrer*; right, Cerasus nigra *Mill.* Middle, left, Buxus sempervirens *Linn.*; right, Lathyrus tuberosus *Linn.* Top, left, catkins and nuts of Corylus avellana *Linn.*, and leaves and acorns of Quercus robur *Linn.*

To face p. 78.

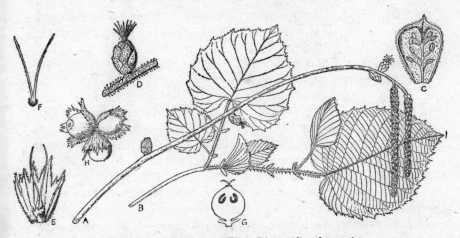

FIG. 29.—*Corylus avellana* Linn. (Corylaceae).

A, spring flowering shoot showing female and male flowers. B, summer shoot. C, male flower. D, female flower. E, same with bracts opened out. F, pistil. G, vertical section of female flower.

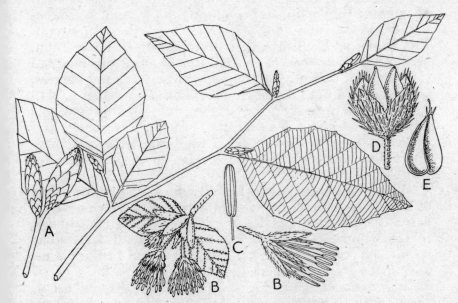

FIG. 30.—*Fagus sylvatica* L. (Fagaceae).

A, winter buds. B, male flowers. C, anther. D, involucre and fruit. E, nut.

middle being fertile; the perianth is four to five-lobed, and the ovary is three-locular with two pendulous ovules in each loculus; styles three. The nuts are two or three, enclosed in a hard prickly involucre composed of the concrescent outer and inner scales.

The genus *Fagus* formerly embraced also those species in the southern as well as the northern hemisphere. But the Dutch botanist Blume separated the southern Beeches under the name *Nothofagus* (false Beech), and this genus is now generally recognised. It seems an interesting parallel development in a widely separated area.

There are seven species of the true Beeches, the genus stretching right across the temperate northern hemisphere. The southern Beeches, *Nothofagus*, are found in extratropical South America, Australia, Tasmania, and New Zealand, and there are about twenty species, most of them evergreen.

Fagaceae also include the Oaks, *Quercus*. To the inhabitants of these islands perhaps no trees have been of greater importance for shipbuilding and constructional work, and they provide excellent firewood. The common English Oak is now called *Q. robur* Linn. (syn. *Q. pedunculata* Ehrhart), and is naturally adapted to a wettish soil, whilst the very closely related species, *Q. petraea* (Matt.) Lieblein (*Q. sessiliflora* Salisb.), will thrive in comparatively dry situations. As the synonyms imply, the former has the fruits borne on a peduncle, and in the latter they are sessile on the branchlets, and there are differences in the shape of the bases of the leaves (Fig. 31).

The pedunculate oak is found wild in the greater part of Europe, Asia Minor, and the Caucasus, and is essentially a tree of the plains and low hills in northern latitudes; in the Pyrenees it grows up to over 3000 feet. The sessile oak, on the other hand, is not found in the plains, and in the Pyrenees ascends as far as 5300 feet.[1]

In some members of the family stellate hairs occur, often with a multiseriate stalk, the simple hairs are unicellular, and glandular hairs are sometimes present.

[1] Elwes and Henry, *Trees of Great Britain and Ireland*, 2 : 297–8.

The genus *Ulmus* has often been included in the family *Urticaceae*, but this group is now generally divided into several families, the **Ulmaceae**, containing the Elms and a few other genera, such as the exotic *Zelkova*, *Celtis*, and *Trema*, the *Moraceae* (Figs, Breadfruits, etc.), *Cannabinaceae* (Hops, etc.), and *Urticaceae* proper (Nettles, etc.). From big trees and shrubs the habit becomes quite herbaceous, even down to small annuals in *Urticaceae*, but most of the herbs, such as the common Nettle,

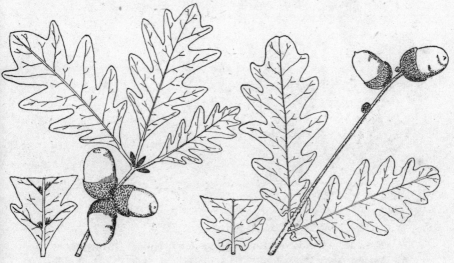

FIG. 31.—The "spotting" features of the two British native oaks are shown here; left, *Quercus petraea* (Matt.) Liebl., right, *Quercus robur* Linn. (Fagaceae).

remain very fibrous, like the family *Malvaceae* in its own group (p. 96).

The common Elm in Britain is *U. procera* Salisb. and is the *Ulmus campestris* of Linnaeus' *Flora Anglica*, and of many British Floras. The Wych or Scotch Elm is *U. glabra* Huds., and is usually found in British Floras under the name *U. montana* Smith. In addition there are *U. carpinifolia* Gleditsch. (*U. nitens* Moench.) (the " U. campestris" of most European Floras), *U. stricta* Lindl., the Cornish Elm, *U. plotii* Druce, and *U. diversifolia* Melville. The *U. elegantissima* Horwood is a hybrid segregate of *U. glabra* × *U. plotii* [1].   Elms are valuable timber trees.

The stomata of the leaves are not surrounded by any specialised cells. Cystoliths and similar bodies are common in the family.

The family **Urticaceae** is treated in my general book in a restricted sense, the *Ulmaceae, Moraceae,* and *Cannabinaceae* being excluded. The remainder is largely a

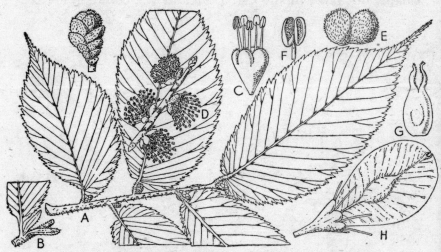

FIG. 32.—The Wych Elm, *Ulmus glabra* Huds.   (Ulmaceae).

A, mature leafy branchlet. B, stipules. C, flower. D, flowers. E, bract. F, anther. G, pistil. H, fruit. J, winter bud (not lettered in the drawing).

herbaceous group, which is represented in Britain by *Urtica* and *Parietaria.*

I now believe this large herbaceous group to have descended from woody ancestors. In my general scheme there were shown as having been derived from *Piperales,* but a more natural place seems to be after *Moraceae.* The flowers are small and unisexual. In *Parietaria* the leaves are alternate, in *Urtica* opposite. The common Nettle, *Urtica dioica* Linn., is a perennial and capable of holding its own on account of its persistent rootstock and

[1] I am indebted to my colleague Dr. R. Melville for this information as to species.

ULMACEAE TO URTICACEAE

Elms and Nettles may not seem to have much in common, though they are distantly related. It may seem at variance with the principles upon which the Dicotyledons are divided in this system to consider large trees like the Elms to be akin to herbs such as the Nettles. The whole of the families have to be studied, however, in order to appreciate this. Though nettles are herbaceous, they are very fibrous, probably because they have been derived from more woody ancestors. This must, of course, remain as a mere speculation, and cannot be proved. But taxonomic botany would be rather a dull subject and would lose much of its fascination if speculation were ruled out. Darwin once wrote to Wallace saying " I am a firm believer that without speculation there is no good and original observation ", so we are in quite good company.

Ulmus is shown representing the ULMACEAE, *Humulus* the CANNABINACEAE, and *Urtica* the URTICACEAE, all with greatly reduced flowers.

The plants illustrated in the coloured plate are : Bottom, Ulmus sp. Left, Humulus lupulus *Linn.* Right, Urtica dioica *Linn.*

To face p. 82.

stinging hairs. Another British species, *U. urens* Linn.,
is an annual (see Fig. 33). The stem of the common
Nettle is rich in fibre and the leaves are used for the
extraction of chlorophyll. The valuable " Ramie " fibre
is obtained from the exotic *Boehmeria nivea* Gaud. The
genus *Humulus*, the Hop, formerly included in *Urticaceae*,
differs from all others in this family in its seed; there is no
endosperm and the embryo is spirally coiled, and the
stipules are interpetiolar. A description of it will be
found under *Cannabinaceae* below.

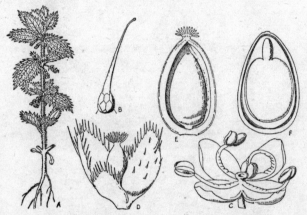

FIG. 33.—*Urtica urens* Linn. (Urticaceae).

A, whole plant in flower. B, stinging hair from the
stem. C, male flower. D, female flower. E, vertical
section of fruit. F, vertical section of seed.

Anatomically the family **Cannabinaceae** resembles
Urticaceae in several characters, such as the simple
perforations of the vessels, the wood prosenchyma with
simple pits, secondary hard bast, long bast-fibres (*Cannabis*), unicellular clothing hairs often containing cystoliths,
and glandular hairs, the heads of which are divided only
by vertical walls. The stomata have no special subsidiary
cells.

The genus *Humulus* is a native of Britain, the well-
known Hop, *Humulus lupulus* Linn., being used for making
beer and for tonic medicines. The flowers of *Humulus*
are dioecious. Hemp, *Cannabis sativa* L., is an important

fibre used for making ropes, string, and sacking, and the seeds are food for cage birds.

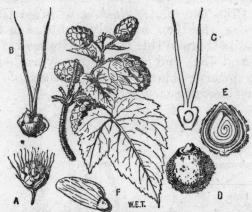

Fig. 34.—An important plant in the brewing industry, the " Hop," *Humulus lupulus* L. (Cannabinaceae).

A, female inflorescence. B, female. C, vertical section of same. D, fruit. E, vertical section of same. F, seed.—After Baill. (From Hutchinson, Families of Flowering Plants).

BIXALES to CUCURBITALES.

18. Cistaceae.   19. Thymelaeaceae.   20. Violaceae.
21. Frankeniaceae.   22. Tamaricaceae.
23. Polygalaceae.   24. Cucurbitaceae.

As pointed out on p. 15, the more primitive families of woody plants are not now found in Britain, having been destroyed by successive Ice Ages. Our next woody family is therefore relatively fairly advanced. This is **Cistaceae**, which belongs to a mainly tropical group, the *Bixales*.

In *Bixales* the carpels have become united and the ovules are inserted on the walls of the ovary (parietal placentation). This seems to be an early type of placentation when carpels become united, and the axile arrangement probably represents a later and more climax stage. *Bixales* are derived from the more primitive *Dilleniales* (see diagram at end of book) and the general relationship is soon appreciated if all their genera be examined and compared.

There is only one genus of *Cistaceae* in Britain— namely, *Helianthemum*, the Rock Roses. It favours limestone and chalky places. In the Bentham and Hooker

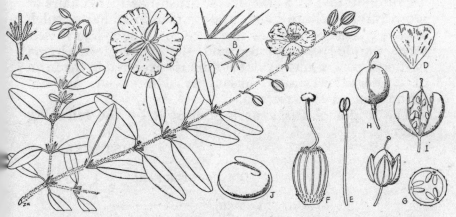

Fig. 35.—*Helianthemum nummularium* (L.) Mill. (Cistaceae). Flowering shoot.

A, stipules. B, stellate hairs of leaves. C, flower from below. D, petal. E, stamen. F, pistil. G, cross-section of ovary. H, fruit. I, the same, open. J, embryo.

system *Cistaceae* followed on closely after the Poppy family (*Papaveraceae*) and the Crucifers (*Cruciferae*). But it is not here considered to be really allied to these, not only because nearly all the exotic members of the family are woody, but it is far more happily placed amongst other woody families such as *Bixaceae* and *Flacourtiaceae*.

Like the Poppies, however, the petals are often very fugitive and crumpled in bud, and the stamens are numerous; also the ovary is one-locular with parietal placentas, though often towards the base the placentas nearly meet towards the middle of the loculus. The absence of nectar is compensated for by the production of large quantities of pollen upon which bees feed.

Three of the British species are undershrubs, showing derivations from more woody types, and one, *Helianthemum guttatum* Mill., has been evolved so much as to have become an annual. Annuals are more recent than perennials. *Cistaceae* are most abundantly represented in the Iberian Peninsula and around the Mediterranean.

They are characterised anatomically by the occurrence of unicellular thick-walled hairs of special structure, which are often united into star-like or brush-like tufted hairs or more rarely peltate hairs, and of glandular hairs which always consist of only one row of cells. The xylem vessels have simple perforations, and the wood-prosenchyma bordered pits, whilst oxalate of lime is excreted in the form of clustered crystals. Special subsidiary cells are not found around the stomata.

The origin of *Cistaceae* is indicated by the following diagram :—

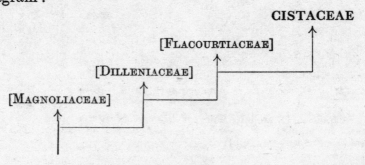

I now consider the **Thymelaeaceae** to be apetalous relatives of the *Bixales*, especially of the exotic family *Flacourtiaceae* and a small linking family, the *Gonystylaceae*. They have a tubular often coloured calyx within which the stamens are sometimes inserted at different levels, but usually no petals. With the single exception of the exotic genus *Drapetes*, all *Thymelaeaceae* are characterised by the presence of intraxylary phloem accompanied by more or less abundant hard bast fibres, and the external bast is likewise distinguished by numerous bast fibres (Solereder). The stomata are not of a special type, and there are no internal secretory organs or external glands. Clothing hairs are unicellular. The family is most abundantly represented in the southern hemisphere, being very numerous in South Africa and Australia. They are of little economic value except in horticulture.

In the northern hemisphere, DAPHNE, the only genus represented in Britain, is very widely distributed, with a few species in the northern tropics. It is absent from North America, however, its place being taken by a related small genus, *Dirca*. The two British species occur in woods, *Daphne mezereum* Linn. having precocious very sweetly scented deep pink flowers and deciduous leaves, whilst *D. laureola* Linn. is evergreen, and the flowers are green and devoid of scent.

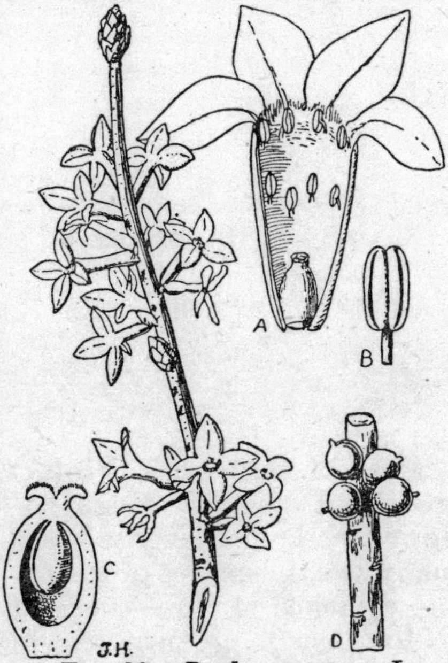

There is no sign of petals in *Daphne*, but many other genera have small petals which have been regarded and described as scales. To my mind they are nothing but reduced petals. Specimens of one large genus are often seen in our greenhouses. This is *Pimelea*, from Australia and New Zealand, and the stamens are reduced to two.

FIG. 36.—*Daphne mezereum* L. (Thymelaeaceae).

A, dissection of flower. B, anther. C, vertical section of ovary. D, fruits. (From Hutchinson, Families of Flowering Plants.

To the student of plant geography and phylogeny the family *Thymelaeaceae* is of particular interest because it seems to show the origin of the wonderful family *Proteaceae*, which is so conspicuous a feature of the landscape at the Cape of Good Hope, and in parts of Australia.

The *Proteaceae,* or at any rate certain of them, such as the genus *Protea* and the "Silver tree," *Leucadendron argenteum* L., may be looked upon as the "Compositae" of this particular group of plants, for the flowers are often collected into heads and surrounded by an involucre of bracts, just as in *Compositae.* This is an excellent example of parallelism, the climax development of an inflorescence often being a head (capitulum).

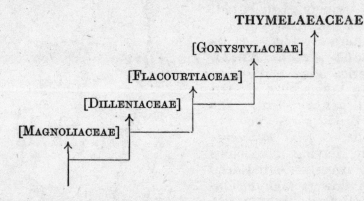

Most of the exotic **Violaceae,** apart from *Viola,* are trees and shrubs. None of these is native of Britain, however, and nearly all are tropical. There are also many woody species of VIOLA. Besides the woody habit, the presence of three parietal placentas is rather foreign to the *Cruciferae,* near to which they are usually placed, and in which there are only two placentas.

It seems very probable that *Viola* originated in the tropics and thence spread into temperate regions. It occupies a position in the family similar to that of the Balsams (*Impatiens*) in the older and wider conception of the *Geraniaceae.* A peculiarity of many of the species of *Viola* found in temperate regions is that the showy perfect flowers rarely produce fertile fruits, these being developed in the minute inconspicuous cleistogamous flowers which appear later in the season. The presence of stipules is also detrimental to the idea of the family having been derived from the same stock as the *Cruciferae,* which have no stipules. And the seeds of *Violaceae* have retained their endosperm; in *Cruciferae* there is none. Bentham and Hooker described six species of *Viola*; the latest London Catalogue enumerates no fewer than twenty-six, a particularly striking example of the divergent views

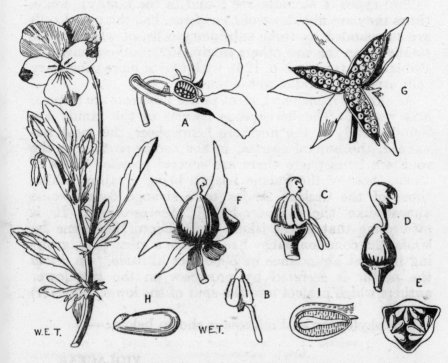

FIG. 37.—Although the British species of *Viola* are herbs, there are many woody exotic species, and the more primitive relatives of *Viola* are trees and shrubs. *Viola tricolor* L. (Violaceae).

A, flower cut lengthwise. B, stamen with spurred anther. C, ovary with 2 stamens. D, ovary with style and stigma. E, ovary in cross section. F, fruit. G, fruit-capsule split into 3 valves. H, seed. I, seed in section.—After Le Maout & Decne.

of botanists in regard to species. Natural hybrids seem to be common and are probably the cause of some of the confusion, the genus still being in a state of flux, like *Rubus, Crataegus, Hieracium*, etc.

The " spotting " characters for the *Violaceae* in Britain

G

the tyro is apt to mistake at first for *Papilionaceae*. This
is, however, entirely due to superficial resemblance, for the
ovary of *Polygala* is formed by the union of two or more
carpels, whilst that of *Papilionaceae* is composed of only
one carpel. The stamens connate into a sheath split on
the upper side sometimes help to complete the downfall
of the novice in his diagnosis. Though our species are
small herbs, most of the exotic genera of the family are
trees and shrubs. The two carpels of *Polygala* have each

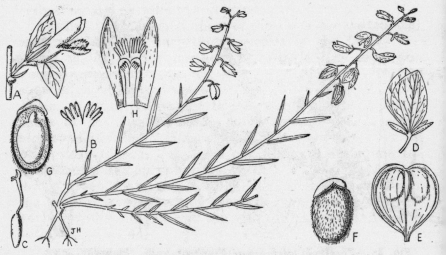

Fig. 39.—*Polygala vulgaris* Linn. (Polygalaceae). Part of flowering
plant.

A, flower and pair of bracteoles, with scar of fallen bract. B, stamens.
C, pistil. D, calyx in fruit. E, fruit with seeds showing through the thin
shell. F, seed with caruncle. G, section of same. H, lower petals and
stamens.

a single pendulous ovule, and the fruit is a compressed
capsule which opens into the loculi along the edges. The
seeds are downy.

The hairy covering in *Polygalaceae* is usually composed
of simple unicellular hairs and there are no glandular
hairs. Likewise, the stomata are not of any special
type.

CISTACEAE TO CUCURBITACEAE

There are many missing links in the chain of evolution shown in this drawing, including the basic group, the family FLACOURTIACEAE, which is found only in the tropics and subtropics. In the British flora the nearest related family is CISTACEAE, of which *Helianthemum* (shown at the bottom) is the only example. Next comes VIOLACEAE (*Viola* is drawn), our native species of which are herbs, but most other genera are woody. This is a good example of the evolution of herbs from woody ancestors, though some Violets in other countries are quite woody. THYMELAEACEAE (*Daphne*, flowers and fruit drawn) are linked by one or two small exotic families with FLACOURTIACEAE, and a further step up the " tree " takes us into the austral family PROTEACEAE. FRANKENIACEAE (*Frankenia*) seem closely connected with these groups. POLYGALACEAE (*Polygala* drawn) are not easy to place, except about here; they, too, are very abundant in southern regions, especially South Africa. TAMARICACEAE (*Tamarix*) seem to be related to FLACOURTIACEAE, but it needs PASSIFLORACEAE (non British) to connect up the evolutionary story of the climax family CUCURBITACEAE shown at the top (*Bryonia*).

The plants illustrated in the coloured plate are : Bottom, Helianthemum nummularium (*Linn.*) *Mill.* Left, berries of Bryonia dioica *Linn.*, with leaf and flowers, top right. Middle, left, flowers and berries of Daphne mezereum *Linn.*; right, Viola tricolor *Linn.*; above, Frankenia laevis *Linn.* (pink); above this, Polygala vulgaris *Linn.*, and top, left, Tamarix gallica *Linn.*

To face p. 92.

POLYGALACEAE

Violaceae

[Flacourtiaceae]

[Dilleniaceae]

[Magnoliaceae]

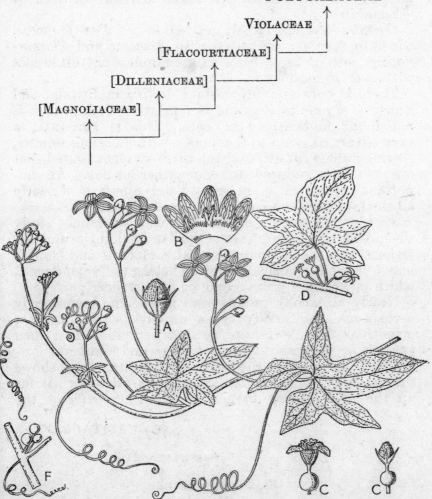

Fig. 40.—White Bryony, *Bryonia dioica* Jacq. (Cucurbitaceae), has yellowish green dioecious flowers, and the berries are poisonous.

A, male flowerbud. B, male corolla (opened) and stamens. C, D, female flowers. F, fruit.

We now come to a climax family also derived from the Bixaceous alliance, the Cucumber family, **Cucurbitaceae.** Because part of the family has a sympetalous corolla, Engler included it in the *Metachlamydeae* (= *Gamo-*

petalae), but this position has found little favour even by
" Englerites ". [1]

Cucurbitaceae are closely related to the *Passifloraceae*,
which in turn are connected with *Bixaceae* and *Flacourtiaceae*, both of these being exotic families not often met
with even in gardens.

There is only one " Cucurbit " native in Britain, and
nearly everyone in England is familiar with it, but it is
not found in Scotland or Eire. This is BRYONIA, a
very advanced genus in the family, with dioecious flowers,
a sympetalous corolla, and the three stamens united, but
one of them reduced to one anther-loculus. An important anatomical character, which is a feature of nearly
all the family, is the bicollateral vascular bundles.

With only a single genus to deal with we cannot study
the phylogeny of the genera of this family, but Cucumbers,
Melons, and the common Vegetable Marrow and Gourds
may be seen in gardens. They all belong to *Cucurbitaceae*,
which makes it of some economic importance.

Nearly all woody groups tend to become increasingly
herbaceous, the woody types usually being the most
primitive. The herbs are at first perennials and then
annuals or they may become trailers and climbers.

This is indicated in the following diagram, which shows
the probable path of evolution of *Cucurbitaceae*. As far
up the evolutionary branch as the *Flacourtiaceae* the

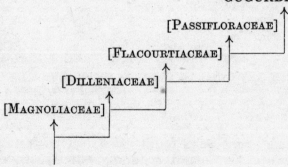

CUCURBITACEAE

[PASSIFLORACEAE]

[FLACOURTIACEAE]

[DILLENIACEAE]

[MAGNOLIACEAE]

[1] Rendle, though otherwise following Engler, placed *Cucurbitaceae*
next to *Passifloraceae*.

habit is arboreal or frutescent; in *Passifloraceae* it is mixed, with many climbers, and finally in *Cucurbitaceae* it becomes largely herbaceous.

TILIALES TO EUPHORBIALES

25. Tiliaceae. 26. Malvaceae. 27. Linaceae.
28. Euphorbiaceae.

We now climb up our woody " tree " a little farther to an almost entirely woody group, the *Tiliales*, represented

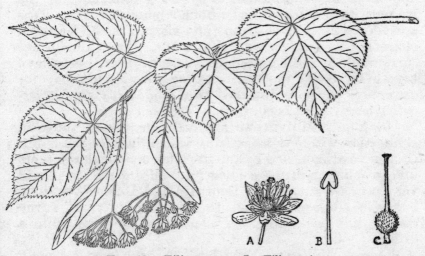

FIG. 41.—*Tilia europaea* L. (Tiliaceae).

A, flower. B, stamen. C, pistil.

in Britain by only one family, **Tiliaceae**. Everyone knows a Lime tree, TILIA. A peculiar situation exists respecting the type of this genus. Most genera are based on a type species, i.e., the first species described under the generic name. But in *Tilia* the first " species ", *T. europaea* L. (*T. vulgaris* Hayne), is now known to be a hybrid between *T. platyphyllos* Scop. and *T. cordata* Mill.

The latter is considered to be indigenous in the south and western parts of England.

Tiliaceae and the closely allied exotic family *Sterculiaceae* are very interesting for students of phylogeny. Their progenitors were probably the family *Dilleniaceae*, which are mostly in the tropics, a " half-way house " being the *Flacourtiaceae*. Considerable advancement on that group in structure is apparent in the *Tiliaceae*; the carpels (free in *Dilleniaceae*) have become united, with axile placentation, and the calyx is *valvate* throughout the group, a character maintained in the still more advanced *Malvaceae*. The valvate calyx and usually stellate hairs are good " spotting " characters for *Tiliaceae*, *Sterculiaceae*, and *Malvaceae*, and there is a strong tendency for the stamens to become united (monadelphous). Many *Tiliaceae* have mucilage-cells in the axis and in the leaves, a character they share with *Malvaceae*. The stomata are surrounded by ordinary epidermal cells. Some herbs have been evolved in *Tiliaceae*, but they are very fibrous; for example, " Jute ", obtained from *Corchorus* spp. *Sterculiaceae* give us Cocoa, from *Theobroma cacao*.

The family **Malvaceae** has been mentioned above in connection with *Tiliaceae*, from which, besides the habit, they are distinguished by the so-called one-locular anthers due to splitting of the connective. *Malvaceae* are placed very near *Geraniaceae* in Bentham and Hooker's system, but as may be seen by inspecting the family " tree " at the end of the book, they are considered to have quite a different affinity.

Whereas *Malvaceae* have been derived from a woody stock (*Tiliaceae*), *Geraniaceae* have arisen quite independently from a herbaceous stock such as *Caryophyllaceae* or even directly from the *Ranales*. I may be quite wrong in all this, being " mere speculation ", but it is the conclusion come to during the course of these studies.

Every taxonomist knows that *Malvaceae* are frequently clothed with stellate hairs. There are also often bristle-hairs, which are unicellular or uniseriate, and sometimes peltate and glandular hairs of varied structure. These characters are also found in *Tiliaceae*, and *Malvaceae* shares with this family in a marked degree secretory organs containing mucilage. From a taxonomic standpoint this character should not be unduly stressed as has been done in the Engler and Prantl system.

There are only three indigenous genera of *Malvaceae* in Britain. These are *Malva*, *Althaea*, and *Lavatera*, and they do not provide very much scope for the study of phylogeny. Of the three, probably *Lavatera* is the most primitive, being rather woody, and it has at least one

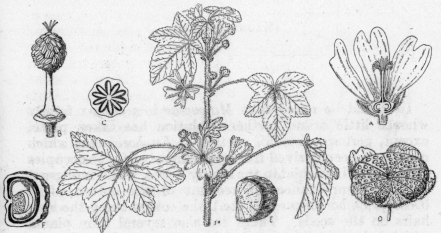

FIG. 42.—*Malva sylvestris* Linn. (Malvaceae).

A, vertical section of flower. B, stamens and style-arms. C, cross-section of fruit. D, fruit. E, segment of fruit. F, vertical section of same.

species which is a tree, *L. olbia* Linn., a South European species, often seen in gardens and in places naturalised. Next in order is *Malva*, and last of all comes *Althaea*, which embraces the Hollyhock. These genera may be keyed out as follows :—

Epicalyx composed of 3 bracts :

    Bracts broad and united at the base, ovate . . . . LAVATERA
    Bracts narrow and free from each other at the base . . MALVA
Epicalyx of 5 or more bracts more or less united at the base ALTHAEA

The two genera of *Linaceae* found in Britain may be separated as follows :—

Flowers pentamerous (sepals, petals, stamens, styles and carpels 5);
    sepals free, entire; leaves alternate or opposite . . .   LINUM
Flowers tetramerous (sepals, petals, stamens, styles and carpels 4);
    sepals united to nearly the middle and toothed; very small annual
    herb; leaves opposite . . . . RADIOLA

And here is suggested their rather long phylogenetic history :—

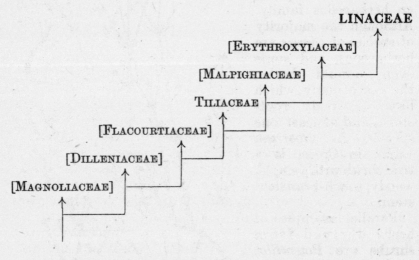

LINACEAE

[ERYTHROXYLACEAE]

[MALPIGHIACEAE]

TILIACEAE

[FLACOURTIACEAE]

[DILLENIACEAE]

[MAGNOLIACEAE]

From the *Malvales* we must take a jump, but not a very big one, into Bentham and Hooker's " Apetalae ", to the **Euphorbiaceae.** This is a very wonderful family with a great variety of floral structure, and I was fortunate in my younger days to examine a great deal of it in detail for the *Flora of Tropical Africa.*

If it be possible for a family name to be a misnomer then *Euphorbiaceae* is one. This is named after the genus EUPHORBIA, which is exceptional and almost unique in its own family. It is a very large and widely spread genus and is represented in Britain by about a dozen species. The inflorescence of *Euphorbia* is indeed a remarkable structure, and about as advanced as it can be. It is composed of an involucre of connate bracts, and between

TILIACEAE TO EUPHORBIACEAE

The paucity of some groups in the flora of the north temperate zone is very evident in the families represented on this page. The basic family is TILIACEAE (*Tilia* is shown), which may be traced right back to the MAGNOLIACEAE through the tropical families FLACOURTIACEAE and DILLENIACEAE. TILIACEAE is also most richly represented in the tropics, like a closely related family, STERCULIACEAE, to which the Cocoa plant (*Theobroma cacao*) belongs. The climax development of the group seems to be the family MALVACEAE (*Malva* is drawn), most of which, but by no means all, have become herbaceous. Their fibrous nature is evidence of descent from arboreal stock. Their united stamens with unilocular anthers is a very advanced character. Several small families link up the TILIACEAE with LINACEAE (*Linum* shown), most of which are woody, but not of course our British species. Then part at least of the great tropical family EUPHORBIACEAE seems closely related, especially to STERCULIACEAE, though the genus *Euphorbia* (drawn) has far outstripped its relatives in the evolution of its remarkable inflorescence and extremely reduced flowers.

The plants illustrated in the coloured plate are : Bottom, Tilia europaea *Linn*. Left, Malva moschata *Linn*. Right, Linum perenne *Linn*. Top, Euphorbia lathyris *Linn*.

To face p. 100.

the bracts, and more or less simulating small petals, are variously shaped, often semilunar, glands. Within the involucre are borne the male and female flowers, the males

FIG. 44.—*Euphorbia* (Euphorbiaceae).

A, inflorescence, showing the involucre (cyathium) with bifid ciliate lobes, four large bilobed disk-glands, several male flowers, and the single central female flower.   B, male flower and bracteole.   C, female flower.   D, pollen grains.

usually numerous and looking like stamens, the females solitary and placed in the middle, and much resembling the ovary of a bisexual flower. The male flower is composed of a short stalk (pedicel) and one stamen. Usually there is a constriction in the middle indicating the junction of the pedicel and the filament, and in some exotic species there is a distinct, though small, calyx. The female flower, again, is composed of a pedicel and an ovary with three bifid styles, and there is sometimes a small calyx at the base of the ovary.

The second genus of *Euphorbiaceae* in Britain is MER-CURIALIS, with two species, *M. perennis* Linn., the " Dog's Mercury ", and *M. annua* Linn. In this genus the flowers are not in an involucre, but are clustered in the leaf-axils or in axillary spikes. The male flowers have three sepals and nine to twelve stamens, and the females three sepals and a two-locular ovary.

The other genus usually placed in *Euphorbiaceae* in most British Floras is *Buxus*, but this is here regarded as a separate and distinct family, more closely related to the " Witch Hazel " family, *Hamamelidaceae*, than to *Euphorbiaceae* (see p. 71).

Euphorbiaceae contain many plants of very great economic value, " Para Rubber " being obtained from *Hevea brasiliensis* Müll. Arg., which is of primary importance in the motor and other industries. When the Japanese occupied the Malay Peninsula and Java in the Second World War, they secured a large percentage of the world's supply of crude rubber. Kew took a hand in introducing the first Para-rubber plants into the Far East. Also to *Euphorbiaceae* belongs the Castor Oil plant, *Ricinus communis* Linn.

On p. 104 is a diagram showing the probable origin of *Euphorbiaceae*, composed of reduced groups which have been assembled into a somewhat heterogeneous family. So much so in fact that one exotic genus, *Jatropha*, not only has petals, but the corolla is actually *sympetalous*.

Even the British species of *Euphorbia* show differences amongst themselves, which in other families are of generic importance. Most of them have alternate leaves without stipules, but in *E. peplis* Linn., for example, the leaves are opposite and stipulate. The seeds of some species furnish valuable taxonomic characters. Many exotic species, particularly those in southern Africa, are of a Cactus habit and covered with thorns. Both species of the

genus *Mercurialis* have opposite leaves with a pair of
stipules on each side between the petioles.

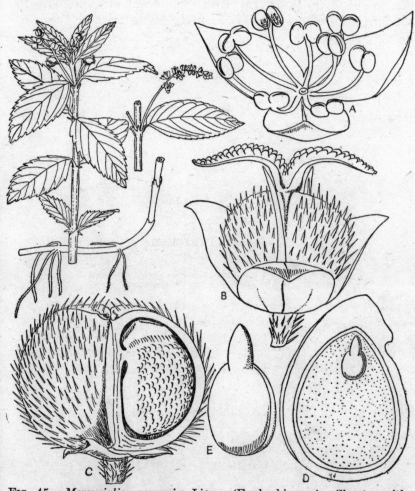

FIG. 45.—*Mercurialis perennis* Linn. (Euphorbiaceae). Shoots with
female (left) and male (right) flowers.

A, male flower. B, female flower. C, fruit, exposing one seed. D,
vertical section of seed. E, embryo.

It may be mentioned here that in the German system of
Engler and Prantl the *Euphorbiaceae* are regarded as
being allied to or even derived from the *Geraniales*

(*Geraniaceae*, etc.). Although both families are only sparsely represented in Britain compared with the rest of the world, I do not think that even the most elementary student of botany would be inclined to regard them as being related.

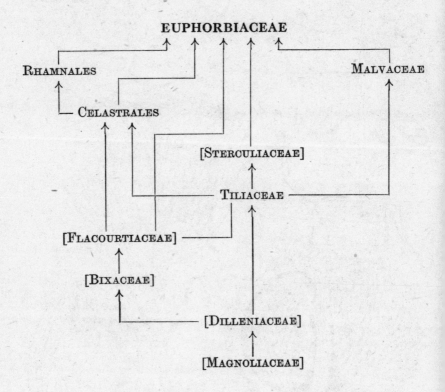

ERICALES and GUTTIFERALES.

29. Ericaceae. 30. Vacciniaceae. 31. Pyrolaceae.
32. Monotropaceae. 33. Hypericaceae.

The fact that the above families are included in one chapter does not indicate that they are all related, *Hypericaceae* having no direct phyletic connection with *Ericales* (see folder diagram). Nor does it mean that because these families follow *Euphorbiaceae* they are in any way remotely allied to that family. They are not. The origin of the family **Ericaceae** is probably to be found in the tea family, *Theaceae*, which shows relationship with *Rhododendron* through the *Saurauiaceae*, a small family close to the *Theaceae*. The exotic *Clethraceae*, whilst no doubt closely allied to *Ericaceae*, are also very near *Theaceae*, their petals being free. The map[1] shows the distribution of this interesting little family (p. 106).

FIG. 46.—*Clethra arborea* L. (Clethraceae).

A, vertical section of flower. B, flower with sepals and petals removed. C, stamens. D, petal. E, style. F, transverse section of ovary. (From Hutchinson, Families of Flowering Plants).

Ericaceae are primitive among the sympetalous families because of the

[1] The student's attention is drawn to this map of the distribution of *Clethraceae*, a small family which seems to represent an ancient stock of *Ericaceae*. It will be observed that the family is found in two widely separated areas, one embracing a large part of America and the island of Madeira, the other Indo-Malaya. It is the latter part of the distribution which deserves special mention.

Some readers may be unaware of the work of Alfred Russel Wallace, a contemporary of Darwin, who studied the distribution of life forms in the Malay Region. Wallace was able to draw a line through the group of islands, and to separate those of an Asiatic type from those of an Australian type of animals and plants. He pointed out great differences between the two types, and scientists were greatly puzzled why there should be a line of separation in a group where the islands lie so close together. Why in the course of geological ages had not the life-forms from one side slowly filtered across to the other until the line disappeared? Wegener's hypothesis of drifting continents published in 1915 seems to supply a reasonable explanation. According to him, Australia, with a few islands north of it, including New Guinea, has but lately (geologically speaking) drifted into this region, and there has not been sufficient time for mingling to occur. It should be noted that *Clethraceae* are almost entirely in Wallace's Asiatic group.

H

structure of their flowers.   Though there is cohesion of the petals there is no adhesion of the different parts.   The stamens are still hypogynous and not attached to the corolla, and usually there is a double row (diplostemonous), one opposite and the other alternate with the corolla-lobes.   The type of opening of the anthers (by pores) is, however, unusual and somewhat advanced.   The ovary is superior, and usually five- or more-locular. In more advanced sympetalous families the stamens are reduced to five, four, two, or even one, and are usually inserted on the corolla, and the carpels are often reduced to two, with usually a corresponding reduction in the

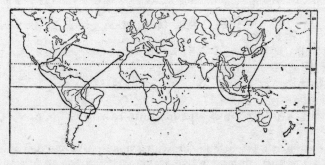

Fig. 47.—Range of *Clethraceae*, a primitive family of *Ericales*, closely related to *Ericaceae*; note the approximate agreement with Wallace's line in the Malaya.

number of ovules.   In *Ericaceae* the ovules are generally very numerous.

It is rather surprising that such a relatively homogeneous family as *Ericaceae* " possesses only a few prominent anatomical characters common to all its members" [Solereder].   One of these is that in nearly all cases the stomata are surrounded by several ordinary epidermal cells.   This important point should be considered in deciding whether *Vacciniaceae* should be merged in *Ericaceae*, as in the Engler and Prantl system, because in *Vacciniaceae* the stomata (also *fide* Solereder) are provided with subsidiary cells on each side of and parallel to the pore.

Some remarkable types of clothing and glandular hairs are found in the family, which are of great taxonomic value, particularly in the genus *Rhododendron*. The majority of Ericaceous plants obtain their organic food through the agency of fungi (mycorrhiza), which become attached to their roots.

The nature of the anthers in *Ericaceae* is of very great interest and has been the subject of a special investigation by Matthews and Knox [1] and others. By studying the development (ontogeny) of the stamen it has been shown that by the complete inversion of the anther during its growth the apparent base is really the organic apex, and though the pores appear to be terminal, they are thus actually basal. This is proved by the course of the vascular strand which supplies the anther. It is curved like a hook and directed towards the apparent base.

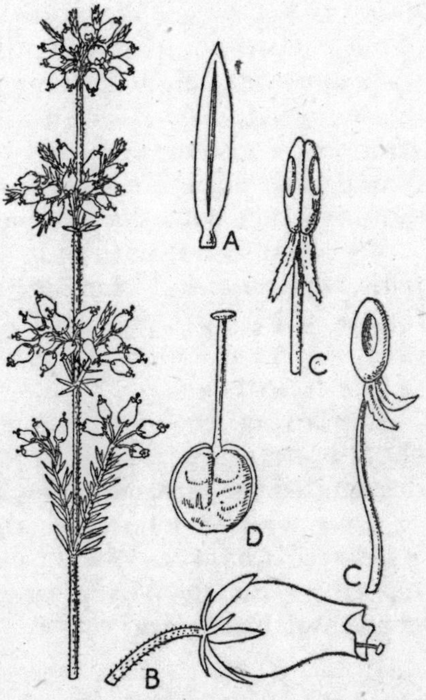

The porous dehiscence of the Ericaceous anthers is of course connected with more effective pollen presenta-

FIG. 48.—The flowers of the Bell Heather, *Erica cinerea* L. (Ericaceae), are often perforated by bumble bees which steal the nectar secreted around the base of the ovary.

A, leaf. B, flower. C, stamens, front and side views. D, pistil.

tion. In all *Ericaceae* the pollen-grains remain in tetrads which are usually shed singly. In *Rhododendron*, however, the tetrads are loosely roped together by slender sticky threads.

To decide which are the most primitive of the British

[1] Matthews and Knox, " The Comparative Morphology of the Stamen in the Ericaceae ", *Trans. Edinb. Bot. Soc.*, 29 : 243 (1926).

genera of the *Ericaceae* we shall have to pin our faith to the nature of the fruit and the largest number of stamens. Some genera have a capsular fruit and others a baccate fruit. Obviously the former is the more primitive, other things being equal, and *Andromeda* and *Phyllodoce* have these two characters in common. Of the other genera with a capsular fruit, *Dabeocia*, *Erica*, and *Calluna* have only eight stamens, and the leaves are opposite or whorled. *Loiseleuria* is further reduced to five stamens, and was included by Linnaeus in *Azalea*, which usually has only five stamens and is now regarded as being synonymous with *Rhododendron*.

We are now left with only two genera, both with baccate fruit, *Arbutus* and *Arctostaphylos*, the former a tree and found wild in the south-west of Eire, the latter low creeping shrublets in the mountains of the northern parts of our country.

Regarding the distribution of *Ericaceae*, the student should note one very interesting point. The family dominates the landscape both in species and/or individuals in two widely separated regions, *Rhododendron* in the Eastern Himalaya–Western China area, whilst in the Cape region of South Africa there are about seven hundred species of Erica and other closely allied genera.

Key to the British genera of *Ericaceae*.

Fruit a capsule; leaves usually quite small :
    Stamens 10; leaves alternate :
        Capsule opening between the loculi; anthers not tailed at the top; leaves crowded, bordered with glandular teeth   PHYLLODOCE [1]
        Capsule opening in the middle of the loculi; anthers tailed at the tip; leaves lax, glaucous below   .   .   .   .   .   ANDROMEDA
    Stamens 8 :
        Leaves alternate, white below; corolla deciduous; anthers not tailed at the top   .   .   .   .   DABEOCIA

---

[1] The *Bryanthus caeruleus* and *Menziesia caerulea* of some Floras and Lists.

ERICALES

The family ERICACEAE, and some smaller ones evidently derived from the same stock, were placed at the bottom of the artificial group *Sympetalae* (or *Gamopetalae*) in the Englerian system. They represent a fairly primitive type of that group, because the stamens have not become epipetalous, as in most other sympetalous families, but have remained inserted directly on the axis. In addition, they are usually double the number of the corolla-lobes, though in more highly evolved groups within the family ERICACEAE itself they are reduced to five—for example, in the *Azalea* section of *Rhododendron*. Even within the confines of this one genus there is evidence of considerable evolution, some species, such as the tree-like *Rhododendron falconeri*, having much more primitive features (15–20 ovary-loculi and 15–25 stamens) than others, such as the lowly *R. lapponicum*. VACCINIACEAE (*Vaccinium*, middle left), with ovary inferior, are a stage higher than ERICACEAE, as also PYROLACEAE (*Pyrola* shown, top left), and MONOTROPACEAE (*Monotropa* shown, top middle), the latter root-parasites or saprophytes. (Bottom left, *Arbutus*, middle, *Erica*, right *Dabeocia*, all ERICACEAE.)

The plants illustrated in the coloured plate are : Bottom, left, Arbutus unedo *Linn.* Middle, Erica cinerea *Linn.* Right, Dabeocia cantabrica (*Huds.*) *C. Koch.* Middle, left, Vaccinium myrtillus *Linn.* Top, left, Pyrola rotundifolia *Linn.*; middle, Monotropa hypopitys *Linn.*

To face p. 108.

Leaves opposite or whorled; corolla persistent :
   Corolla divided nearly to the base . . . . . . CALLUNA
   Corolla shortly lobed or toothed, tubular-campanulate ERICA
Stamens 5; leaves opposite; corolla campanulate, 5-lobed
                                  LOISELEURIA
Fruit a berry; leaves alternate :
   Shrubs or trees; loculi of the ovary with several ovules; berries
     verrucose and strawberry-like . . . . ARBUTUS
   Low creeping shrublets; loculi of the ovary 1-ovulate; berries
     smooth . . . . ARCTOSTAPHYLOS

The decorative value of *Ericaceae* in horticulture is very considerable. Our gardens and woods would not be so gay in spring without the genus *Rhododendron*. As evidence of its popularity and importance there is a society devoted to it, "The Rhododendron Society." The common *Rhododendron* grown and naturalised on nearly every country estate is *R. ponticum* Linn., a native of Asia Minor (and South Spain [1]), and in some places it regenerates very freely. Great collectors' names connected with the introduction of Rhododendrons from Asia are Hooker, Fortune, Wilson, Forrest, Kingdon-Ward, and Rock, whilst the late Professor Sir Isaac Bayley Balfour was the doyen of botanists devoted to it.

An interesting alien established in Scotland is *Ledum palustre* Linn.,

Bentham and Hooker treated **Vacciniaceae** as a separate family, but Drude, in the Engler and Prantl System, included them as a subfamily of *Ericaceae*. Towards the close of the nineteenth century some teachers of botany in this country began to follow rather blindly the German system, and it became the fashion to put on one side the more classical work of our two famous Kew botanists, G. Bentham and J. D. Hooker. In my own scheme I maintained *Vacciniaceae* as a separate family, and it is noteworthy that Matthews and Knox (see p. 107), after a study of the stamens in the two groups, came to the conclusion that the differences were sufficient to warrant the retention of *Vacciniaceae* as a distinct family. They regarded the distal prolongations of the anther-lobes which occur in *Vacciniaceae* as awns and distinct from the bristle-

[1] Rather doubtfully indigenous in Spain.

like appendages of the *Ericaceae* (absent from the Rhododendron group). The awns of the *Vacciniaceae* are thus, morphologically, prolongations of the base of the anther. As already noted under *Ericaceae*, there is also an important anatomical difference, the stomata of *Vacciniaceae* being accompanied by a pair of special subsidiary cells parallel to the pore, a feature not present in *Ericaceae*. An anatomical character is in this instance of great assistance to the taxonomist.

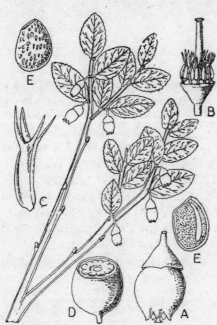

Vacciniaceae are represented in Britian by four species, three of them belonging to *Vaccinium*, and the fourth is now usually separated under *Oxycoccus*. *Vaccinium myrtillus* Linn., the "Bilberry," is confined to Europe and Russian Asia; *V. vitis-idaea* Linn. and *V. uliginosum* Linn. extend across the north temperate zone from Europe to North America.

Fig. 49.—*Vaccinium myrtillus* L. (Vacciniaceae) is very common on mountain and heath often with the heather.

A, flower.   B, pistil and stamens.   C, anther.   D, fruit.   E, seed and vertical section of seed.

Oxycoccus differs from *Vaccinium* in having the corolla-segments free nearly to the base and abruptly reflexed. Our species is *O. quadripetalus* Gilib. (*Vaccinium oxycoccus* Linn.), and is widely spread across the cooler parts of the northern hemisphere. Here are the differences of the two genera:—

Corolla divided nearly to the base into segments, these sharply reflexed, anthers not awned. . . . . Oxycoccus
Corolla campanulate, with short lobes, anthers usually awned on the back . . . . Vaccinium

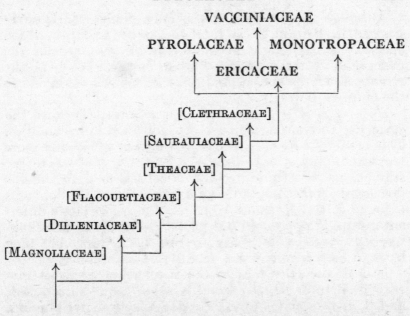

Although in my full system *Pyrola* was included in the *Ericaceae*, as in Bentham and Hooker, there is perhaps justification for regarding it and *Moneses* as a separate family, **Pyrolaceae**. There are two genera; *Pyrola* is represented by four species, with racemose flowers, five free incurved petals, anther-loculi not or very slightly produced into the pore, short stigmatic lobes, and with the valves of the fruit connected by fibres. *Moneses* (*M. uniflora* L.) has solitary (rarely two) flowers, the petals slightly connate at the base and spreading, the anther-loculi with tubular porous tips, long stigmatic lobes, and the valves of the fruit free. All are low herbs with slender creeping rootstocks and rounded, sometimes whorled leaves.

Monotropaceae, also formerly included in the *Ericaceae*, are represented in Britain by only one species, *Monotropa hypopitys* Linn. It is a parasite on the roots of trees, and the leaves are reduced to scales. It differs from *Ericaceae* in the dehiscence of the anthers, which open by transverse slits and not by pores.

Although HYPERICUM is the only genus of **Hyperi-caceae** in Britain, it is represented by about a dozen species. These might give one the impression that the general habit of the genus is herbaceous, but nearly all the remainder of the species and of other genera belonging to the family are woody.

Hypericaceae is a fairly advanced family, because the stamens, though numerous, are collected into bundles. This is more fully carried out in a closely allied and more tropical family, the *Guttiferae* (or *Clusiaceae*), where the stamens are mostly united into a central column and the flowers are sometimes unisexual. A parallel development is found in the *Malvales*, which is otherwise quite a different group. As pointed out at the beginning of this chapter, *Hypericaceae* are not related to the *Ericales*, but they have to be put somewhere in the linear sequence.

It is noteworthy that in the two shrubby species met with in Britain, *Hypericum calycinum* Linn. (introduced) and *H. androsaemum* Linn., the stamens are in five bundles, whilst the herbaceous species have them in three bundles, a reduction corresponding with the more advanced habit. These herbs, then, have been derived from woody ancestors, as in the case of the herbaceous *Rosaceae*.

The leaves of *Hypericaceae* are opposite and gland-dotted, and the seed has no endosperm. The calyx has remained imbricate, however, and has not become valvate, as in the generally more advanced *Malvales*.

The translucent or black dots of the leaves of *Hypericaceae* are caused by schizogenous secretory cavities, and schizogenous secretory canals occur in the phloem of the axis, and sometimes in the cortex and pith. In *Hypericum* the stomata are surrounded by three epidermal cells, but in some exotic genera there are two subsidiary cells parallel to the pore. Glandular hairs are not recorded for the family, but stellate hairs occur in some exotic genera.

The diagram on page 113 shows the probable path of evolution of the *Hypericaceae*.

Again, as shown in our diagram for *Cucurbitaceae*, herbs are indicated as having been evolved from ligneous ancestors. As far up the " tree " as *Theaceae* the habit is

arboreal and frutescent, and the same obtains for most of
the *Hypericaceae* except for certain species of the genus

                                        HYPERICACEAE
                                              ↑
                        [THEACEAE]
                             ↑
            [BIXACEAE] ┌──────────┘
                 ↑   │
      [DILLENIACEAE] ┌──┘
            ↑   │
[MAGNOLIACEAE] ┌─────┘
      ↑   │
   ┌───────────┘
   │

Hypericum, which have become herbaceous.   The family
is mainly of horticultural value.

CELASTRALES TO SAPINDALES.

34. Aquifoliaceae.   35. Empetraceae.   36. Celastraceae.   37. Loranthaceae.   38. Santalaceae.
39. Rhamnaceae.   40. Elaeagnaceae.   41. Aceraceae.

The family **Aquifoliaceae** has only one representative
in Britain.   The common " Holly " needs no introduction
to students, though it is mainly conspicuous in the fruiting
stage at Christmas-time and is often not noticed when in
flower.   The family is widely spread over the world, and
has probably been derived from *Theales* (*Theaceae*, the
Tea family, etc.).   Only a few species have prickly leaves
like our native species, *Ilex aquifolium* Linn.   The corolla
of this is slightly sympetalous.   The fruit is not a real
berry, though very like one, but is really a drupe containing four stones each enclosing a single seed.   *I. aquifolium* extends from western and southern Europe eastwards to the Caucasus, and is found all over Britain.
Although the genus is spread nearly all over the world,

Euphorbiaceae may have been derived from the same stock as *Celastraceae*.

The family is most abundant in warmer climates than ours, and only one genus and species occurs in Britain. This is *Euonymus europaeus* Linn., the " Spindle Tree ", common in England, but rare in Scotland and Eire.

In Britain the family **Loranthaceae** is represented by only one, but very familiar example, the Mistletoe, *Viscum album* Linn. In a wild state it is confined to England and

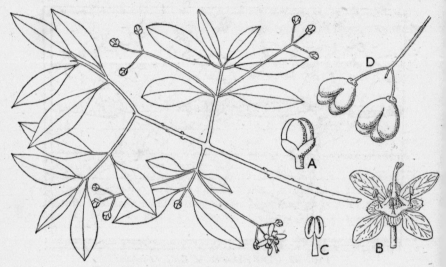

Fig. 53.—*Euonymus europaeus* L. (Celastraceae).
A, flower bud. B, flower. C, stamen. D, fruits.

Wales only as far north as Yorkshire, growing parasitically on various species of trees. This species is widely spread through Europe and Asia, and is most commonly found on the Black Poplar, *Populus nigra* Linn. Distribution is brought about by birds which feed on the berries and deposit the seeds on the branches of trees.

The leaves of *Viscum album* Linn. are opposite or in whorls of three on the jointed branchlets. The flowers are unisexual, small and green, the great attraction being the white berries which are so popular as a decoration at Christmas-time. A peculiarity of the seed is the possession

AQUIFOLIACEAE TO ACERACEAE

It will require some imagination for those whose knowledge of plants is mainly confined to the flora of Britain to detect much relationship amongst the plants shown here. All are trees and shrubs. At the bottom is shown the familiar Holly (*Ilex*), a genus comprising most of the family AQUI-FOLIACEAE. Above is the equally well-known Mistletoe (*Viscum*), which is parasitical on other trees, and belongs to LORANTHACEAE. At the top (left) are shown the fruits of the Sea Buckthorn (*Hippophaë*), the sole British member of the ELAEAGNACEAE, and the winged fruits of the Maple (*Acer*) of the family ACERACEAE, formerly classed with the Horse-chestnuts (SAPINDACEAE). All these families have small and inconspicuous flowers, and are found mainly in the warmer parts of the world, those in Europe being but outliers from the main centres of distribution. Their fruits are often either baccate and distributed by birds, or winged and borne hither and thither by the wind.

The plants illustrated in the coloured plate are : Bottom, Ilex aquifolium *Linn.* Middle, left, Viscum album *Linn.*; right, Frangula alnus *Mill.* Top, left, fruits of Hippophaë rhamnoides *Linn.*; right, Acer campestre *Linn.*

of more than one embryo, sometimes as many as three, and when paired they are often united by the cotyledons.

The stomata of *Loranthaceae* are of the Rubiaceous type, i.e., they are accompanied by special subsidiary cells parallel to the pore. They frequently occur on the branches and are often arranged transversely to the longitudinal axis of the shoot. There are no glandular hairs, and the clothing hairs are either simple, stellate, or peltate, and in some the candelabra type are recorded.

The family is most abundantly represented in the tropics, and there are over 1000 species distributed under about twenty-five genera. *Loranthus* is the largest, with about 500 species. For example, in tropical Africa alone there are over 200 species, many with handsome flowers which brighten the branches of otherwise sombre forest trees and shrubs.

The paucity of species of the families of the *Celastrales* in the British flora is remarkable. It applies particularly to the **Santalaceae**, which is represented by a single genus and species, *Thesium humifusum* DC., the "Bastard Toadflax". This is widely distributed in temperate Europe and Asiatic Russia, and in Britain is found only in the southern counties, in chalky pastures, where it attaches itself to the roots of a great variety of plants.

Santalaceae are not related to *Thymelaeaceae*, near which they are placed in the Bentham and Hooker system, at least not in my opinion. The stomata are of the same type as described for *Loranthaceae*, and they are similarly arranged on the shoots.

Rhamnaceae is one of the most easily recognised families, for there is at least one constant feature. The stamens are alternate with the calyx-lobes, and therefore opposite the petals when these are present, which is usually the case.

The two British species of *Rhamnaceae* have usually been included in *Rhamnus*, but recently Hegi in his *Illustrierte Flora von Mittel-Europa* (Vol. V, i, p. 343) has restored the genus *Frangula*. I consider this to be sound. In *Rhamnus* Linn. (*sensu stricto*) the winter-buds are covered with scales and there is no terminal bud, the flowers are polygamo-dioecious, the style two to four-parted, and the seeds have a dorsal groove, with thin curved epigeal cotyledons. In *Frangula*, on the other hand, the winter-buds are naked, the flowers are bisexual, the seeds have no groove, and the hypogeal cotyledons are thick. *Rhamnus* proper embraces the bulk of the species, including the British *R. cathartica* Linn., whilst *Frangula* includes our native *F. alnus* Mill. (*Rhamnus frangula* Linn.), and also *F. purshiana* (DC.) Cooper, the

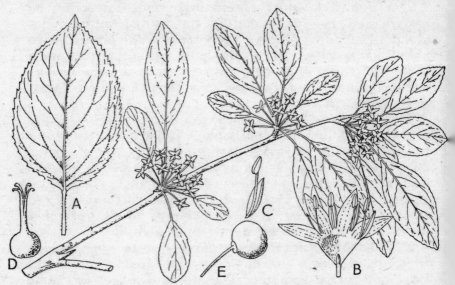

Fig. 54.—Male flowering shoot of *Rhamnus cathartica* L. (Rhamnaceae); the flowers are unisexual and dioecious.

A, mature leaf. B, male flower. C, stamen and petal. D, pistil. E, fruit.

source of the drug Cascara Sagrada from western North America, and a few other species. Botanists dealing with very local floras are apt to take rather a restricted view of genera, but the present example seems entirely justified having regard to the characters employed to distinguish other genera in the family, which is a very natural one. The wood of *Frangula alnus* is used in the manufacture of a high-grade gunpowder.

The fruit of *Rhamnus* and *Frangula* is a berry enclosing

small drupes, and the seeds contain endosperm. The stomata of the leaves are not of any special type. Some exotic genera of *Rhamnaceae* have a stellate indumentum.

I believe **Elaeagnaceae** to be a more advanced group than and related to *Rhamnaceae*. The stellate indumentum already present in some exotic *Rhamnaceae* has in

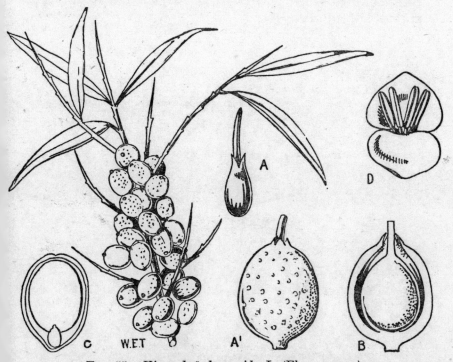

FIG. 55.—*Hippophaë rhamnoides* L. (Elaeagnaceae).

A, female flower. A 1, fruit. B, section of same. C, section of seed. D, male flower. (From Hutchinson, Familes of Flowering Plants).

Elaeagnaceae become almost universally lepidote, scales being a more advanced type of stellate or branched hair. These peltate scales consist of a large number of narrow ray-cells which do not all reach to the centre of the shield from which they spread out. The exotic genus *Elaeagnus*, often cultivated in gardens for ornament, is the largest and most primitive, with bisexual flowers and alternate leaves. The "Sea Buckthorn", *Hippophaë rhamnoides*

L., is maritime in Britain, but not always so on the continent of Europe. The leaves are densely covered with silvery peltate scales, the flowers are dioecious, the males in axillary clusters, the females solitary, and the fruit is a yellow or brown berry.

The vessels have simple perforations, and the wood prosenchyma bears bordered pits. The stomata have no special subsidiary cells.

FIG. 56.—The Maple, *Acer campestre* Linn. (Aceraceae), is readily recognised by its opposite leaves and winged fruits.

A, flowering shoot. B, male flower. C, bisexual flower. D, branchlet in fruit. E, fruit.

The only indigenous species of **Aceraceae** is *Acer campestre* Linn., the Common Maple, with flowers in loose erect corymbs. Another species, the Sycamore, *A. pseudoplatanus* Linn., is naturalised in Britain and has the flowers in closer pendulous racemes. ACER is the type genus of the small family *Aceraceae*, formerly included in the *Sapindaceae*. *Acer campestre* is a tree up to about 70 feet high, with opposite cordate leaves five-lobed at the base. The fruits have two widely spreading wings. It is widely distributed in Europe, reaching the Caucasus and Persia, and it is found in the south-west, in Spain and Portugal, and in one or two localities in Algeria. It is abundant as a wild tree in England as far north as the middle of Northumberland. Nectar is secreted in the thick fleshy disk of the flowers.

LOGANIALES to RUBIALES and VERBENALES.

42. Oleaceae.   43. Apocynaceae.   44. Rubiaceae. 45. Caprifoliaceae.   46. Verbenaceae.

From the Celastrales we must now move up our " tree " to a mostly sympetalous group, the *Loganiales*. These are represented by one family, the **Oleaceae**. In my scheme for the whole of the families [1] it was shown that *Loganiales* were probably of mixed origin, and this may be understood by examining only the British examples. These are the Common Ash, *Fraxinus excelsior* Linn., and the Privet, *Ligustrum vulgare* Linn., the one a tree with pinnate leaves, no perianth, and a dry oblong-linear fruit, the other a shrub with simple leaves, a double perianth, and a baccate fruit. I am, therefore, rather doubtful whether *Fraxinus* and *Ligustrum* are really closely related. Probably the former is more closely allied to *Sapindaceae* and *Aceraceae*, whilst *Ligustrum* may be a reduced example of the *Loganiaceae*.

The wood of the Ash is put to many uses, the seeds are rich in oil, and the young green " keys " when pickled taste rather like walnuts treated in the same way.

The spotting feature for most *Oleaceae* is the two stamens, and this one character may be responsible for bringing together a rather heterogeneous assemblage of plants,

[1] Hutchinson, *Families of Flowering Plants*, **1** : phylogenetic diagram (1926).

I

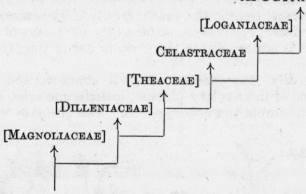

We have now climbed nearly to the top of one of the branchlets, that is to say of the woody branch, of our phylogenetic " tree " and reached another climax family, **Rubiaceae**, in which the ovary is inferior. It is mostly a tropical and subtropical family, but the distinct tribe, the *Galieae*, to which the British genera belong, is mainly found in temperate regions. It is also one of the most advanced groups, which leads us to the belief that *Rubiaceae* originated in tropical and spread into cooler regions.

Galieae are advanced because the leaves are accompanied by precisely similar foliaceous stipules. Usually the real leaves may be detected by the buds in their axils.

The fruits of many of the species of *Galium* are admirably adapted for dispersal by animals, *G. aparine* Linn., the Goosegrass or Cleavers, being now widely spread nearly throughout the northern hemisphere.

Rubiaceae is a very important family economically, because it furnishes among other things Coffee (*Coffea*), and Quinine (*Cinchona*), the latter helping to make life possible for the white man among the deadly mosquitoes of the tropics.

Key to the British genera of *Rubiaceae*.

Corolla-tube as long as or longer than the lobes :
  Flowers in panicles; calyx much reduced . . . . ASPERULA
  Flowers in heads surrounded by an involucre of bracts. SHERARDIA
Corolla-tube very short :
  Fruit dry; corolla usually 4-lobed. . . . . . . GALIUM
  Fruit fleshy; corolla usually 5-lobed . . . . . . RUBIA

Here and there the stomata of various families have been referred to as being of the Rubiaceous type. This type (see sketches Fig. 59) is so-called because it is characteristic of the whole family, which is a very large one with more than 400 genera, and about 6,000 species. The stomata are invariably accompanied by subsidiary cells parallel to the pore. Accompanying this feature, which must be of considerable importance to be characteristic of so large and natural a group, is the absence of glandular hairs from the leaves. The vascular bundles are collateral.

Although for the present we include *Sambucus* (the Elder), and *Viburnum*, with *Lonicera* and *Linnaea* in **Caprifoliaceae**, I suspect this family to be of mixed origin. *Lonicera* and *Linnaea* are no doubt related, but the other two genera seem very different from them. They have several

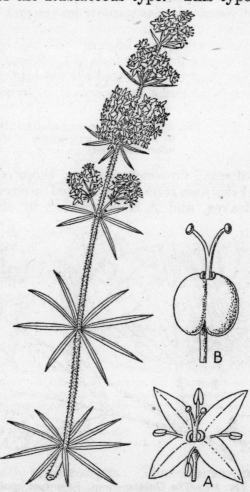

Fig. 58.—The family *Rubiaceae* stands high in the " family tree " (see folder at end of book), and particularly the tribe *Galieae*, to which the Lady's Bedstraw, *Galium verum* L., belongs. The whorls are composed of leaves plus stipules, which are not distinguishable from each other, the calyx is much reduced, and the corolla has 4 lobes and 4 stamens.

A, flower. B, pistil.

killed by frost during the winter. This loosens the pith, which readily falls out. Elderberry wine and jam are too well known, of course, to need more than casual mention here.

All naturalists should have a warm place in their hearts for the delightful little *Linnaea borealis,* named after Carl Linnaeus, " the father of modern botany ". In this the ovary is three-locular, one of the loculi being one-ovulate, the others with two or more ovules. This seems to show an intermediate stage in the reduction of ovules from several to one, and on the other hand it may show a tendency to the abortion of some of the loculi of the ovary so characteristic a feature of the family *Valerianaceae.* A common garden hedge plant in Britain is the Snowberry, *Symphoricarpus albus* Blake (*S. racemosus* Michx.), which also belongs to this family.

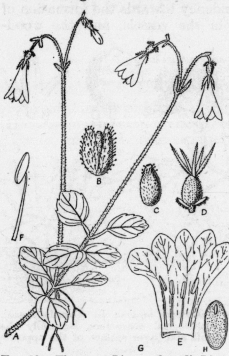

Fig. 62.—The name *Linnaea borealis* Linn. (Caprifoliaceae) commorates that of the " Father of Modern Botany."

A, flowering branch. B, ovary and sepals. C, ovary. D, bracts, ovary and calyx. E, corolla laid open. F, stamen. G, cross-section of ovary. H, vertical section of seed.

An exotic and a more primitive genus than *Lonicera* is *Leycesteria* in Eastern Asia, with a subactinomorphic corolla-limb and a five-locular ovary.

Here is a key to the British genera :—

Leaves pinnately divided; flowers in spreading flat cymes SAMBUCUS
Leaves simple :

OLEACEAE TO CAPRIFOLIACEAE

One would have to involve the aid of many strange tropical families in order to show clearly the reason for associating those represented in the drawing given here. At the bottom is the family OLEACEAE, represented by the common Ash (*Fraxinus*, left) and the Privet (*Ligustrum*, right, in flower and fruit). They are related to the Spindle-tree family, CELASTRACEAE, with free petals. But all the families shown have acquired a sympetalous corolla, and are therefore more highly evolved with respect to this part of the flower A family leading up towards the APOCYNACEAE (*Vinca*, with blue flowers) is the exotic LOGANIACEAE, of which *Buddleja* is a well-known cultivated example. In APOCYNACEAE the ovary has remained superior, but in the other two families shown, RUBIACEAE and CAPRIFOLIACEAE, the ovary has become inferior. RUBIACEAE (*Galium*, top left) are nearly all found in the tropics, and are a completely climax group, with constantly opposite, stipulate leaves, and actinomorphic corolla. The zygomorphic corolla of some CAPRIFOLIACEAE, such as *Lonicera* (top, right) places this family even a little higher than the RUBIACEAE.

The plants illustrated in the coloured plate are : Bottom, Fraxinus excelsior *Linn.* Right, Ligustrum vulgare *Linn.*, in flower and fruit. Middle, Vinca minor *Linn.* Top, left, Galium verum *Linn.*; right, Lonicera periclymenum *Linn.*

To face p. **128.**

Corolla rotate, actinomorphic; ovule solitary in each loculus of the
ovary . . . . VIBURNUM
Corolla tubular or campanulate; ovules 2 or more in some of the
ovary-loculi :
Corolla subactinomorphic; small creeping evergreen shrublet
LINNAEA
Corolla zygomorphic; stems twining . . . . . . LONICERA

The family **Verbenaceae** need not occupy us long, for it
is mainly found in the tropics, and in the temperate regions
of the southern hemisphere. It is largely a woody group
and has perhaps not been evolved by the same evolutionary path as the *Labiatae*, next to which it is usually
placed. With the latter it shows some parallelism in the
zygomorphic corolla of some of its genera and reduction to
four or even two stamens. The ovary is usually entire,
however, and not deeply lobed as in *Labiatae*.

The only Verbenaceous plant in Britain is *Verbena
officinalis* Linn., an erect perennial with small flowers in
long slender spikes. It is found mostly on roadsides and
in waste places.

Solereder mentions several anatomical characters of
importance for the family. We need only note the
stomata, which are either surrounded by several ordinary
epidermal cells, or very rarely by two subsidiary cells
placed *transversely* to the pore, as in most *Caryophyllaceae*.
There are no internal secretory organs.

The tribes *Cordieae* and *Ehretieae* of *Boraginaceae*,
which are perhaps not naturally placed with the true more
herbaceous *Boraginaceae*, seem to connect *Verbenaceae*
with *Loganiaceae*. In my general work they will be
treated as a separate family, *Ehretiaceae*. They are not,
of course, represented in the British flora.

Dicotyledones—*Herbaceae*.

RANALES to ARISTOLOCHIALES.

47. Ranunculaceae. 48. Ceratophyllaceae.
49. Nymphaeaceae. 50. Berberidaceae.
51. Aristolochiaceae.

In the Introduction (p. 10), it is mentioned that in a first attempt at a new classification based on phylogeny I pointed out the desirability of separating the *Magnoliaceae* and allied families from the *Ranunculaceae* and its relatives, because I could find no real affinity between them, and considered their similarity in floral structure to be due to parallel development.

The differences between the two families are shown in the following :—

MAGNOLIACEAE.	RANUNCULACEAE.
Trees and shrubs.	Herbs or rarely soft-wooded climbers.
Leaves stipulate; stomata with special subsidiary cells parallel to the pore.	Leaves without stipules [1]; stomata without special subsidiary cells.
Perianth not or rarely differentiated into sepals and petals, 3- or more-seriate.	Perianth differentiated into sepals and petals and usually not more than 2-seriate, or the petals reduced or absent.
Floral axis usually elongated.	Floral axis usually short.

It is contended therefore that the resemblance of the flowers of these two families is only superficial and that each family represents a basic group, *Magnoliaceae* for the woody subphylum *Lignosae*, and *Ranunculaceae* for the herbaceous subphylum *Herbaceae* (see p. 40).

In Britain there are over a dozen genera of this first and most primitive family of herbs, **Ranunculaceae**. Perhaps the most ancient of these is Helleborus, with two

---

[1] There are stipule-like appendages in *Thalictrum* spp.

130

species, *H. viridis* Linn., and *H. foetidus* Linn., in these
islands. The petals are leaf-like and tubular and are still
similar in texture and colour to ordinary leaves. To
compensate for the dull colour of the petals, however, the
sepals of some species, such as the " Christmas Rose ",
Helleborus niger L., are white. In other species the sepals
have remained green like the leaves from which they have
been derived. Note also the *leaf-like* carpels, each with
several ovules along the infolded margins.

The " Paeony ", *Paeonia mascula* Mill., is found
(presumably naturalised) in the island of Steep Holme in
the Severn Estuary. It is distantly related to the Helle-
bore; the petals, however, are large and attractive and
conspicuous to insects. But *Caltha palustris* Linn., the
" Marsh Marigold ", has probably lost its petals, and in
order to compensate for this its sepals are a beautiful
buttercup yellow, and it has invaded the marshes, where
it has few competitors. On the other hand, *Caltha* may
never have had petals !

More recent representatives of this ancient stock will be
found mainly in gardens or naturalised. They are
Aquilegia, Aconitum, and *Delphinium,* probably evolved
in the order named. We have here, then, in one and the
same family, examples of the most primitive and of
considerably advanced structures, for *Delphinium* and
Aconitum are to the other members of the *Ranunculaceae* as orchids are to *Liliaceae,* or *Labiatae* to
Boraginaceae.

Evolution has taken place in different ways in these
three genera. In *Aquilegia,* the " Columbine ", all the
five petals have long spurs to conceal the honey, but the
corolla has remained actinomorphic (" regular "). In
the British species of *Delphinium, D. ajacis* Linn., there
are only two petals, and they have spurs within the spur of
the calyx; and the carpels, instead of being five, are
reduced to only one. This in fact is almost a leguminous
ovary, and a good example of how a legume may have
been evolved. But *Leguminosae* have descended from the
apocarpous *Rosaceae,* and not from *Ranunculaceae.* The
beautiful blue colour of the flowers of *Delphinium* should

also be noted.   Blue is an advanced colour and present
only in the more highly evolved *Ranunculaceae*, such as
Anemone and *Clematis*.   There are no blue buttercups,
for example; they are yellow or white, yellow being a
primitive colour and white an easy variant.

The British " Aconite ", *Aconitum anglicum* Stapf,
known as " Monkshood ", is a parallel of the *Delphinium*,

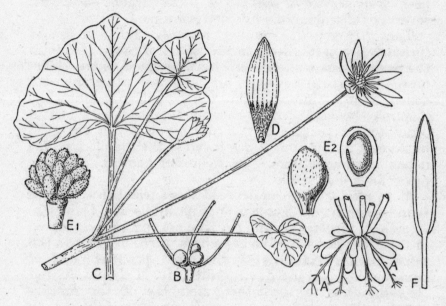

FIG. 63.—The Lesser Celandine, *Ficaria verna* Huds. (Ranunculaceae),
    besides being a welcome Spring flower, has several interesting morpho-
    logical features; its leaves are sub-opposite and anisophyllous, there
    are only three sepals and more than five petals.

A, rootstock with tubers.   B, bulbils in the leaf-axils.   C, mature leaf.
D, petal.   E 1, carpels, 2, same enlarged and vertical section.   F, stamen.

but the petals, though modified, are not spurred.   There
are still three to five carpels, so the " Aconite " is less
advanced than the *Delphinium* in that respect.   The
upper sepal is hooded and forms an effective protection for
the other parts of the flower, besides being of an attractive
colour.   In both *Delphinium* and *Aconitum* the flowers are
gathered into inflorescences, thus making them more con-

spicuous and attractive to insects, ensuring cross-pollination and so making for a virile, successful race. An inflorescence is therefore more advanced than a single flower, except when the latter is due to reduction, as is sometimes obvious— for example, in the "Snowdrop" (see p. 269).

We must now deal with another group of the family which on the whole may be regarded as being on a higher plane than the *Helleborus* alliance. Of this group *Myosurus*, the "Mousetail", and *Ranunculus*, the "Buttercup", are the most ancient, the former with a long carpellary axis just as in *Magnolia*. *Ranunculus* is very similar but with a more contracted axis. The character for the whole group is the uniovulate carpel. That must surely be a reduction from those, such as *Helleborus*, with several ovules. It is a mark of greater efficiency and economy by which one seed can do the work of many. *Ranunculus* has managed to spread itself nearly all over the world. This may be due

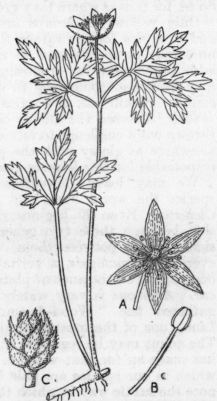

FIG. 64.—Wood Anemone, *Anemone nemorosa* L. (Ranunculaceae), has lost its petals and has no nectaries; but the sepals do the work, that of protection and attraction, insects visiting the flower to collect the pollen.

A, flower. B, stamen. C, carpels.

to the little nectary near the base of the petal which attracts insects. Or it may have been the looking-glass wherein an insect sees its reflection. Many of us as children determined our liking for butter with this mirror of nature. Those were happy days and we

PLATE NINE

RANUNCULACEAE

The Buttercup family, RANUNCULACEAE, provides
a most interesting group for the study of the
evolution of genera. In few families is there such
a wide range of floral structure, particularly with
regard to the sepals and petals. For example, the
gap between a primitive type such as *Paeonia* (red
flower at the base) and the Aconite (*Aconitum*, blue
flower) is almost as great as that from the family
taken as a whole to the Dead-nettle family, LABI-
ATAE, or, say, from the Lilies, LILIACEAE, to the
Orchids, ORCHIDACEAE. *Trollius* (middle left) and
Ranunculus (right), with yellow flowers, are shown,
whilst *Anemone*, a herb, is a more primitive example
than *Clematis* (a climber with opposite leaves and
valvate petaloid sepals). The more primitive
flowers are red or yellow; the more advanced blue,
pink or white.

The plants illustrated in the coloured plate are : Bottom, Paeonia
mascula *Mill.* Middle, left, Trollius europaeus *Linn.*; right, Ranunculus
flammula *Linn.* Top, left, Aconitum anglicum *Stapf*; middle,
Anemone nemorosa *Linn.*; right, Clematis vitalba *Linn.*

To face p. 136.

culus, which has few carpels in a single whorl; it is a native of Asia Minor, and is found in Britain only as a cultivated plant.

In *Ranunculaceae* the attraction of the flower is not always due to the petals as in most other families. Of the British genera the petals are the conspicuous feature in *Ranunculus* and *Paeonia*; in others it is the calyx, i.e., in *Clematis, Anemone, Caltha, Trollius, Helleborus,* and *Aconitum,* whilst both the calyx and corolla are coloured in *Aquilegia*; and in *Thalictrum* it is the anthers that are most prominent. There is no nectar in the flowers of *Clematis, Anemone,* and *Thalictrum,* and this might have had a serious effect with respect to insect visitors during the course of evolution, were it not for the fact that food is provided for them in the shape of pollen, as well as for pollen-devouring flies.

With respect to the anatomical characters, Solereder enumerates

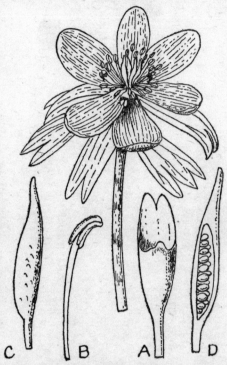

FIG. 67.—The petals of the naturalised "Winter Aconite," *Eranthis hyemalis* Linn. (Ranunculaceae), are reduced, green and tubular; their lack of attraction is compensated for by the bright yellow sepals, whose protective function is undertaken by a whorl of leaf-like bracks.

A, petal. B, stamen. C, carpel. D, vertical section of carpel.

several of importance. These are: the xylem of the vascular bundles is V-shaped and encloses the phloem in the arms of the V; the perforations of the vessels are simple; wood prosenchyma simply-pitted. The clothing hairs are mostly unicellular, except in

K

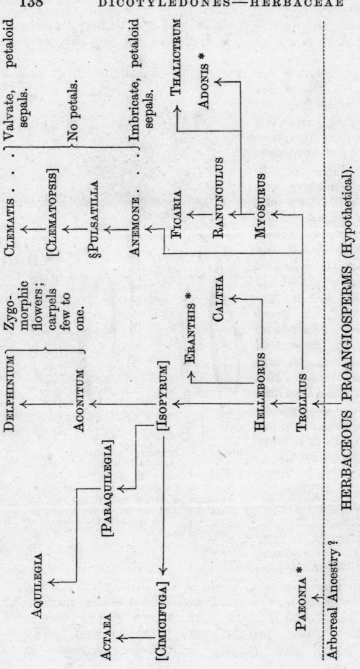

HERBACEOUS PROANGIOSPERMS (Hypothetical).

Diagram showing the relationships of the British genera of RANUNCULACEAE. From TROLLIUS to DELPHINIUM and AQUILEGIA there is more than one ovule and the fruit is a follicle. From MYOSURUS to THALICTRUM and to CLEMATIS there is only one ovule and the fruit an achene (ANEMONE sometimes has an additional abortive ovule). PAEONIA rather stands apart and may have had a separate ancestry, probably from a more woody stock. (Genera in square brackets not represented in the British flora.)

Thalictrum. Glandular hairs are always unicellular. The stomata of this family have already been mentioned, and are frequently spoken of in the text as being of the Ranunculaceous type, i.e., they have no special subsidiary cells, but are surrounded by a number of ordinary epidermal cells.

Here is a key to the British genera of *Ranunculaceae* arranged so far as possible on phylogenetic lines :—

Carpels with more than one ovule; fruit usually with more than one seed :

Flowers actinomorphic (" regular ") :

Sepals smaller than the large petals; radical leaves twice ternate
PAEONIA*

Sepals larger than the petals (when present) and mostly brightly coloured :

Petals present, though often much modified; sepals pale yellow, greenish or white :

Petals not spurred :

Petals tubular, green :

Sepals greenish or tinged with purple; flowers several together
HELLEBORUS

Sepals yellow; flowers solitary, subtended by a whorl of leaf-like bracts . . . . ERANTHIS *

Petals not tubular :

Carpels several; flowers large, yellow . . . . . TROLLIUS

Carpel solitary; flowers small, whitish, racemose . ACTAEA

Petals spurred . . . . AQUILEGIA

Petals absent; sepals bright yellow (very like the petals of a Buttercup (Ranunculus); growing in or near water; nectar secreted by the carpels . . . . CALTHA

Flowers zygomorphic (" irregular ") :

Upper sepal hood-like, not spurred; carpels 3. . . ACONITUM

Upper sepal not hood-like, with a long spur at the base; carpel 1
DELPHINIUM*

Carpels with only one fertile ovule (and one seed) (sometimes abortive ovules in *Anemone*) :

Leaves radical, or if cauline then alternate or rarely subopposite; herbs :

Petals present; sepals not petaloid :

Carpels arranged on a long floral axis; sepals spurred; petals narrow, clawed . . . . MYOSURUS

Carpels in the flowering stage arranged on a globose or short floral axis; sepals not spurred; petals usually broad :

Petals with a nectariferous claw, yellow or white; mostly perennials :

Petals 5; sepals 5; leaves alternate or all radical . RANUNCULUS

Petals more than 5; sepals 3; leaves subopposite. . FICARIA

it is reasonable to assume that one of their characters, in this case trimery, may have been developed in some of the descendants of *Ranales* which have remained Dicotyledons.

In *Berberidaceae* the stamens are the same number as the petals and opposite to them, and the anthers are peculiar in their dehiscence, by valves or flaps opening from the bottom upwards. This peculiar opening of the anthers is uncommon. It is characteristic, however, of the family *Lauraceae*, not represented in this country except in cultivation; but *Lauraceae* are not related to *Berberidaceae*.

To understand the morphology of the shoots and leaves of *Berberis* the student should study the allied and more primitive exotic genus *Mahonia*, with pinnate leaves. It will be observed that in *Berberis* the leaves are always simple and may be either evergreen or deciduous, whereas in *Mahonia* they are always imparipinnate and evergreen. The simple leaf of *Berberis*, however, is articulated at the base in the same way as the terminal leaflet of *Mahonia*, so that it may be looked upon as a reduced imparipinnate leaf. Again, the inflorescence of *Berberis* is situated at the apex of a short shoot which arises in the axil of a leaf-thorn, whilst in *Mahonia* it arises from the axil of a scale of the winter bud which terminates a long shoot. In *Berberis* the flower, with few exceptions, consists of six sepals in two whorls of three, six sepals in two whorls, six stamens in two whorls, and a single carpel forming the pistil. For training the eye in the appreciation of morphological differences the study of these two genera is recommended.

The genus *Epimedium*, which is often found naturalised, is an escape from gardens. It is a striking contrast in habit to *Berberis* and *Mahonia*, but other exotic genera bridge the apparently large gap between them.

The stamens of *Berberis* and *Mahonia* are sensitive to touch, which ensures a good dose of pollen on the head of a visiting insect and increases the chance of cross-pollination. Nectar is secreted on the inner side of the base of each petal. The stamens when touched by insects move

RANUNCULACEAE TO CRUCIFERAE

The families represented in this plate are closely connected phylogenetically. The basic family is RANUNCULACEAE, which is the most primitive of the herbaceous subphylum (*Caltha* is drawn). Related to them are the NYMPHAEACEAE (*Nymphaea* is shown), which are entirely aquatic. Then there is a clear line of development through the herbaceous BERBERIDACEAE (not represented in Britain, except by *Berberis*, which is woody) to PAPAVERACEAE (*Papaver* is illustrated), and finally to the large and very successful climax family CRUCIFERAE (*Cardamine* shown). From the RANUNCULACEAE to the CRUCIFERAE there is a gradual reduction in the number of stamens and carpels, and the latter become united in PAPAVERACEAE and reduced to two in CRUCIFERAE. ARISTOLOCHIACEAE (*Asarum* drawn) are mainly tropical, and need the equally tropical family MENISPERMACEAE to link them up with BERBERIDACEAE. Of the latter family *Berberis* and *Mahonia* (the second not native) are exceptional in being woody.

The plants illustrated in the coloured plate are : Bottom, Caltha palustris *Linn.* Middle, left, Nymphaea alba *Linn.*; right, Papaver rhoeas *Linn.* Top, left, Asarum europeum *Linn.*; right, Cardamine pratensis *Linn.*

To face p. 142.

suddenly towards the pistil. Because of this Sprengel considered them to be self-pollinated, but another observer, H. Müller, proved this to be erroneous, because the insect's head or proboscis is inserted between the dehiscing anthers and the stigmatic margin which is at the same level. When it visits another flower and touches the stigma with the side of its body dusted with pollen, pollination is effected.

The Barberry, *Berberis vulgaris* Linn., was once common as a hedge plant until it was found to be a host for wheat rust. Its fruits, like many similar Chinese species grown in our gardens, make a jelly of good flavour.

One of the extreme limits of reduction of the series of orders beginning with the *Ranales* is the family **Aristolochiaceae**, represented in Britain by a single species, *Asarum europaeum* Linn., though *Aristolochia clematitis* L. is found natu-

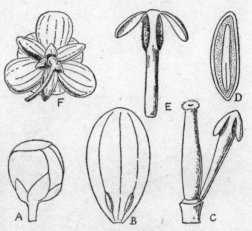

FIG. 68.

A, flower-bud of the Barberry, *Berberis vulgaris* Linn. (Berberidaceae). B, petal with the two nectaries. C, pistil and one stamen. D, vertical section of seed. E, stamen. F, flower from below.

ralised. With only these before us it would be very difficult to imagine that the family has descended from the Ranales, but if we examine the world species the evidence is much clearer. For example, there is one genus, discovered comparatively recently, which provides a link between *Aristolochiaceae* and the *Ranales*. This is *Saruma*, a monotypic Chinese genus, with cordate leaves, terminal, solitary flowers, and with three, large, rounded, *very conspicuous petals* and free carpels (see Fig. 69).

The wood of *Aristolochia* is very similar to that of

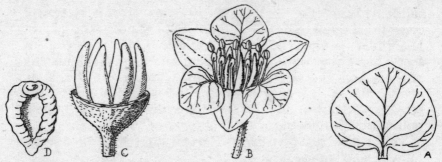

FIG. 69.—*Saruma* (*S. henryi* Oliv.) (Aristolochiaceae), a Chinese genus more or less intermediate between *Menispermaceae* and *Aristolochiaceae*. Note the three well-developed petals and free carpels.

A, petal.   B, flower.   C, calyx-cup and carpels.   D, seed.

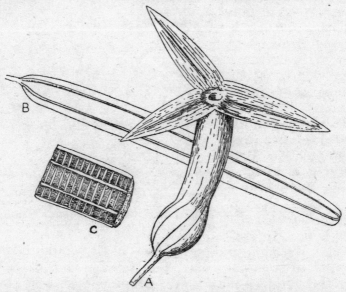

FIG. 70.—*Pararistolochia*, a more primitive genus than *Aristolochia*, with an actinomorphic (regular) 3-lobed calyx and elongated hard-ribbed indehiscent fruit, grows in the forests of West tropical Africa.

A, flower.   B, fruit.   C, longitudinal section of fruit.

Clematis, with broad medullary rays; but this, of course, is due to parallelism and not generic relationship. The stomata are of the Ranunculaceous type. Again, as in *Berberidaceae*, a monocotyledon-like trimerous type of flower has been evolved. *Asarum* is a small rhizomatous herb, with inconspicuous flowers; calyx three-lobed and coloured, no petals, and there are twelve stamens; ovary six-locular with axile placentation. Some years ago I

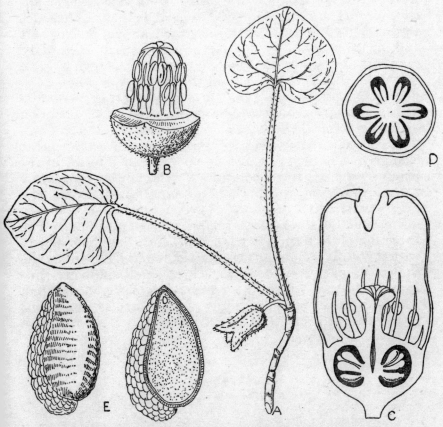

FIG. 71.—*Asarum europeum* Linn. (Aristolochiaceae). A, whole plant. B, flower with calyx (perianth) removed. C, vertical section of flower. D, cross-section of ovary. E, whole and vertical section of seed.

described an interesting genus from West Africa, and called it *Pararistolochia*, which has a regular, three-lobed, tubular calyx, and it is probably an ancestral type of the larger genus *Aristolochia*, with an oblique entire often petaloid calyx. Some species of the latter genus are familiar climbers in our greenhouses. A sketch of *Pararistolochia* is shown in Fig 70.

It seems probable that there are two types of climbers amongst Dicotyledons, one kind having been evolved from woody ancestors, the other from herbaceous ancestors. These climbing Aristolochias belong, I consider, to the latter, for their wood, as stated above, is very soft and in cross-section shows strikingly broad medullary rays just as in *Clematis*, which has also been shown to have had an herbaceous ancestor in the genus *Anemone*.

Asarum europaeum Linn. is a low-growing perennial herb arising from a creeping rhizome such as are common in herbaceous *Berberidaceae*. And the floral parts run in threes as in that family. But there has been a great change in the ovary, which is inferior, an inferior ovary being a very advanced condition. The flowers grow close to the ground and are often hidden among fallen leaves. The calyx (perianth) is greenish-brown outside, and dull brown inside, and the odour is rather sharp and camphorlike. The three lobes are narrowly triangular, and they open slowly with their tips remaining for some time curved inwards while the lower part spreads out. Three small splits are thus formed, behind which the mature stigmas are situated, which are touched by intruding insects, such as small flies.

The diagram below shows the short path of evolution of *Aristolochiaceae*.

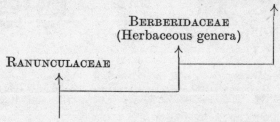

ARISTOLOCHIACEAE

BERBERIDACEAE
(Herbaceous genera)

RANUNCULACEAE

RHOEADALES to RESEDALES.

52. Papaveraceae.   53. Fumariaceae.   54. Cruciferae.
55. Resedaceae.

Having dealt with the *Ranales* and their more immediate reduced derivatives, we pass on to a more advanced group, the *Rhoeadales*, the name originating from the specific epithet of *Papaver rhoeas* Linn., the common Field Poppy. The principal family is **Papaveraceae**, familiar to everyone. In contrast with the *Ranunculaceae*, the car-pels are completely united, but their con-crescent walls are not produced right into the middle of the ovary or very rarely so, and even in the latter case the ovules are not borne on the inner angle of the loculi but on the intrusive walls (Fig. 72, B); thus the placentation of the ovules is parietal and not axile, and we shall find that, other things being equal, parietal placentation is usually the first stage when carpels are united, and axile placentation a later development. Most of the higher fami-lies have axile placenta-tion or some modifica-tion of it (such as the families *Malvacaeae, Geraniaceae, Rubiaceae, Compositae, Labiatae,* etc.). We may trace the descent of the

FIG. 72.—The Field Poppy, *Papaver rhoeas* L., has no nectaries but provides pollen for insects; interesting features are the two caducous sepals, the crumpled petals in bud, the placentation of the ovules and the dehiscence of the fruit (by pores).

A, flower-bud. B, cross-section of ovary. C, fruit. D, seed. E, vertical section of seed.

Papaveraceae from the Ranalean stock by *Platystemon,* a Californian genus with torulose loosely united carpels, which become quite free in fruit (see Fig. 75, p. 150).

It happens that in Bentham and Hooker's *British Flora* the genera are arranged very nicely on phylogenetic lines, except that No. 3, *Chelidonium*, should be placed at the end, being the most highly advanced and nearest to the more specialised family *Cruciferae*. The student should

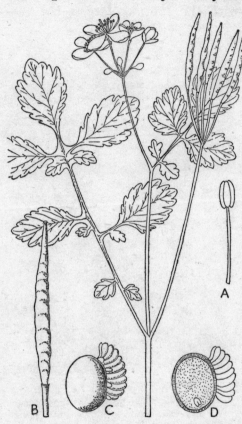

note in *Papaver* the reduction of the number of sepals to two or rarely three, and they fall away early, the four petals which are crumpled in bud, the numerous stamens, and the sessile stigmas. *Meconopsis cambrica*, the Welsh Poppy, has the stigmas raised on a distinct style. It is the type of the genus *Meconopsis*, and has an "Atlantic" distribution, being confined in a wild state from Westmorland, south through Wales and South-west England as far as the Pyrenees. The three other genera have a linear fruit very similar to many *Cruciferae*. There are no nectaries on the petals of *Papaveraceae*, and insects visiting the flowers are concerned only with collecting the pollen which they eat. In

Fig. 73.—The Greater Celandine, *Chelidonium majus* L. (Papaveraceae), has at least one good spotting feature, the leaf-opposed inflorescence; like the Horned Poppy, its fruits resemble those of the next family Cruciferae.

A, stamen. B, fruit. C, seed. D, vertical section of seed showing abundant endosperm and tiny embryo.

the beds of herbaceous plants at Kew, where the families are arranged according to the Bentham and Hooker system, it is an interesting and not too difficult task to observe the relationships and connections from the *Ranunculaceae* to the *Papaveraceae* and finally to the *Cruciferae*.

FIG. 74.—The Horned or Sea Poppy, *Glaucium flavum* Crantz (Papaveraceae), has a fruit which is a transition to the Cruciferous type. A, leaf.

The following key serves to distinguish the genera :—

Ovary and fruit globose or ellipsoid; stamens very numerous :
 Stigmas sessile on top of the ovary . . . . PAPAVER
 Stigmas supported on a distinct style . . . . . . MECONOPSIS
Ovary and fruit linear; stamens not very numerous :
 Flowers yellow, large, solitary; seeds not crested; sea-coast plants
 GLAUCIUM
 Flowers violet, large, solitary; seeds not crested; field weeds
 ROEMERIA*
 Flowers yellow, small, umbellate; seeds crested at one end
 CHELIDONIUM

There are no glandular hairs in *Papaveraceae*, and no special subsidiary cells associated with the guard-cells of the stomata. Laticiferous canals, cells, and sacs are widely distributed in the family, and their nature, according to Solereder, may be used to distinguish genera. The latex is white in *Papaver*, orange in *Chelidonium*, and watery in *Glaucium*.

Although many continental botanists still retain the family **Fumariaceae** in the *Papaveraceae*, the two are really very distinct. In the *Genera Plantarum*, Bentham and Hooker united them, but in their *British Flora* they separated them. In one respect they differ markedly from *Papaveraceae* in that their flowers are nectariferous, the nectar being secreted in the pouches of the upper petals. The stomata are similar to those of *Papaveraceae*. There are two genera in our flora, *Corydalis*, with two species, one of them naturalised, and *Fumaria*. The family marks

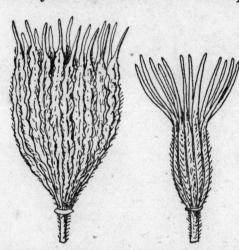

FIG. 75.—*Platystemon californicus* Benth. (Papaveraceae), a Californian genus, with numerous loosely united carpels which become quite free from one another in the fruiting stage, provides a link between the *Papaveraceae* and the *Ranunculaceae*.

a considerable advancement on *Papaveraceae*, but is too poorly represented to warrant remarks on phylogeny. The two genera are distinguished as follows :—

Fruit dehiscent, linear, with several seeds . . . . . CORYDALIS
Fruit a small rounded 1-seeded nut . . . . FUMARIA

The diagram on page 151 shows the probable phylogeny.

We have next to consider a large and most successful climax family derived from the Papaveraceous stock and

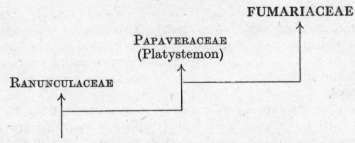

linked, as has been pointed out, by the more advanced
genera of that family, namely, *Glaucium*, *Roemeria*, and
Chelidonium. This
great family is
Cruciferae. It is so
natural that the non-
botanical person can
see very little differ-
ence between the
genera. In spite of
this difficulty, how-
ever, botanists recog-
nise about three
hundred and fifty,
though the differ-
ences amongst them
would in other fami-
lies be regarded as
little more than
specific. These char-
acters are nearly all
derived from the
fruit and seed, and
ripe fruit and seed
are therefore essen-
tial for the deter-
mination of the genus
of a Crucifer. The

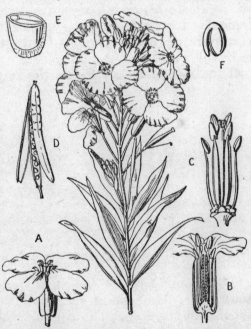

FIG. 76.—*Cheiranthus cheiri* L. (Cruciferae).

A, flower. B, flower cut vertically. C,
stamens and ovary. D, fruit splitting from
below. E, section of seed. F, embryo.—
After Baill. (From Hutchinson, Families of
Flowering Plants.)

flowers are of a most uniform structure, and those of the
common Wallflower are quite familiar to most students as
being the first they examined on taking up the study of

botany. The formula runs thus :—K4 C4 A4 + 2 G2. These characters are associated nearly throughout the whole family, and it may be said that in this group, perhaps more than in any other, the resemblances are more emphatic than the differences. All *Cruciferae* have nectar in their flowers.

Taking the structure of the fruit into consideration, we may either consider that those with a lomentum are the most advanced; i.e., those that have transverse partitions between the seeds, or that this type, already evolved in the *Papaveraceae*, is primitive. The student may be able to decide to his own satisfaction which view be the more logical. I consider the lomentum in the *Cruciferae* to be the more advanced type of fruit, just as it undoubtedly is in the *Papilionaceae*.

The diagram below shows the phylogeny :—

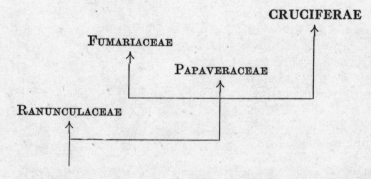

The stomata of the leaves of *Cruciferae* are very characteristic. The guard-cells are surrounded by three subsidiary cells, which are not, however, as in *Magnoliaceae* and *Rubiaceae*, parallel to the pore. One of these subsidiary cells is smaller than the other two. All Cruciferae possess characteristic secretory cells which contain myrosin, and these cells are known as myrosin cells. Clothing hairs in *Cruciferae* are always unicellular, but they vary from unbranched to two-armed (T-shaped), stellate, peltate, or dendriform (tree-like) hairs.

Cruciferae provide some salads and several important vegetables, including the Cabbage (*Brassica oleracea*

Linn. var. *capitata* Linn.), Cauliflower (*B. oleracea* var. *botrytis* Linn., subvar. *cauliflora* DC.), Brussels Sprout (*B. oleracea* var. *bullata* DC.), Kohlrabi (*B. oleracea* var. *gongyloides* Linn.), Savoy (*B. oleracea* subvar. *subauda* O. E. Schulz), Turnip (*Brassica campestris* Linn. var. *rapa* Hartm.), White Mustard (*Sinapis alba* Linn.), Black Mustard (*B. nigra* (Linn.) Koch), Horse Radish (*Armoracia lapathifolia* Gilib.), Radish (*Raphanus sativus* Linn.), Watercress (*Nasturtium officinale* Linn.); also many beautiful garden plants.

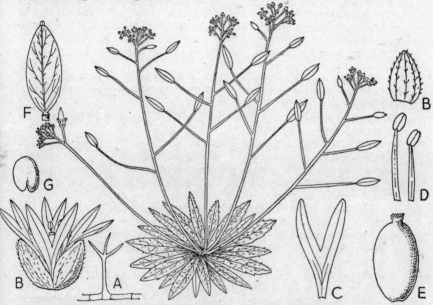

FIG. 77.—The Whitlow-Grass, *Erophila verna* (L.) E. Mey., was described by Linnaeus as *Draba verna*, hence the (L.) after the name. It may be recognised by its habit, stellate indumentum, and bilobed petals.

A, stellate hair. B, flower. C, petal. D, stamens. E, pistil. F, fruit. G, seed.

Key to genera of *Cruciferae*.

1. Fruits divided by a *longitudinal* partition, usually opening by two valves :
  2. Fruits at least 3 or 4 times as long as broad :
  3. Flowers white, mauve, purple or red (not yellow) :
  Petals large, on long claws, purple or rarely white; stigmas 2, very short, erect or parallel :

L

Leaves hoary and soft with stellate hairs; stigmas thickened at the base; pods long and narrow . . . . MATTHIOLA

Leaves green, with coarse hairs; stigmas not thickened; pods much contracted between the seeds . . . . HESPERIS*

Petals small, or the claws scarcely longer than the calyx; stigma capitate, entire :

Leaves all undivided; flowers white :

Leaves all stalked, large and broad; seeds in a single row
ALLIARIA

Upper leaves sessile or auricled; seeds in one or two rows
ARABIS

Leaves (at least the lower) pinnate :

Seeds in one or two distinct rows in each cell; pod rather short and curved; flowers white . . . . . . NASTURTIUM

Seeds merged into one row in each cell; pod straight, long or slender :

Stem leaves undivided, narrowed at the base; flowers white
ARABIS

Stem leaves pinnate or divided; flowers white or pinkish mauve
CARDAMINE (Dentaria)

3. Flowers yellow :

All the leaves entire or at most toothed; plants pale or hoary, with minute appressed hairs :

Fruits flattened; radicel accumbent . . . . CHEIRANTHUS*

Fruits nearly quadrangular; radicle incumbent. . ERYSIMUM

Leaves (at least the lower) pinnate or lobed at the base; plants glabrous or hairy with rough or spreading hairs :

Cotyledons accumbent; pods ending in a very short style; plants glabrous, with lyrate or pinnate leaves :

Fruits relatively short (0·8 cm.), on slender spreading pedicels, valves not ribbed . . . . NASTURTIUM (Radicula)

Fruits longer (2·5 cm. or more), on stiff short pedicels, valves ribbed . . . . BARBAREA

Cotyledons incumbent; valves of the fruit opening to close under the stigma with 3 ribs; plants hairy or glabrous, the leaves deeply pinnate . . . . SISYMBRIUM

Cotyledons conduplicate; fruit ending in a beak or conical style, up to 1 cm. long; leaves irregularly pinnate or lyrate, or the upper ones undivided :

Seeds in a single row; fruits terete or angular :

Valves of fruit 1-nerved . . . . BRASSICA

Valves of fruit 3–7 nerved . . . . SINAPIS

Seeds in 2 rows; fruits compressed . . . . DIPLOTAXIS

2. Fruits less than 3 times as long as broad :

4. Fruits globular or oblong, or compressed; valves flat or convex, *parallel with the false septum* :

5. Fruits nearly globular or cylindric (not compressed or flattened) :

Small aquatic plants with subulate leaves and minute white flowers . . . . SUBULARIA

Terrestrial plants with flattened leaves :
  Flowers white ; radicle accumbent :
    Plants glabrous ; fruits globular or shortly ovoid or oblong :
      Valves of fruit 1-nerved . . . . COCHLEARIA
      Valves of fruit not nerved . . . . ARMORACIA

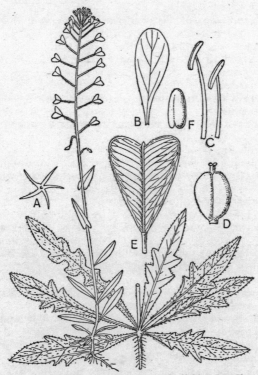

FIG. 78.—The common weed "Shepherd's-
Purse, *Capsella bursa-pastoris* L. (Cruciferae), is an "aggregate" species, with
several forms; a useful plant to test the
young student's powers of observation,
with several interesting morphological
features.

A, stellate hair. B, petal. C, stamens.
D, pistil. E, fruit. F, seed.

Plants hoary or rough with short hairs; fruits somewhat
  flattened or oblong. . . . . ALYSSUM*
Flowers yellow :
  Leaves pinnately lobed, or, if entire, narrowed at the base;
    cotyledons accumbent . . . . NASTURTIUM

Leaves entire or toothed, the upper ones auricled and clasping
the stem; radicle incumbent . . . . . CAMELINA*
5. Fruits distinctly compressed or flattened :
Fruits orbicular or oval; flowers white or pale yellow ALYSSUM*
Fruits longer than broad; flowers white or yellow :
Petals entire or at most toothed . . . . DRABA
Petals deeply 2-lobed . . . . EROPHILA
4. Fruits compressed or flattened laterally *at right angles to the false
septum*; valves more or less boat-shaped :
6. Seeds 2 or more in each loculus of the pod :
Fruits winged all around; flowers small, white :
Leaves entire . . . . THLASPI
Leaves pinnate . . . . TEESDALIA
Fruits not winged, obcordate or wedge-shaped; several seeds in
each loculus . . . . CAPSELLA
Fruits not winged, oval, very small; seeds 2 in each loculus
HUTCHINSIA
6. Seeds solitary in each loculus of the pod :
Fruits opening by two valves; upper leaves undivided :
Two adjacent outer petals much larger than the others; flowers
white . . . . IBERIS
Petals equal-sized; flowers white . . . . . LEPIDIUM
Fruits indehiscent or separating laterally into two nuts; trailing
plants with pinnate or bipinnate leaves; flowers white
CORONOPUS (*Senebiera*)
1. Fruits not dehiscent, with 1 seed or with several seeds separated by
transverse partitions (false septa) :
Fruits flattened :
Fruits obovate, pendulous, 1-seeded; tall plants with auriculate
based leaves and yellow flowers . . . . . . ISATIS*
Fruits small, broad; trailing plants with pinnate or bipinnate leaves,
with small white flowers . . . . CORONOPUS
Fruits globular, cylindrical, or conical :
Fruits globular, 1-seeded, shortly stipitate, bilobed at the top;
perennials with coarse glabrous leaves pinnately lobed with wavy
toothed margins; flowers white . . . . . . CRAMBE
Fruits not globular:
Fruits containing several seeds separated by transverse partitions;
flowers white, pale yellow or lilac . . . . . RAPHANUS
Fruits 2-locular, each with one seed; flowers yellow; leaves lanceolate; jagged-toothed . . . . BUNIAS*
Fruits composed of two joints, only the upper joint fertile and
1-seeded, beaked; leaves pinnately lobulate; flowers purplish or
white; annuals . . . . CAKILE

Resedaceae is an advanced family of this alliance.
Anatomically it shares some characteristics with *Cruciferae*, particularly the occurrence of myrosin-cells in the

genus RESEDA, which also has the same type of histo-
logical differentiation of the epidermis of the leaf. There
are no special subsidiary cells to the stomata, however, as
in *Cruciferae*. The petals are small and inconspicuous, and
they are valvate in bud. Valvate sepals or petals are
very rare in primitive groups of families and occur only
in advanced tribes or genera. The valvation of members

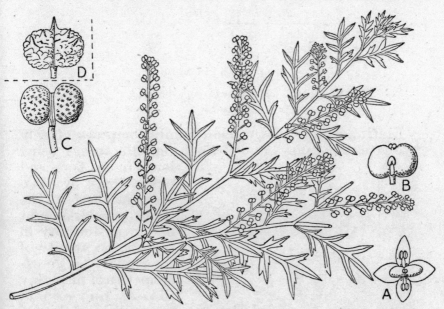

FIG. 79.—The Wart Cress, *Coronopus didymus* (L). Sm. (Cruciferae), is almost
exceptional in the family in having only two stamens; as in the Greater
Celandine (fig. 73), its inflorescence is leaf-opposed.

A, flower. B, pistil and stamens. C, fruit. D, fruit of the second
species *C. procumbens* Gilib.

of the same whorl means the complete or almost complete
suppression of the internodes between them. Although
the petals of *Reseda* are small, they make up for their
deficiency in size by their sweet scent (cf. Mignonette of
gardens). *Reseda* is the only genus represented in Britain,
with two native and one naturalised species, which grow
mostly in waste places or in limestone soil. The seeds
of *Resedaceae*, like *Cruciferae*, have no endosperm, and the
group is no doubt derived from the same stock, being

something of a climax in its own little sphere. *Resedaceae* are mostly semi-desert plants and are numerous in the Mediterranean region.

CARYOPHYLLALES.

56. Elatinaceae.   57. Caryophyllaceae.   58. Portulacaceae.

Elatinaceae is a very small family composed of only two genera, ELATINE and BERGIA, only the former being found in our flora, and represented by two very small herbs. The student would no doubt find great difficulty in tracing the affinity of the family from an examination of these tiny plants, but exotic species help in this respect. The stipules are paired, and the family is distinguished from *Caryophyllaceae* by the completely septate ovary and the seeds without endosperm. The exact phylogenetic position is somewhat doubtful, but I would rather regard them as being related to *Caryophyllaceae* or *Crassu-*

FIG. 80.—The resemblance of the Soapwort, *Saponaria officinalis* L. (Caryophyllaceae) and *Phlox* in the *Polemoniaceae* gives colour to the idea that the two families are closely related.

A, petal. B, pistil. C, stamen. D, capsule.

laceae, than place them, as Engler does, between the
Dipterocarps and Tamarisks. *Elatinaceae* are indeed
probably little more than syncarpous *Crassulaceae*,
which, instead of inhabiting dry regions as most of that
family does, have
adopted an aquatic
or semi-aquatic
habitat.

Our next family,
Caryophyllaceae, is
a very important one
and quite richly re-
presented in the
British flora by thir-
teen genera. These
fall into two well-
marked subfamilies,
the more primitive,
Alsinoideae, with
free or nearly free
sepals, and the more
advanced *Silenoi-
deae*, with the sepals
united into a tube.
This difference of
freedom and cohe-
sion of parts, were it
to be found in the
petals, would place
the two groups into
separate subdivi-
sions, the "Poly-
petalae" and
"Gamopetalae" re-
spectively, but the

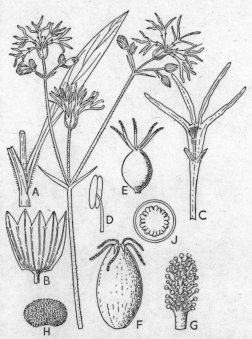

FIG. 81.—The flowers of the "Ragged Robin,"
Lychnis flos-cuculi L. (Caryophyllaceae), are
arranged in cymes, the oldest flower being
in the middle; as in nearly all *Caryophyllaceae* the ovary is 1-locular with the
numerous ovules attached to the central
axis.

A, node. B, calyx opened out. C, petal.
D, stamen. E, pistil. F, fruit. G, ovules
on central axis. H, seed. J, cross-section
of ovary.

union of the sepals is quite rightly not regarded as of
so much importance as that of the petals. Nevertheless,
Caryophyllaceae are closely connected with the "Gamopetalae", in that they seem to be the basal stock from
which *Primulaceae* have been derived. But I have shown

already (p. 169) that part of *Primulaceae* may have also come directly from the same stock as the *Saxifragaceae.* Then there are connecting links between the *Caryophyllaceae* and *Geraniales* (sensu stricto), and with certain families formerly widely separated and placed in the old group "Apetalae", such as *Polygonaceae, Chenopodiaceae,* etc., which we shall examine presently.

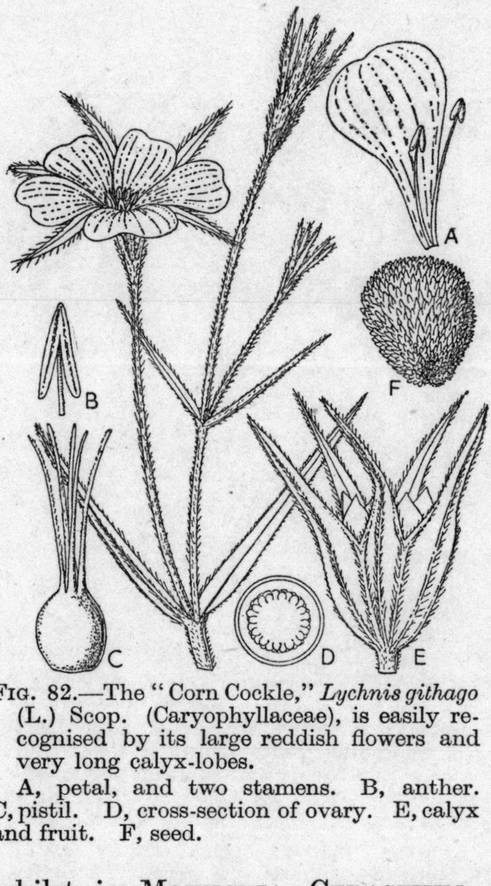

As stated above, the genera with free sepals are probably more primitive than those with united sepals. Those with free sepals may be again grouped into two sections, one with stipules and the other without stipules. Then the capsule provides most useful characters; in SAGINA, ARENARIA, and STELLARIA, it opens by valves, a common and normal mode of dehiscence, whilst in MOENCHIA, CERASTIUM, and HOLOSTEUM, the capsule opens at the top by short teeth, a much less common method of setting free the seeds. All those genera with stipules, SPERGULARIA, SPERGULA, and POLYCARPON, have capsules opening by valves.

The more advanced group, characterised by the gamosepalous calyx, has, without exception, capsules which open at the top by teeth or short valves. Except

FIG. 82.—The "Corn Cockle," *Lychnis githago* (L.) Scop. (Caryophyllaceae), is easily recognised by its large reddish flowers and very long calyx-lobes.

A, petal, and two stamens. B, anther. C, pistil. D, cross-section of ovary. E, calyx and fruit. F, seed.

PLATE ELEVEN

CARYOPHYLLACEAE TO PLANTAGINACEAE

Caryophyllaceae are represented at the base of the drawing by two genera, left, *Dianthus*, and right, *Lychnis*. Both have a gamophyllous calyx, a character used to separate about half of the family from the other half, which have free sepals. It is not a far cry from the Caryophyllaceae to the Gentianaceae, represented on the right (middle) by *Blackstonia*, and on the left by *Gentiana*. Here sympetaly is well established, and in the latter the stamens are reduced to five. These are alternate with the corolla-lobes, but in the parallel and similarly derived family Primulaceae the stamens are opposite the corolla-lobes, the alternate series having been dispensed with. The relationship between *Blackstonia* (Gentianaceae) and *Lysimachia* (Primulaceae), shown on the right-hand side at the top, is probably more than superficial. Further evolution of the same subphylum is shown by Plumbaginaceae (*Armeria*, top left), and Plantaginaceae (*Plantago*, top middle). In these higher families the free central placentation of the Caryophyllaceae has become free basal by reduction of the central axis of the ovary.

The plants illustrated in the coloured plate are : Bottom, left, Dianthus caesius *Sm.*; right, Lychnis dioica *Linn.* Middle, left, Gentiana pneumonanthe *Linn.*; right, Blackstonia perfoliata *Huds.* Above middle, left, Primula vulgaris *Linn.*; right, Lysimachia vulgaris *Linn.* Top, left, Armeria maritima *Linn.*; middle, Plantago media *Linn.*

To face p. 160.

for DIANTHUS, a very natural and widely spread genus, the other genera are somewhat artificial, these being LYCHNIS with usually five, SILENE and CUCUBALUS* with three, and SAPONARIA (Fig. 80) with two styles. Note the great similarity of *Saponaria* or *Silene* and *Phlox* (*Polemoniaceae*).

The guard cells of the leaf-stomata are surrounded by

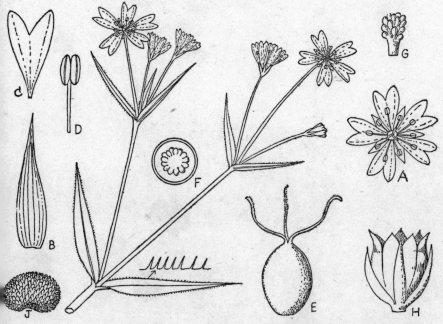

FIG. 83.—*Stellaria holostea* Linn., shows many of the characteristics of the family *Caryophyllaceae*. Flowering shoot with portion of leaf margin (enlarged).

A, flower from above. B, sepal. C, petal. D, stamen. E, pistil. F, cross-section of ovary. G, free basal placenta. H, fruit. J, seed.

two subsidiary cells placed transversely to the pore. This is known to anatomists as the Caryophyllaceous type of stoma, though they do not occur in every genus, being rare in *Arenaria*, *Cerastium*, and *Stellaria*. The hairy covering consists of simple, uniseriate hairs, and of similarly constituted glandular hairs with a unicellular glandular head.

Many of the *Caryophyllaceae* of Britain are weedy plants and widely distributed. But one species, at any rate, is very rare. This is the " Cheddar Pink ", *Dianthus*

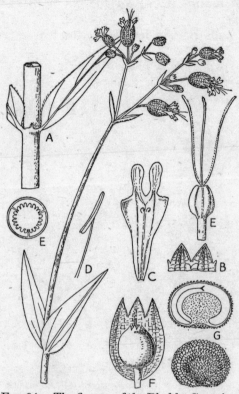

Fig. 84.—The flowers of the Bladder Campion, *Silene cucubalus* Wibel (Caryophyllaceae), are not always bisexual, some being male and some female, each sex with vestigial organs of the other.

A, node. B, calyx-teeth. C, petal. D, stamen. E, pistil and cross-section of ovary. F, fruit. G, seed and longitudinal section.

caesius Linn., which is found only on the limestone rocks in and near the Cheddar Gorge, in Somerset, but nowhere else in these islands. It occurs also in similar situations in western and southern Europe.

Key to the genera of *Caryophyllaceae*.

Sepals free or only slightly united at the base Subfamily **Alsinoideae**
  Stipules absent :
    Capsule opening by valves :
      Petals entire :
        Sepals 5 or 4, with the same number of styles . . . Sagina
        Sepals 5; styles 3 or rarely 4 . . . . Arenaria
        Petals 2-lobed; styles usually 3 (rarely 5) . . . Stellaria
      Capsule opening at the top by short teeth :
        Styles 5–4; capsule with 10–8 teeth :
          Petals entire; stiff glabrous plants . . . . . Moenchia
          Petals notched; much branched hairy plants . . Cerastium
        Styles 3; capsule with 6 teeth; small viscid annual . Holosteum
    Stipules present; capsule opening by valves :
      Styles 5; leaves in whorls, narrow . . . . . . Spergula
      Styles 3 :
        Leaves in pairs, opposite, narrow . . . . . . Spergularia
        Leaves in whorls, spathulate . . . . Polycarpon
Sepals united into a tube; capsule opening by teeth at the top or by
  short valves; stipules absent . . . . Subfamily **Silenoideae**
  Calyx-tube not bracteate at the base :
    Styles 5 *or* 4; capsule with 10 or 5 teeth . . . . . Lychnis
    Styles 3 :
      Fruit a capsule with 6 teeth . . . . Silene
      Fruit at first fleshy, indehiscent. . . . . . . Cucubalus*
    Styles 2; capsule with 4 teeth . . . . Saponaria*
  Calyx-tube scaly-bracteate at the base; styles 2; capsule with 4
    teeth . . . . Dianthus

It has been mentioned that *Caryophyllaceae* and *Saxifragaceae* probably represent the basal stock whence *Primulaceae* have been evolved. There is, in fact, a small family which forms something of a link between them.

If we examine a Caryophyllaceous flower—for example, that of the common stitchwort, *Stellaria holostea* Linn. (Fig. 83), remove the five stamens which are alternate with the petals, and imagine the petals to be joined into a tube, we have then practically the Primulaceous type of flower. The family **Portulacaceae** seems to be the link between these two families. In Britain it is rather poorly represented by only two genera, but there are

several to be seen in gardens.   In CLAYTONIA* the petals
are five and free, and the five stamens are opposite to
them, just as in *Primulaceae*.   In the second genus

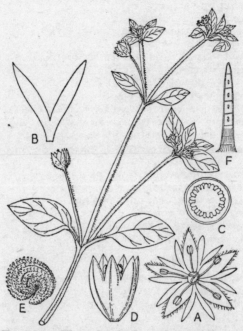

FIG. 85.—The despised and troublesome
    Chickweed, *Stellaria media* Vill. (Caryo-
    phyllaceae), is of great biological interest,
    not the least of which is that its seeds
    provide food for small birds nearly all the
    year round; sometimes it has less than five
    stamens; a good "spotting" feature (if
    needed!) is the line of hairs down one side
    of the stem, these hairs conducting water
    to the special absorbing cells of hairs (F) in
    the leaf-stalks.

A, open flower.   B, petal.   C, cross-section
of ovary.   D, capsule.   E, seed.

MONTIA, the petals are united into a tube, which, however, is split on one side and the stamens are reduced to
three; in fact, nearly as advanced in its androecium as
some *Scrophulariaceae*.

The family *Portulacaceae* is best " spotted " by the sepals usually being two in number, a very rare feature. It is widely spread all over the world, and some of the exotic genera, such as *Anacampseros* and *Portulacaria*, are adapted for growing under extremely dry conditions like the Karoo region of South Africa.

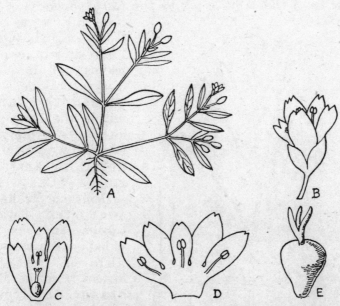

Fig. 86.—Although a member of the *Portulacaceae*, the genus *Montia* (*Montia fontana* Linn.) has a highly advanced sympetalous corolla, and the stamens reduced to three, equalling the stage of evolution exhibited by *Scrophulariaceae*.

The phylogenetic history is shown as follows :—

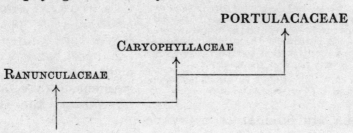

GENTIANALES to PLANTAGINALES

59. Gentianaceae. 60. Menyantheceae. 61. Primulaceae. 62. Plumbaginaceae. 63. Plantaginaceae.

The family **Gentianaceae** is probably a direct development from the same stock as the *Caryophyllaceae*. *Gen-
tianaceae* agree with *Caryophyllaceae* in their mostly opposite leaves, but the corolla is sympetalous, which placed the family within the concept of the *Metachlamydeae*, here abandoned as being an artificial group.

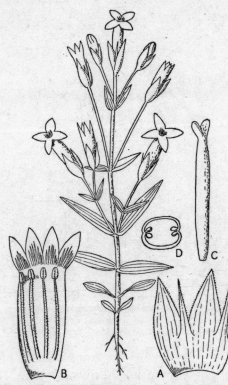

Gentianaceae have a contorted (twisted) corolla, and are pro-vided with intraxylary phloem, which is absent from the *Meny-anthaceae*, often in-cluded with them. BLACKSTONIA (*Chlora*), which greatly re-sembles some *Caryo-phyllaceae*, has per-foliate leaves as in CLAYTONIA (*Portu-lacaceae*) (the opposite leaves are united at the base), and six to eight corolla-lobes and stamens. CENTAURIUM (*Erythraea*) and GEN-

FIG. 87.—The Field Gentian, *Gentiana campestris* L. (Gentianaceae), has only four corolla-lobes, and the nectar secreted at the bottom of the tube is protected from many insects by the dense fringe of bristly hairs at the mouth.

A, calyx laid open. B, corolla laid open.
C, pistil. D, cross-section of ovary.

TIANA are familiar to many people.

Key to the genera of *Gentianaceae*.

Corolla-lobes and stamens 8; corolla yellow; leaves perfoliate
BLACKSTONIA (Chlora)

Corolla-lobes and stamens 5–4 :
  Anthers remaining straight :
    Calyx divided to the base into narrow segments; corolla pink
CICENDIA

    Calyx at most divided to the middle :
      Flowers yellow . . . . MICROCALA
      Flowers blue . . . . GENTIANA
  Anthers becoming spirally twisted; flowers pink or red
CENTAURIUM (Erythraea)

The following shows the probable phylogenetic history of *Gentianaceae* :—

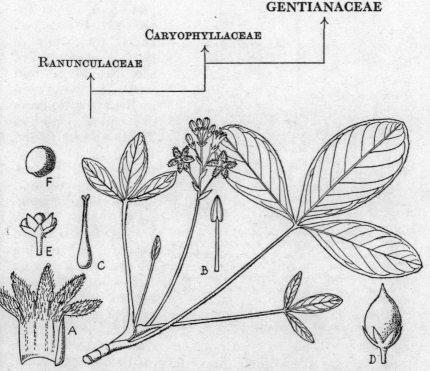

FIG. 88.—The Buckbean, *Menyanthes trifoliata* L. (Menyanthaceae), has alternative leaves and valvate corolla-lobes, characters used to distinguish the family from the Gentianaceae.

A, opened corolla. B, stamen. C, pistil. D, fruit. E, open fruit with seeds. F, seed.

Menyanthaceae have usually been included in *Gentianaceae*, but the leaves are alternate, the vascular bundles of the stem are collateral (i.e., without intraxylary phloem), and the corolla-lobes are induplicate valvate. Many of the family have intercellular sclerenchymatous idioblasts. These are branched thick-walled cells which have pointed arms projecting into the intercellular spaces, and they occur in the parenchyma of the leaf, stem, and root. The two genera in Britain are marsh or aquatic plants. *Menyanthes trifoliata* Linn. is a marsh plant with three-foliolate leaves, and *Limnanthemum nymphaeoides* Link (*Nymphoides*), an aquatic, has floating peltate cordate leaves, and the seeds are winged and ciliate. The separation of this group from *Gentianaceae* leaves

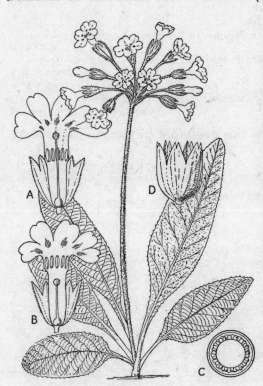

FIG. 89.—In the deliciously fragrant flowers of the Cowslip, *Primula veris* L. (Primulaceae), the anthers are inserted either in the middle or near the top of the corolla-tube, with long and short styles respectively; nectar is secreted around the base of the ovary.

A, long-styled form. B, short-styled form. C, cross-section of ovary showing free basal placenta. D, fruit.

these two families much more natural or homogeneous, an ideal taxonomic botanists have been sometimes slow to adopt owing to custom, convenience, or conservatism.

The family **Primulaceae** has a very similar phylogenetic history to that of *Gentianaceae*. That is to say,

both families have probably arisen from the Caryophyllaceous stock. It seems possible, however, that
Primula and *Cyclamen*
may have descended
more directly from
Saxifragaceae, rather
than through the more
advanced *Caryophylla-*
ceae. Notes on this

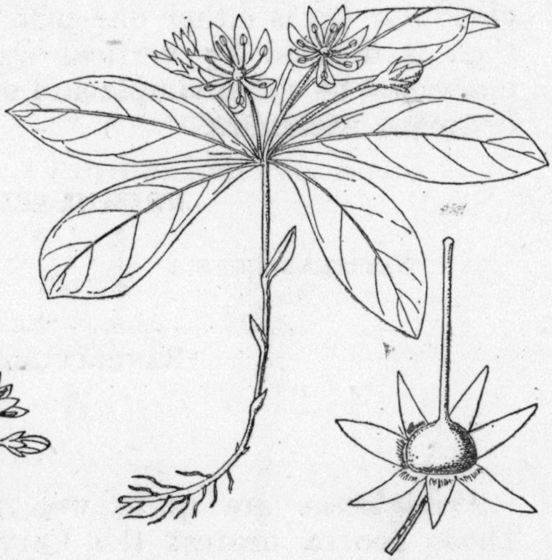

FIG. 90.—A denizen of northern
woods, flowering in early summer, *Trientalis europaea* Linn.
(Primulaceae), with fruit; corolla-lobes more than 5, with a
stamen opposite each.

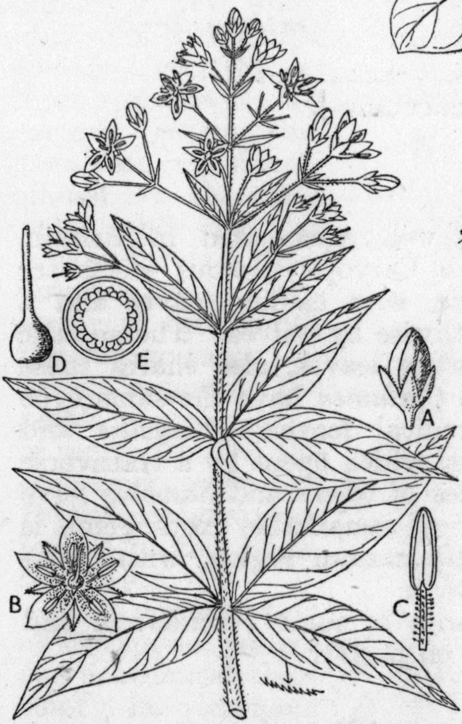

FIG. 91.—In the Yellow Loose-strife,
Lysimachia vulgaris L., the stamens are
shown to be opposite the corolla-lobes,
a characteristic feature of the family
Primulaceae to which it belongs.

A, flower bud. B, open flower. C, stamen. D, pistil. E, cross-section of ovary.

interesting point are
given under *Saxifraga-*
ceae on p. 188.

The " spotting " fea-
tures for *Primulaceae*
are the free basal pla-
centa in the one-locular
ovary, and the stamens
inserted opposite the
corolla-lobes. It should
be remarked, however,
that in *Glaux* there is no
corolla, but the stamens
are *alternate* with the
calyx-lobes. *Samolus* is an outstanding genus with
alternate leaves and an inferior ovary.

M

stalked glandular hairs is also similar. This type of hair-structure is met with in *Primulaceae*.

There are two genera in Britain, and they occur mainly within the influence of the sea, but the common Thrift, *Armeria maritima* (Mill.) Willd., also occurs inland on some of the Scottish mountains.

The two genera are distinguished as follows :—

Flowers in panicles ; styles free from the base.   LIMONIUM (Statice)
Flowers in an involucrate head subtended by an inverted cylindrical sheath ; styles shortly connate at the base . . . . . ARMERIA

The most familiar exotic species of this family is *Plumbago capensis* Thunb., a greenhouse climber with beautiful blue flowers and indigenous in South Africa.

Here is the probable path of descent of *Plumbaginaceae* :—

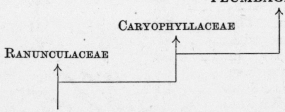

PLUMBAGINACEAE

CARYOPHYLLACEAE

RANUNCULACEAE

Our next family is **Plantaginaceae.** This was placed at the end of the *Gamopetalae* in the Bentham and Hooker system, but it seems to have a general affinity with the *Primulaceae*. The heads of the glandular hairs of PLANTAGO and LITTORELLA are mostly divided by vertical walls only, as in *Primulaceae* and *Plumbaginaceae*, whilst the stomatal apparatus throws back as far as the *Caryophyllaceae*, i.e., the guard cells are accompanied by subsidiary cells placed *transversely* to the pore. In connection with these interesting linking anatomical characters the student should glance at the folder family " tree " based mainly on floral structure. The family embraces only three genera, two of which, *Plantago* and *Littorella*, are found in Britain. In both these genera the flowers are anemophilous and there are no nectaries.

CARYOPHYLLACEAE TO CHENOPODIACEAE

More than one segment of our hypothetical family tree is shown to branch off from the *Caryophyllaceous* stock. As we have seen in the diagram on p. 172, the families PRIMULACEAE, PLANTAGINACEAE, and PLUMBAGINACEAE, are shown to be closely related, having become sympetalous with a reduced number of stamens. These families are more closely related to the half of CARYOPHYLLACEAE which have a tubular calyx. The families shown here have evolved in a different way, and from the other half of CARYOPHYLLACEAE, in which the sepals are free. But in this case the petals have been dispensed with and the inflorescences have become spicate or paniculate. There is also a much greater economy in the ovary, which has become unilocular, and in the number of ovules, the latter being reduced to one. The curved embryo characteristic of the CARYOPHYLLACEAE has persisted almost throughout the subphylum. Many are weeds of fields and waste places, and some are adapted to more saline conditions near the sea. The families shown from the bottom upwards are CARYOPHYLLACEAE (left, *Stellaria*, right, *Spergularia*), ILLECEBRACEAE (right, *Scleranthus*), POLYGONACEAE (left, *Polygonum*), and CHENOPODIACEAE (top right, *Chenopodium*, and left, *Salicornia*).

The plants illustrated in the coloured plate are : Bottom, left, Stellaria holostea *Linn.*; right, Spergularia campestris (*All.*) *Aschers.* Middle, left, Polygonum persicaria *Linn.*; right, Scleranthus annuus *Linn.* Top, left, Salicornia herbacea *Linn.*; right, Chenopodium album *Linn.*

To face p. 172.

In *Plantago* the flowers are bisexual; in *Littorella* they are unisexual, rather a rare feature in plants with sympetalous corollas; but the females have no corollas. In the latter genus also the male flowers are pedicellate and the anthers are borne on long slender filaments exserted from the corolla, whilst the female flowers are concealed amongst the leaves and consist of a sessile calyx split into unequal-sized sepals and enclosing a small ovary with a long thread-like style. *Littorella* grows in mud and wet sand on the margins of pools, or sometimes under water, in which case it usually fails to flower and is propagated by long runners.

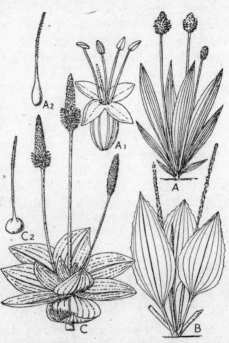

FIG. 93.—The distinctive habits of three of the five native species of *Plantago* are shown in the sketch.

A, *P. lanceolata* L. B, *P. major* L. C, *P. media* L.

A genus which is almost a parallel to this is *Lilaea* [1], constituting the family *Lilaeaceae* (*Heterostylaceae*), an aquatic or marsh herb of Western America and belonging to Monocotyledons.

POLYGONALES and CHENOPODIALES.

64. Polygonaceae.   65. Illecebraceae.   66. Chenopodiaceae.   [66a. Amaranthaceae].

Polygonaceae is the next family. In Bentham and Hooker's system there are very many pages, in fact a

[1] See Hutchinson, *Families of Flowering Plants*, 2 : 41, fig. 8 (1934).

whole volume, between the *Caryophyllaceae*, in the group
"Polypetalae", and the *Polygonaceae*, in the " Monochlamydeae ".   But these two families are rather closely
related, especially through those genera of *Caryophyllaceae*
which have stipulate leaves such as *Spergularia*.   To
see this the student might with advantage compare, for
example, a living plant of *Spergularia campestris* (All.)
Aschers. with one of *Polygonum aviculare* Linn., when the
general relationship may be appreciated.   In the latter
species the stipules are not of such an advanced type as
in most other species of POLYGONUM.   Indeed, in such
a species as *Polygonum bistorta* Linn. it is not easy to
recognise the stipular organs as such.   They look much
more like the glorified ligule of a grass, being intra-petiolar
and sheathing the stem.   That is perhaps why they are
designated by a special term, the *ochrea*.

Polygonum is probably the most ancient of the three
genera represented in Britain.   In this genus the species
range from those with axillary flowers to others with
terminal spikes or racemes.   It almost equals *Ranunculus*
in the variety of its morphology and range of habitat.
For example, *P. aviculare* is a troublesome weed of
cultivation, *P. maritimum* Linn. favours maritime sands,
P. amphibium Linn. and *P. hydropiper* Linn. grow in
ponds and ditches, whilst *P. convolvulus* Linn. and *P.
dumetorum* Linn. are climbing.

RUMEX, the second largest British genus, is much more
homogeneous than *Polygonum* both in morphology and
habitat.   To this genus the common garden rhubarb
belongs.   It shows a parallelism with the Monocotyledons
in that the perianth is six-parted, the three inner segments
being much larger than the outer, especially in fruit,
when they enlarge and close over the triangular nut.
The latter resembles that of many *Cyperaceae*, the parallelism with Monocotyledons thus being carried a little
farther.

A reduced relative of *Rumex* is the third genus, *Oxyria*,
with four sepals; and the nut is winged.   It is related
more particularly to the *Acetosa* group of *Rumex*, with
similar radical and cordate-based leaves and scapose

panicle.   It occurs only on high mountains in its southern range, descending to low levels northwards, being found at sea-level near Aberdeen.

In addition to these three genera, the " Buckwheat ", *Fagopyrum*, is cultivated in fields.

In *Polygonaceae* there is no special type of stoma; the vessels have simple perforations and the wood prosenchyma bears simple pits.   The indumentum consists chiefly of simple unicellular and glandular hairs.   The head of the latter may be either unicellular or divided by vertical walls.

Key to the genera of *Polygonaceae*.

Sepals (perianth-segments) 5, subequal, not enlarged or only slightly so in fruit; flowers axillary, or in spikes or panicles of spikes; stipules sometimes sheathing the stem within the petiole Polygonum
Sepals 6, the inner larger than the outer especially in fruit, and enclosing the nut; flowers usually in terminal panicles; lower leaves often long-stalked and large; stipules soon split and jagged . . Rumex
Sepals 4, the inner two enlarged; fruit flat, winged; leaves radical, cordate at the base. . . . . Oxyria

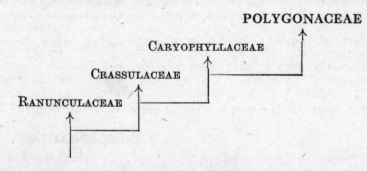

Illecebraceae are more highly reduced types also derived from the Caryophyllaceous stock, particularly from the *Paronychieae*, a tribe of *Caryophyllaceae*.   In Corrigiola there are well-developed petals and the leaves are alternate and stipulate.

The other genera in Britain have opposite leaves and there are no petals.   In *Herniaria* and *Illecebrum* the sepals are free. In the latter they are rather remarkable, being thick and white and hooded at the top with a subulate point. *Herniaria glabra* L. is anisophyllous (a large and small leaf in each pair), and the stipules are interpetiolar.

In *Scleranthus* the sepals are united into a tube and the stamens are perigynous. The leaves are small and connate at the base without apparent stipules. It is interesting to note that in this genus the Caryophyllaceous type of stomata is found, i.e., they are accompanied by two subsidiary cells placed transversely to the pore.

The ovary in *Illecebraceae* is reduced to one loculus and there is only one ovule and seed, the latter with endosperm and a more or less curved embryo as in *Caryophyllaceae*. The very small flowers of this family should be dissected under the microscope by students.

Key to the genera of *Illecebraceae*.

Leaves alternate; embryo ring-like (annular). . . . CORRIGIOLA
Leaves opposite :
  Sepals free or nearly so :
    Flowers green; embryo ring-like (annular); sepals obtuse or at most
    muticous; leaves anisophyllous (one large and the other smaller)
                             HERNIARIA
    Flowers white and scarious; embryo slightly curved; sepals aristate
    at the apex . . . . ILLECEBRUM
  Sepals united into a tube; stamens perigynous; embryo ring-like
  (annular) . . . . SCLERANTHUS

And below is the phylogenetic history of the family :—

ILLECEBRACEAE
↑

(Tribe Paronychieae)
CARYOPHYLLACEAE
↑

CRASSULACEAE
↑

RANUNCULACEAE
↑

As there are no *Molluginaceae* in Britain, the student will not be able to appreciate the very close affinity of that family with **Chenopodiaceae**, unless he examines the two families side by side in a large herbarium such as that at Kew and the British (Natural History) Museum.

Most of our species of *Chenopodiaceae* are found in maritime habitats or within the influence of the sea. An exception is the genus *Chenopodium* the several British species of which grow mostly in cultivated and waste places, the commonest being " Fat Hen ", *Chenopodium album* Linn. The key to genera will show some of their chief characteristics.

Stems not jointed; stamens 5 :
  Leaves flat :
    Fruiting perianth not enlarged or only slightly so, herbaceous
                                                        CHENOPODIUM
    Fruiting perianth enlarged :
      Fruiting perianth with 5 more or less equal segments . . . BETA
      Fruiting perianth with 2 flat much enlarged segments . ATRIPLEX
  Leaves very narrow or nearly completely reduced :
    Leaves with very sharp hardened tips . . . . . . SALSOLA
    Leaves fleshy, linear, without hardened tips. . . . . SUAEDA
Stems succulent and jointed; stamens 2–1 . . . . SALICORNIA

For an account of the most striking anatomical feature, the peculiar anomalous structure of the stem, Solereder's book [1] should be consulted. There are no special subsidiary cells around the stomata, but the hairy covering is very diverse, and sometimes characteristic of certain genera or groups of genera. There are no unicellular hairs, but uniseriate hairs are widely distributed.

The origin of *Chenopodiaceae* is indicated below :—

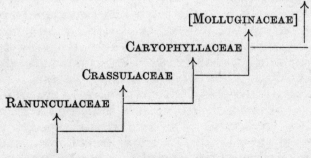

                                    CHENOPODIACEAE

                  [MOLLUGINACEAE]

            CARYOPHYLLACEAE

        CRASSULACEAE

    RANUNCULACEAE

[1] Solereder, *Syst. Anat. of the Dicotyledons,* 2 : 655 (1908).

Closely related to the *Chenopodiaceae* is the family **Amaranthaceae***, of which there is one genus naturalised as a weed, namely *Amaranthus**. They are annual herbs with alternate long-petiolate leaves and dense axillary clusters or spikes of very small unisexual or polygamous flowers without petals and with three to five stamens, and a one-locular ovary with one erect ovule.

LYTHRALES.

67. Lythraceae.   68. Onagraceae.   69. Halorrhagaceae.
70. Callitrichaceae.

Lythraceae is rather a puzzling family from the phylogenetic standpoint. The first tribe, *Ammannieae*, is composed of herbs with a strong tendency to an aquatic habit. It is this tribe which shows most closely the connection with *Caryophyllaceae*. Two exotic genera, *Hydrolythrum* (India) and *Quartinia* (Abyssinia and Uganda), are completely submerged aquatics and resemble some *Podostemaceae*. *Quartinia* grows on the rocks of the cataracts at the outlet of Lake Tana, Abyssinia, and is more luxuriant where the rush of water is most violent, appearing like a mass of dark-green *Algae*, a remarkable habit for a flowering plant.

It is not very difficult to visualise the British herbaceous genera as being perigynous representatives of the *Caryophyllaceae*. Their flowers at most show but an imperfectly formed type of perigyny, for the stamens are usually inserted, not with the calyx-lobes and petals, but lower down within the tube of the calyx or receptacle, whichever one prefers to call it. There are only two genera in Britain, LYTHRUM and PEPLIS, which grow mostly in wet ditches and moist or muddy places.

Lythrum is distinguished by its sepals being united into a tube conspicuously ribbed like some of the gamosepalous *Caryophyllaceae*. The two British species are very different in appearance, *L. hyssopifolium* L. with small, inconspicuous axillary flowers, and *L. salicaria* L., which is an ornament to the bank of any pond, with large showy whorled flowers collected into terminal leafy racemes after the manner of some *Labiatae.*

Peplis is a small creeping annual in wet places, with opposite or subalternate spathulate leaves, and small axillary sessile flowers, with globose capsule and very short style; there is only one species in Britain, *P. portula* Linn., the Water Purslane.

The epidermal cells around the stomata are usually of

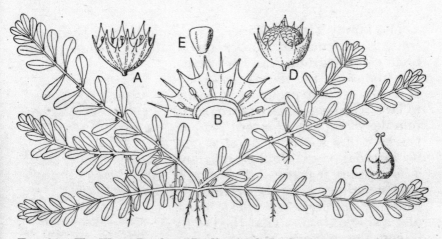

FIG. 94.—The Water Purslane, *Peplis portula* L. (Lythraceae) is probably not very distantly related to the *Caryophyllaceae*, from the stock of which *Lythraceae* is indicated as having been possibly derived.

A, calyx and stamens. B, same opened out. C, pistil. D, fruit. E, seed.

the ordinary type, but sometimes like those of *Cruciferae.* Intraxylary phloem is always present. In *Lythrum salicaria* L., simple conical one- or two-celled hairs occur.

Key to British genera of *Lythraceae.*

Calyx tubular, much longer than broad; style distinct; petals distinct or showy; leaves lanceolate or linear; tall perennials or dwarf annuals . . . . LYTHRUM

Calyx shortly campanulate; style very short; petals minute or absent; leaves spathulate; dwarf annual creeping and rooting at the nodes
PEPLIS

And the phylogenetic history may be shown as follows :—

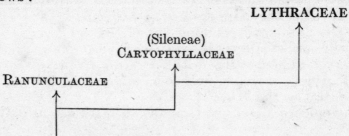

The family **Onagraceae** gets its name from the genus *Onagra*, a synonym of *Oenothera*. It is a much more homogeneous group than *Lythraceae*. Anatomically the family is characterised by the presence of intraxylary phloem, the occurrence of bundles of raphides (except *Trapa*), the lack of a special type of stoma, no internal or external glands, and a few other features. The ovary, almost without exception, is inferior, there is a definite number of stamens, and a single style. That the family is considerably advanced is shown by its general tendencies, and the instability of the species of some of its genera, such as *Oenothera*, the Evening Primrose. Some genera are very advanced within the family; for example, in *Lopezia*, indigenous

Fig. 95.—In *Lopesia racemosa* Cav., a Central American species of *Onagraceae*; reduction almost equal to that of Orchids and Gingers in the Monocotyledons has been reached; though there are two stamens, only one of them is fertile.

in Central America, and sometimes seen in greenhouses, there are only two stamens, one bearing an anther, the other being petaloid and sterile. In this genus, therefore, we find a reduction in the androecium almost equivalent to that of the Orchids or Gingers in the Monocotyledons.

Excellent characters are obtained from the nature of the fruit. In the majority it is a many-seeded capsule, as in the British genera *Epilobium, Chamaenerion,*

CARYOPHYLLACEAE TO HALORRHAGACEAE

CARYOPHYLLACEAE again figures at the base of this small subphylum. *Lychnis* (*L. viscaria*) is shown on the right-hand side. Possibly derived from this section of the family is LYTHRACEAE (*Lythrum* shown at the bottom left), with perigynous sepals, petals and stamens, whilst ONAGRACEAE provides a local climax (*Epilobium* in the middle), in which the completely inferior ovary acts as a stalk to the other parts of the flower, and in which epigyny is completely attained. A highly advanced member of the last family is *Circaea* (top right), with the sepals, petals and stamens reduced to two each, and the fruit efficiently adapted for dispersal by means of numerous hooked bristles. An even more evolved family is HALORRHAGACEAE, represented by *Myriophyllum* (left), an aquatic with whorls of deeply divided leaves and unisexual flowers, the males in the upper axils, the females below.

♥

The plants illustrated in the coloured plate are : From left to right, Myriophyllum verticillatum *Linn.*, Lythrum salicaria *Linn.*, Epilobium hirsutum *Linn.*, Lychnis viscaria *Linn.* Top, right, Circaea lutetiana *Linn.*

J.H.

To face p. 180.

*Oenothera** (naturalised) and *Ludwigia*. In others—for
example, in tribe *Gaureae* (American only)—the fruit is
nut-like and contains only one to four seeds. In the
well-known *Fuchsia* [1] of our greenhouses, which forms a
tribe of its own, the fruit is a berry. This genus has an
interesting distribution, mainly in Central and South
America, but with a few in far distant New Zealand.
In the exotic Water Chestnut, *Trapa natans* L., the fruit is

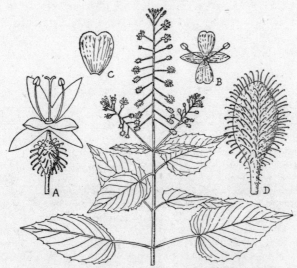

Fig. 96.—*Circaea lutetiana* L. (Onagraceae).
A, flower. B, flower from above. C, petal. D,
fruit.

indehiscent and armed with the persistent spine-like
calyx-lobes.

In the remaining British genus, *Circaea*, the fruit is
indehiscent, two-celled, two-seeded, and covered with
hooks. Its flower is peculiar in that the floral axis is
produced beyond the ovary. About seven species of this
genus are recognised, two only in Britain, one *C. lutetiana*
Linn., Enchanter's Nightshade, being common in woods
and rather a puzzle to elementary students, the other, *C.*

[1] Mispronounced by most laymen, gardeners, and even by some
botanists as " Feushia "; but named in honour of Fuchs, and therefore
should be pronounced in the German way, with the " *c* " hard.

alpina Linn., occurring only in the northern parts of the British Isles, and extending right across Europe and Asia to North America, often growing at high altitudes.

Epilobium is the largest British genus, and the flowers of some of the species are markedly Caryophyllaceous in appearance. The genus *Chamaenerion* is recognised by some botanists, and it seems distinct enough from *Epilobium* to be kept separate. The differences are shown in the key, and in its floral characters it is a more highly evolved group of about four species than *Epilobium*, the best known species being *Chamaenerion augustifolium* Schur. (*Epilobium augustifolium* L.).

Key to the British genera.

Stamens 8 ; petals 4 ; capsule elongated :
  Flowers reddish, pink or white ; seeds with a tuft of hairs :
    Perennials or annuals ; flowers in the axils of the upper leaves,
      actinomorphic ; calyx-lobes and petals forming a tube ; stamens
      2-seriate, not declinate ; filaments not dilated at the base
                                               EPILOBIUM
    Perennials ; flowers mostly in long racemes with small bracts, slightly
      zygomorphic, strongly protandrous ; calyx-lobes free to the top
      of the ovary, spreading ; stamens 1-seriate, declinate ; filaments
      dilated at the base . . . . CHAMAENERION
  Flowers yellow ; seeds without a tuft of hairs . . . . OENOTHERA*
Stamens 4 ; petals small or none ; capsule very short . LUDWIGIA
Stamens 2 ; petals 2, bilobed . . . . CIRCAEA

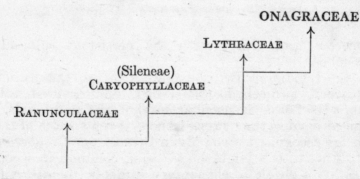

The flowers of **Halorrhagaceae** are so much reduced that it is very difficult to trace the true affinities of the family. I feel this after having dissected flowers of most of the genera. The two British examples are *Myrio-phyllum* and *Hippuris*. Both are aquatics, but some exotic genera are terrestrial. A striking example of the latter is the genus *Gunnera*, to be seen in some gardens, with very large Rhubarb-like leaves, which ought to be called "Robinson Crusoe's Umbrella", because there are fine examples on Juan Fernandez, where his prototype, Alexander Selkirk, was marooned.

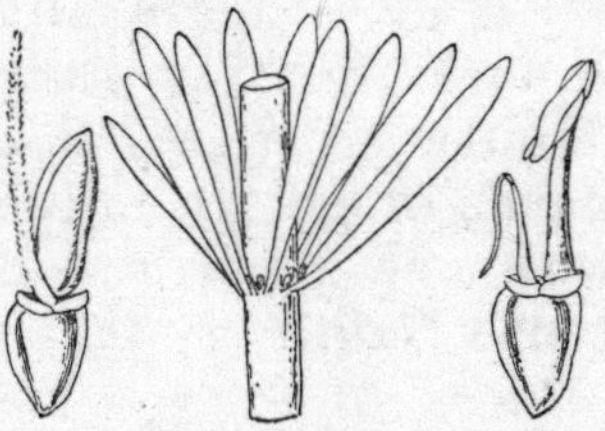

In *Myriophyllum* the whorled leaves are deeply pinnate, the flowers are unisexual and monoecious, the calyx four-lobed, and the male flowers have four petals, but the females have these very minute or absent; the stamens are eight to four, the ovary four-locular, with one ovule in each loculus, and the fruit is a capsule.

FIG. 97.—The limit of reduction in a bisexual flower is shown in *Hippuris vulgaris* Linn. (Halorrhagaceae); the calyx is very small, there are no petals, there is only one stamen, which is at first sessile, one style and the ovary is inferior, with one ovule.

Hippuris is much more highly evolved in other ways. The habit is similar to *Myriophyllum*, but the leaves are not divided, the calyx of the bisexual flowers is very minute around the top of the inferior ovary, there are no petals, there is only one stamen, one subulate style, one pendulous ovule, and of course only one seed in the small nut-like fruit. Reduction could hardly go any farther in a bisexual flower!

Anatomical characters are not particularly helpful in determining the position of this family. There is no intraxylary phloem as in *Onagraceae*, no special type of stoma, and no internal secretory organs. The hairy covering is formed of simple, unicellular or uniseriate

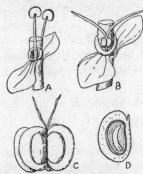

FIG. 98.—*Callitriche verna* L. (Callitrichaceae).

A, male flower. B, female flower. C, fruit. D, section of same to show seed.

trichomes, peltate hairs, glandular shaggy hairs, and other external glands of complicated structure.

An even more advanced family is **Callitrichaceae**, aquatic floating herbs with opposite leaves and very minute unisexual flowers in their axils. There are no sepals or petals, only one stamen, and four-locular ovary with a single pendulous ovule in each loculus. The single genus *Callitriche* is very widely distributed.

SAXIFRAGALES, SARRACENIALES, and UMBELLALES.

71. Crassulaceae.   72. Saxifragaceae.   73. Adoxaceae.
74. Droseraceae.   75. Umbelliferae.

The family **Crassulaceae** is the next in our phylogenetic system. It has arisen probably direct from the Helleboroid group of the Ranalian stock. This seems likely because it has retained free carpels, each with several ovules attached to the adaxial side. In fact there is very little to separate the flower from the *Ranunculaceae*, except that the arrangement of the sepals, petals, and stamens is slightly perigynous, the receptacle being a little expanded; and the seeds have a larger embryo with a less amount of endosperm. In Bentham and Hooker's system the *Crassulaceae* were far removed from the *Ranunculaceae* because of this slight difference in the receptacle (or thalamus), the importance of which was over-emphasised.

Apart from the flowers, however, the *Crassulaceae* are much more advanced from the *Ranunculaceae*. Many of them are very fleshy and adapted to grow in warm, dry climates, such as the Canary Islands and South Africa, where they are very numerous. There is a very peculiar combination of characters in some genera of this family. For example, in *Umbilicus*, *Cotyledon*, and *Kalanchoe*, the corolla is sympetalous, a feature very rarely associated with an apocarpous gynoecium. In one British species, *Sedum rhodiola* DC., the flowers are remarkable in being dioecious.

There are four genera of *Crassulaceae* represented in
Britain, but one of them, *Sempervivum*, is introduced and

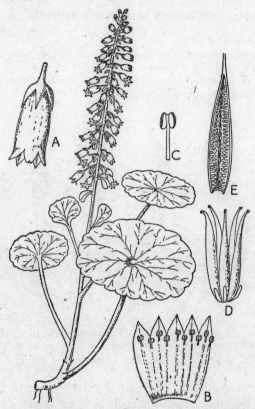

Fig. 99.—The " Navel-Wort " or " Penny-
Wort," *Umbilicus pendulinus* DC. (*Cotyledon
umbilicus* L.) belongs to the otherwise usually
polypetalous family *Crassulaceae*.   It shows
the unusual combination of free carpels and
united petals.

A, flower.   B, corolla laid open.   C, stamen.
D, carpels.   E, carpel opened out.

naturalised, the genus *Tillaea* being now generally merged
in *Crassula*.   In the flowers nectar is secreted at the base
of the ovary.

N

Here is a key to the British genera :—

Petals free or nearly so :
  Stamens twice as many as the petals, but sometimes half of them
    abortive; flowers conspicuous, in cymes or corymbs :
    Petals and sepals usually 10 or 12; flowers sessile on the branches
      of the cyme . . . . SEMPERVIVUM*
    Petals and sepals 5 or 6 . . . . SEDUM
  Stamens the same number as the petals, all fertile; very small plants
    with minute axillary flowers . . . . CRASSULA
  Petals united into a tubular corolla; leaves peltate; flowers pendulous,
    in simple (rarely branched) racemes . . . . . . UMBILICUS

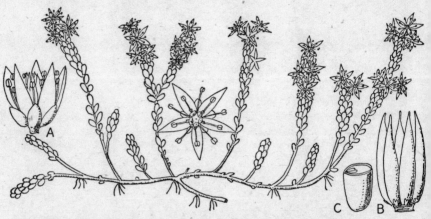

FIG. 100.—The "Golden Stonecrop," *Sedum acre* L. (Crassulaceae) is
familiar in tufts on walls, rocks, and in sandy places.
A, flower. B, carpels. C, section of carpel.

In most members of the family the stomata are charác-
teristic. The pair of guard cells is surrounded by a simple
or multiple girdle of three subsidiary cells. In addition,
water-pores occur in many examples.

Our next family, **Saxifragaceae**, is a very interesting
one. In Bentham and Hooker's *Genera Plantarum* it
was a regular *pot pourri*, containing such widely different
plants besides its namesake *Saxifraga*, as *Hydrangea*,
Escallonia, *Grossularia*, etc., genera representing small
groups which may show great similarity in general
flower-plan but which many botanists now consider are
not truly related. Most students will probably agree
that a Meadow Saxifrage, as representing the genus

Saxifraga, a *Hydrangea*, and a Gooseberry are not really very closely related to one another, if at all.   As a phylogenetic classification could not therefore possibly admit them into one family, I limited the group, in my book, to the two tribes *Saxifrageae* and *Francoeae*, all herbs and mostly scapigerous. The *Francoeae* are confined to Chile and therefore do not come under review in the present book.

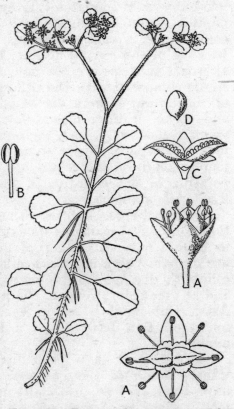

   Saxifragaceae, as thus defined, are found almost exclusively in the north temperate and Arctic regions.   They are extremely rare in Australasia and Polynesia. *Saxifraga* and *Chrysosplenium* are circumboreal in the northern hemisphere and both have isolated representatives in the Andes of South America.   In Britain, the family is poorly represented in genera, but comparatively rich in species. Of these *Saxifraga* is generally the most primitive, with ten stamens all bearing

Fig. 101.—Because there are no petals, the family of the Golden Saxifrage, *Chrysosplenium oppositifolium* L. (Saxifragaceae) is not so easy to recognise as its relative *Saxifraga*.

A, flower from above and the side.   B, stamen.   C, fruit.   D, seed.

anthers; and of this genus there are about eighteen species represented in Britain.   In *Saxifraga* the carpels are reduced to two, the styles being free.

   The Meadow Saxifrage, *S. granulata* L., is one of our earliest flowering plants and well worth a place in a garden. The flowers are strongly proterandrous, and a study of their development is instructive. The central (terminal) flower of the cyme opens first and differs markedly from the lateral flowers in having the large fat papillous stigmas borne on long styles which become very conspicuous after the stamens have shed their pollen. In some of the central flowers, I have observed that the alternate stamens are less polleniferous or indeed almost sterile compared with the others, whilst all the stamens of the lateral flowers are equally fertile. The stigmas and styles of these lateral flowers are smaller and less stout, respectively, than those of the central flower. In fact, this type of flower seems to be heading towards a female condition and to a reduction of its stamens to five, pointing to the evolution of *Parnassia*, which has only five fertile stamens.

Another British species, *S. cernua* Linn., is of exceptional interest because of its extreme rarity. It is found in Britain only on the top of Ben Lawers. The species has probably been left there in isolation, and is perhaps a relic of the Ice Age. It occurs all around the Arctic Circle and at great elevations on the mountains of Europe and Asia. Only slightly less rare is *S. rivularis* Linn., also found on Ben Lawers and a few other high Scottish mountains.

Saxifragaceae have probably been the basal stock whence some of the herbaceous sympetalous families have been evolved, especially part of the " bicarpellatae ", such as *Solanaceae* and *Scrophulariaceae*, etc. In this connection it is very interesting to note that in *Saxifraga* and some other genera the two carpels are arranged *obliquely* to the floral axis, a character many of us learned in our student days was a feature of *Solanaceae* and serving to separate that family from *Scrophulariaceae*, in which the carpels are median to the axis. In the family-tree shown in the folder an arm points directly from the stock of the *Saxifragaceae* to the *Solanaceae*.

Possibly also part of *Primulaceae* find their origin in the same stock, the habit of some being more in keeping with the *Saxifragaceae* than with the *Caryophyllaceae*, whence it is generally supposed they have been derived. In some exotic genera of *Saxifragaceae* the placentas are basal, which is also a marked feature of the *Primulaceae*. As indicated in the family " tree ", the family has been derived from the Ranunculaceous stock, and it provides an interesting parallel with the *Papaveraceae*. This is with reference to the position of the stigmas. Normally, the stigmas of an ovary are immediately above their own carpels and alternate with the placentas, but in certain genera of *Papaveraceae* the stigmas are opposite the placentas, a position known as commissural. One of the British genera of *Saxifragaceae* shows this same feature, namely *Parnassia*. This is an excellent example of a particular character which has arisen quite independently in two separate phyla.

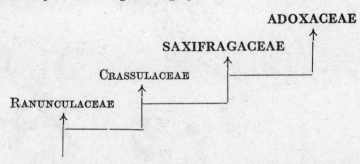

The student may like to know here why many gardeners still confuse the genus *Astilbe*, which belongs to *Saxifragaceae*, with *Spiraea* (Rosaceae). This is because there is a very close resemblance between *Astilbe japonica* Thunb., grown in pots in our greenhouses, and the " Meadow-sweet ", *Filipendula ulmaria* (L.) Maxim., included by some botanists in *Spiraea*.

Key to the British genera of *Saxifragaceae*.

Petals present :
  Stamens 10, all bearing anthers; ovary 2-locular; styles 2; seeds with endosperm; flowers mostly in cymes; leaves cauline or in a basal rosette . . . . SAXIFRAGA

Stamens 5, bearing anthers, with 5 barren filaments with globular
    heads; stigmas 4; ovary 1-locular; seeds without endosperm;
    flowers solitary on long slender stalks; leaves nearly all radical
                                                            PARNASSIA
Petals absent; stamens 8 or 10; ovary 1-locular; seeds with endosperm;
    flowers mostly in cymes; leaves cauline, alternate or opposite
                                                        CHRYSOSPLENIUM

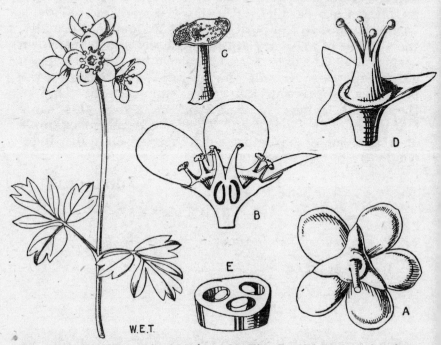

W.E.T.

FIG. 102.—The Moscatel, *Adoxa moschatellina* L. (Adoxaceae), has been
    something of a stormy petrel among botanists, having been bandied
    about between *Caprifoliaceae* and *Saxifragaceae*. It now finds sanc-
    tuary as a separate family.
    A, flower showing the 3 calyx-lobes. B, same in vertical section. C,
stamen. D, ovary. E, transverse section of same. (From Hutchinson,
Families of Flowering Plants.)

The genus *Adoxa* is monotypic (*Adoxa moschatellina*
Linn.), and has been placed in various families, in *Saxifragaceae*, *Araliaceae*, and *Caprifoliaceae*, but is now
generally regarded as an independent family **Adoxaceae**.
From my own studies of the genus, and the viewpoint
of the present system, I should exclude it entirely from
the *Araliaceae* and *Caprifoliaceae*, both of which are

CRASSULACEAE TO UMBELLIFERAE

Apart from BERBERIDACEAE and PAPAVERACEAE, most herbaceous families have advanced very considerably from the *Ranunculaceous* stock. At least one, however, shows a close link. This is CRASSULACEAE, in which the carpels have remained free, and often with as many as ten stamens. In addition, there is slight perigyny, which accounted for the wide separation of the family from RANUNCULACEAE in the Bentham and Hooker system, to which students of the British flora are accustomed. In CRASSULACEAE the leaves are often succulent, and plants of this family are well adapted for life in dry regions, particularly the Canary Islands, North and South Africa. *Sedum* is shown at the bottom, and on the left the genus *Umbilicus*, which has the very rare combination of *free* carpels and a *sympetalous* corolla. Closely related are the SAXIFRAGACEAE (*Saxifraga*), with even more perigynous flowers, and with the carpels united and reduced to two. Equally close is the small insectivorous family DROSERACEAE (*Drosera* shown), and also the monotypic ADOXACEAE (*Adoxa*). Finally the author considers that UMBELLIFERAE have been derived from the *Saxifragaceous* stock, i.e. independently of the ARALIACEAE (see p. 192), with which hey have been associated in most other systems of classification. *Sium* is shown at the top of the picture.

The plants illustrated in the coloured plate are: Bottom, right, Sedum acre *Linn.*; left, Umbilicus pendulinus *DC*. Middle, Drosera rotundifolia *Linn.*; right, Saxifraga granulata *Linn*. Top, Left, Adoxa moschatellina *Linn.*; right, Sium angustifolium *Linn.*

J.H.

To face p. 190.

basically woody. The student should read a very comprehensive account of *Adoxa* published in 1927 [1], where it is shown to have most in common with *Saxifragaceae*, and I am in agreement with this view. In my *Families of Flowering Plants* I placed *Adoxaceae* near *Valerianaceae*, in the *Asterales*, which will be found a few pages farther on in the present book.

Our next British family in the phylogenetic sequence, the **Droseraceae**, is a very specialised one. The family contains only four genera, one of which is represented in our flora, namely *Drosera*. The group is little more than a specialised type of *Saxifragaceae*, the ovary being one-locular with parietal placentas, as in some *Saxifragaceae*. *Drosera* is a large genus, spread all over the world and always occurring in boggy places, mainly on peaty soil. The common Sundew, *D. rotundifolia* L., is not difficult to find in such places in Britain, and may be at once recognised by its rosette of rounded leaves covered with sticky gland-tipped hairs which trap small insects. The structure of these is well described and figured by Solereder.[2] An allied genus, the Venus' flytrap, *Dionaea muscipula*, performs a similar function in a different way. It is native of the south-eastern United States of North America. Two other exotic genera, *Roridula* and *Byblis*, found in South Africa and Australia respectively, are now separated as a distinct family, *Byblidaceae*, and are really more closely related to *Tremandraceae* and *Pittosporaceae*.

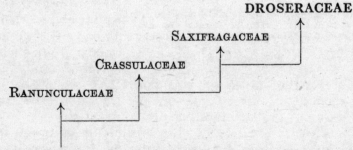

----

[1] T. A. Sprague, " The Morphology and Taxonomic Position of the *Adoxaceae* " (*Journ. Linn. Soc.*, 47 : 471–487; 1927).
[2] Solereder, *Syst. Anat. Dicots.*, 1 : 324.

A peculiarity of *Droseraceae* is that the leaves in bud are *circinnate* after the manner of a fern. Circinnate vernation in Flowering Plants is very rare. It is found in the petals of the Wych Hazels, *Hamamelis*.

As may be seen in the linear sequence of families (p.

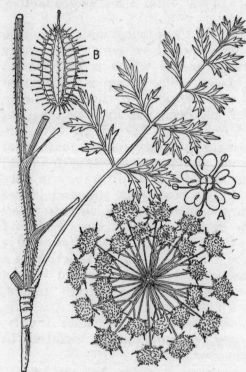

FIG. 103.—The fruits (B) of the "Wild Carrot," *Daucus carota* L. (Umbelliferae) are well adapted for dispersal by animals, including man.

A, flower.

30), and in the diagram at the end of the book, the family **Umbelliferae** is regarded as having been derived from the same stock as the *Saxifragaceae*, i.e., from an entirely herbaceous group, and its relationship with *Araliaceae* is questioned. The theory is advanced that these two families, though nearly always associated in the same group, may have had quite different phylogenetic histories, and that their supposed affinity is more apparent than real, *Araliaceae* having probably been evolved from a woody group such as *Celastrales* and *Rhamnales*. Further notes on this point have been given in the account of *Araliaceae* on p. 69, where the main characters of the two families are contrasted.

Umbelliferae are nearly always difficult to name in a herbarium or from books because of the necessity of having ripe fruits. Often it fell to the lot of the writer to name in the Kew herbarium an alien to the British flora, and of which the native country was unknown. Such a specimen would almost invariably be received in flower and without fruit! To run a plant of this kind down to its genus from Bentham and Hooker's *Genera Plantarum* or other work was nearly always impossible, and sometimes the only way to name it was to search laboriously through the family from cover to cover.

With this experience in mind, therefore, the following key has been compiled on rather different lines, the primary divisions being based, not on the fruit, but on the *presence or absence of bracts.* These characters are always to be observed on a specimen, whether in flower or fruit, and by this means the genera represented in Britain are

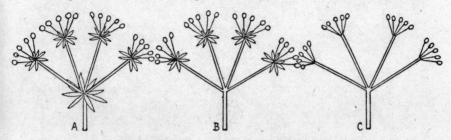

FIG. 104.—Diagrams showing the three artificial series into which the genera of Umbelliferae are arranged in the key.
A, BRACTEATAE.　B, SEMIBRACTEATAE.　C, EBRACTEATAE.

subdivided into three somewhat artificial, though not entirely artificial, series. In the first, and probably the most primitive series, the primary and secondary (or ultimate) umbels are all provided with an involucre of bracts. As the bracts of *Umbelliferae,* and indeed of almost any family, are derived from foliage-leaves, it seems reasonable to assume that the most primitive group would possess these organs throughout the inflorescence. I have called this first series the BRACTEATAE.

The next stage in evolution would probably be the suppression of at least one set of bracts, perhaps of those subtending the primary umbel, those below the ultimate umbels being retained to protect the flowers in bud, which is probably their function. This series has been called the SEMIBRACTEATAE.

And, finally, in several genera the bracts of all the umbels have been completely reduced, and these are placed in the third series, EBRACTEATAE.   In only a few cases has it been necessary to insert a genus in more than one group.

Thereafter in the key, leaf-characters are employed as much as possible, followed by the colour of the petals, and

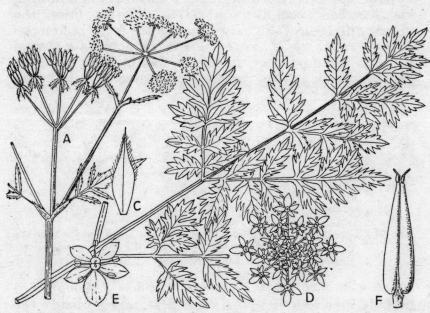

FIG. 105.—This common member of the Carrot family, " Wild Parsley " or " Kech," *Anthriscus sylvestris* Hoffm. (Umbelliferae), is not difficult to name because it is the first of the British members to flower.   Note the beautiful pattern of the flowers in each partial umbel (D).

A, flowers and fruit.   C, bract.   E, flower.   F, fruit.

finally the nature of the fruit.   By the use of such easily ascertainable features, therefore, it is hoped that the task of the beginner will not be so formidable as when the fruit-character is given greater prominence.   It is not denied, of course, that the fruit-characters are of primary importance in the classification of the genera, and the accompanying drawings of them may prove useful for identification.

Some of the genera represented in Britain are easily

recognised by the possession of one or more outstanding characters. Thus *Bupleurum* is distinguished from all the others by its entire leaves. *Hydrocotyle* has orbicular, peltate leaves. *Crithmum* is confined to maritime habitats and has very fleshy stems and leaves. *Eryngium* is unique in having strongly-nerved leaves with very sharp prickly teeth. The basal leaves are palmately lobed in *Astrantia* and *Sanicula*. The involucral bracts are pinnatifid in *Daucus*; and *Aethusa* may be at once

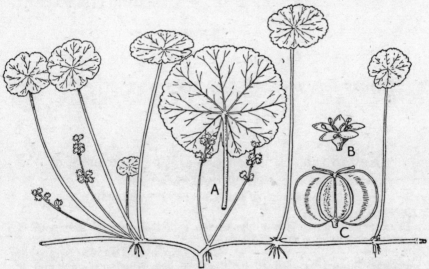

Fig. 106.—The " Marsh Penny-wort," *Hydrocotyle vulgaris* L. (Umbelliferae) does not advertise its relationship with other members of the family, though its fruits give it away at once.

A, leaf. B, flower. C, fruit.

recognised by the reflexed bracts which are longer than the ultimate peduncles. In *Conium* the bracts of the ultimate umbels are all turned to one side.

Only a few genera have yellow flowers; these are *Petroselinum, Smyrnium, Silaus, Foeniculum, Bupleurum, Peucedanum* sp., and *Pastinaca*. All the others have white or very rarely pink or blue flowers. *Trinia* is unique in having unisexual, dioecious flowers, and the resin canals are *below* the ribs of the fruit.

Some genera have outstanding fruit-characters.

Oenanthe is the only genus with sessile or subsessile fruits; they are very shortly stalked in *Scandix*. The carpels are much compressed in *Tordylium, Peucedanum, Angelica, Pastinaca,* and *Heracleum.* In *Petroselinum* the axis of the fruit splits to the base when ripe. There are no resin canals in the fruits of *Astrantia, Eryngium, Scandix, Coriandrum, Anthriscus,* and *Myrrhis.*

The phylogeny of the *Umbelliferae* is repeated here from p. 71.

UMBELLIFERAE

SAXIFRAGACEAE

CRASSULACEAE

RANUNCULACEAE

Key to the artificial series and to the genera of
Umbelliferae

(For drawings of fruits see pp. 198 and 200).

Leaves not peltate :
  Primary and secondary umbels with a well-developed involucre of several bracts or modified leaves
                1. BRACTEATAE (Diagram A, p. 193)
  Primary umbel without an involucre of bracts or with only one or two small bracts or modified leaves :
  Secondary umbels with an involucre of bracts or with one or two bracts or modified leaves
                2. SEMIBRACTEATAE (Diagram B, p. 193)
  Secondary umbels entirely without bracts or bract
                3. EBRACTEATAE (Diagram C, p. 193)
Leaves peltate, orbicular . . . . HYDROCOTYLE

Series 1. BRACTEATAE.

Leaves undivided, ovate to linear, not toothed; petals yellow; fruit ovoid or oblong, somewhat laterally compressed; carpels with 5 more or less prominent ribs, with or without resin canals BUPLEURUM
Leaves variously divided or coarsely and spinous-toothed :
  Leaves and flower-heads not prickly (to p. 199 :
    Stems and leaves very thick and succulent; maritime plants; fruits ellipsoid; carpels with 5 ridges prominent when dry; resin canals numerous and slender, irregular . . . . . . CRITHMUM

Stems and leaves not or only slightly succulent :
  †Fruits smooth (neither prickly nor hairy) :
    Fruits not compressed or only slightly so, globular, ovoid or
      oblong :
      Petals yellow; axis of the fruit splitting to the base when ripe;
      leaves once or twice pinnate . . . . . Petroselinum
      Petals white or pink :
        Fertile flowers and fruits pedicellate :
          Lower leaves once or twice pinnate; petals usually notched,
            with an inflexed point :
            Fruit oblong or narrowly ellipsoid :
              Leaves cut into small very narrow segments . .   Carum
              Leaves cut into few elongated toothed lobes . Falcaria*
            Fruits nearly globular, scarcely 2 mm. diam.; bracts of
              secondary umbels turned to one side, those of the primary
              umbels usually 2; carpels with single resin canals between
              each rib . . . . Sison
            Fruits ovoid, about 4 mm. long; bracts of secondary umbels
              not to one side; carpels with several resin canals between
              each rib; leaflets sessile. . . . . . . Sium
          Lower leaves twice or thrice ternate :
            Bracts of secondary umbels not turned to one side :
              Fruits oblong-ovoid; carpels with 5 prominent acute ribs
              and several resin canals between each; petals white,
              emarginate, with an inflexed point . . . Ligusticum
              Fruits of two globular lobes attached by a narrow edge, each
              carpel with five indistinct rays and single resin canals
              between them; petals white; leaf-segments deeply cut
                        Physospermum (Danaa)
            Bracts of secondary umbels all turned to one side . Conium
        Fertile flowers and fruits sessile or very shortly stalked;
        fruit ovoid to narrowly oblong; carpels corky, with
        five convex ribs and single resin canals between them
                          Oenanthe
    Fruits very much compressed :
      Fruits rough, surrounded by a thick edge, the ribs scarcely visible
      and with 1 or 3 resin canals between each; petals pink, the
      outer often larger . . . . Tordylium*
      Fruits smooth; carpels broad, with three prominent ribs on the
      back, the edges expanded into a wing; resin canals solitary
      between the ribs; petals white or yellow . . Peucedanum
  †Fruits prickly, bristly or hairy :
    Leaves palmately divided, mostly radical :
      Involucral bracts coloured; carpels with 5 plaited ribs and
      without resin canals . . . . Astrantia*
      Involucral bracts not coloured; [carpels covered with short,
      hooked prickles . . . . Sanicula
    Leaves pinnately or ternately divided :
      Fruits ovoid or oblong, not bordered :

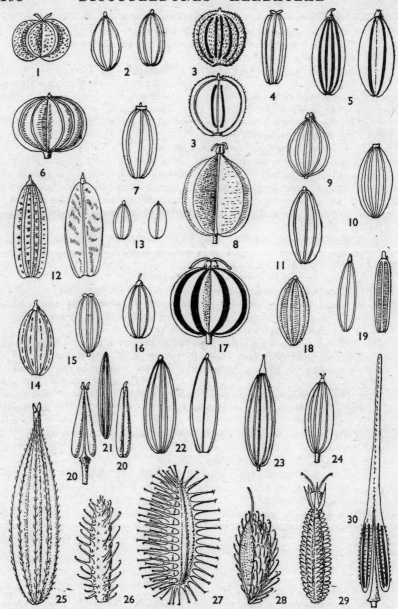

FIG. 107.—Fruits of British genera of UMBELLIFERAE.
1, *Hydrocotyle vulgaris* L., × 6.   2, *Sison amomum* L., × 6.   3, *Tordylium maximum* L., outer (above) and inner (below) faces, × 3.   4, *Bupleu-*

Bracts entire :
  Umbels of few (up to 10) rays; fruits covered with hooked
    bristles; general involucre of one or few bracts; flowers
    white to pink or purple :
  Carpels with the bristles confined to the primary ridges
                                                    CAUCALIS
  Carpels with the bristles between as well as on the primary
    ridges . . . . TORILIS
  Umbels of numerous (20 or more) rays; fruits hairy; carpels
    with 5 prominent thick ribs and one or rarely two resin
    canals between each; petals white . . . . .   SESELI
  Bracts mostly pinnatifid; wings of fruit pectinate; leaves
    twice or thrice pinnate with deeply lobed segments DAUCUS
  Fruits flat, with a thick cartilaginous border, hispid, the ribs
    scarcely visible and with 1 or 3 resin canals between each;
    petals pink, the outer often larger   . . . . TORDYLIUM*
Leaves and flower-heads prickly :
  Stem-leaves lobed, markedly nerved and veined, and with sharp
    prickly teeth; fruit ovoid, without resin canals . . ERYNGIUM
  Stem-leaves palmately lobed; fruit ovoid or oblong, crowned by the
    long pointed teeth of the calyx; carpels with 5 plaited or crumpled
    ribs and without resin canals . . . . ASTRANTIA*

Series 2. SEMIBRACTEATAE.

Leaves undivided, ovate or elliptic to linear, not toothed; petals
  yellow; fruit ovoid or oblong, somewhat laterally compressed;
  carpels with 5 more or less prominent ribs, with or without resin
  canals between . . . . BUPLEURUM
Leaves divided :
  *Fruits not prickly (to p. 202) :
    †Carpels not compressed or only slightly so, subturgid, globular,
      ovoid or more less oblong to almost linear :
    Petals yellow or greenish-yellow :
    Fruits of 2 globular carpels; carpels attached by the very narrow
      face, each with 3 prominent angular ribs and several resin canals
      between them . . . . SMYRNIUM

---

rum rotundifolium L., × 8. 5, Outer and inner faces of *Foeniculum
vulgare* Gaertn., × 4. 6, *Cicuta virosa* L., × 4½. 7, *Conium maculatum*
L., × 7. 8, *Smyrnium olusatrum* L., × 3. 9, *Petroselinum crispum*
Nym., × 4½. 10, *Helosciadium nodiflorum* Koch, × 7. 11, *Pimpinella
saxifraga* L., × 7. 12, *Ligusticum scoticum* L., × 4. 13, *Apium graveo-
lens* L., × 7. 14, *Crithmum maritimum* L., × 3. 15, *Carum carvi* L.,
× 3. 16, *Silaus pratensis* Bess., × 3. 17, *Physospermum cornubiense*
DC., × 4½. 18, *Trinia vulgaris* DC., × 8. 19, *Aegopodium podagraria*
L., × 4½. 20, *Anthriscus sylvestris* L., × 3. 21, *Chaerophyllum temulum*
L., × 5. 22, *Meum athamanticum* Jacq., × 4. 23, *Conopodium denudatum*
Koch, × 5. 24, *Oenanthe phellandrium* Lam., × 4. 25, *Myrrhis odorata*
L. (whole fruit), × 3. 26, *Caucalis daucoides* L. (whole fruit), × 3.
27, *Daucus carota* L. (whole fruit), 4½. 28, *Sanicula europaea* L., × 7.
29, *Astrantia major* L. (whole fruit), × 4¼. 30, *Scandix pecten-veneris*
L. (whole fruit), × 1½.

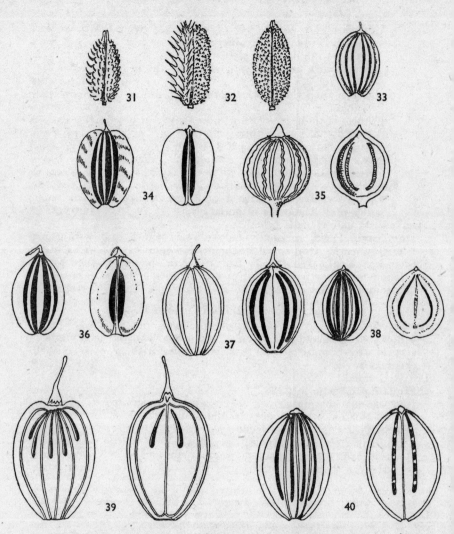

FIG. 108.—Fruits of British genera of UMBELLIFERAE.

31, *Anthriscus scandicina* (Weber) Mansf. × 4½. 32, *Torilis nodosa* × 4½. 33, *Peucedanum palustre* Moench., × 3. 34, *Angelica sylvestris* L., × 3. 35, *Coriandrum sativum* L., × 4½. 36, *Selinum carvifolium* Crantz, × 4½. 37, *Seseli libanotis* Koch, × 4½. 38, *Aethusa cynapium* L., × 4½. 39, *Heracleum sphondylium* L., × 3. 40, *Pastinaca sativa*, L. × 4. All showing outer (left) and inner (right) faces of the carpels, except 33, outer face only.

Fruits ovoid; ribs scarcely acute; resin canals inconspicuous
SILAUS
Petals white or pink :
Fertile flowers and fruits sessile or nearly so (at most on very
short thick stalks) :
Fruits shortly beaked . . . . OENANTHE
Fruits with a very long beak . . . . SCANDIX
Fertile flowers and fruits pedicellate :
Umbels mostly lateral and nearly sessile; fruits short, slightly
laterally compressed, the carpels ovoid, with 5 slender ribs
and single resin canals between; basal leaves with sessile
leaflets or the leaflets much dissected when growing in water
HELOSCIADIUM
Umbels terminal and pedunculate :
Bracts of the ultimate umbels all towards the outside of the
cluster, reflexed and longer than the pedicels; fruit ovoid;
carpels with 5 thick prominent ribs and narrow spaces with 1
resin canal under each . . . . AETHUSA
Bracts of the ultimate umbels not as described above :
Flowers bisexual :
Fruits without visible resin canals between the ribs or sutures :
Fruits 2 cm. long or more, much longer than broad :
Fruits not ribbed except at the base, with a long thick beak
SCANDIX
Fruits ribbed the whole length, with sometimes a few short
bristles on the ribs . . . . MYRRHIS
Fruits much less than 2 cm. long, narrow, lanceolate in out-
line; bracts reflexed in fruit . . . . . ANTHRISCUS
Fruits with visible resin canals between the ribs :
Fruits globular or kidney shaped in outline, nearly as broad
as or broader than long :
Fruits more or less 2-lobed (didymous) :
Leaves with a long sheathing base . . . . CICUTA
Leaves with a very short sheathing base . PHYSOSPERMUM
Fruits not 2-lobed (not didymous); leaves with a short
sheathing base . . . . CORIANDRUM*
Fruits not globular or kidney-shaped, longer than broad :
Fruits about half as long as broad, acutely ribbed
LIGUSTICUM
Fruits much less than half as long as broad :
Fruits very prominently ribbed; leaves finely cut and
feather-like . . . . MEUM
Fruits not prominently ribbed; leaves not feather-like
CHAEROPHYLLUM
Flowers unisexual, dioecious; fruit short, with ovoid carpels
and single resin canals underneath the 5 ribs . . TRINIA
†Carpels very much compressed :
Carpels with 3 ribs on the back, the marginal ribs forming wings;
petals entire, white :

o

Leaves with very large broad basal sheaths :
Carpels with a single vitta between the ridges . . ANGELICA
Carpels with more than one vittae between the ridges
ARCHANGELICA*
Leaves with narrow basal sheaths, cut into narrow linear segments
SELINUM
Carpels not winged :
Lower leaves of 3 large 3-lobed segments; petals white or
yellowish; carpels broad, with 3 prominent ribs on the back
PEUCEDANUM
Lower leaves pinnate; flowers yellow; resin canals reaching
nearly to the base of the carpel . . . . . . PASTINACA
*Fruits covered with sometimes hooked prickles; primary involucre
sometimes of a single bract :
Carpels at least 1 cm. long, with stiff stout bristles and 3 to 7 dorsal
ribs and 2 on the face :
Carpels with the bristles confined to the primary ridges CAUCALIS
Carpels with the bristles between as well as on the primary ridges
TORILIS
Carpels not ½ cm. long; with very short fine bristles . ANTHRISCUS

Series 3. EBRACTEATAE.

Leaves undivided, orbicular, peltate, crenate; mostly aquatic, creeping
herb, rooting at the nodes; fruit laterally compressed; carpels flat,
nearly orbicular, placed edge to edge and with 1 prominent rib on
each side . . . . HYDROCOTYLE
Leaves variously divided :
†Fruits not prickly :
Fruits globular, ovoid, lanceoloid, or shortly oblong; scarcely
compressed :
Petals yellow or greenish yellow :
Basal leaves two or three times ternate, with large broad segments;
fruit of 2 globular carpels, each with 3 prominent angular ribs
and several resin canals between each, attached by a very narrow margin to the central axis; petiole with a broad thin sheath
at the base . . . . SMYRNIUM
Basal leaves pinnate or much divided; fruit ovoid or oblong;
carpels with 5 prominent ribs and single resin canals between
each. . . . . FOENICULUM
Petals white or pink :
Flowers bisexual :
Basal leaves twice or thrice ternate, with large broad segments,
broadly sheathing at the base; fruits ovoid-oblong, somewhat
laterally compressed; carpels with 5 slender ribs but no resin
canals . . . . AEGOPODIUM
Basal leaves once pinnate, with several pairs of sessile rounded
or ovate-lanceolate or much dissected segments; carpels with
5 slightly prominent ribs and 2–3 resin canals between, and
with several on the inner side . . . . . . PIMPINELLA

Basal leaves once pinnate with 2–3 pairs of stalked broad cuneate
leaflets . . . . APIUM
Basal leaves soon disappearing, much dissected, with small or
narrow segments; carpels with 5 obscure ribs and several very
slender resin canals between each; rootstock a tuber
CONOPODIUM
Basal leaves much dissected, with narrow segments and with a
large sheathing base; rootstock not a tuber . . . CARUM
Flowers unisexual, dioecious; leaves finely cut into stiff narrowly
linear or subulate segments, the radical ones twice pinnate;
carpels ovoid, with 5 prominent ribs and a single resin canal
under or within the ribs . . . . TRINIA
Fruits much compressed, much less than half as thick as wide :
Flowers white; resin canals reaching only half way down the
carpel; leaf-lobes stalked on the rhachis. . . . HERACLEUM
Flowers yellow; resin canals reaching nearly to the base of the
carpel; leaf-lobes sessile on the rhachis . . . . PASTINACA
†Fruits covered with short hooked prickles :
Leaves much dissected; flowers in umbels; fruit ovoid; carpels
with 3 or 7 dorsal ribs and 2 on the inner face. . . CAUCALIS
Leaves palmately divided; flowers in small heads; fruit crowned
by the 5 prickly teeth of the calyx. . . . . . . SANICULA

VALERIANALES.

76. Valerianaceae.   77. Dipsacaceae.

IN Bentham and Hooker's system all the sympetalous
families with an inferior ovary were grouped together in
one series called INFERAE, and those with a superior
ovary disposed in two other series, the HETEROMERAE
and BICARPELLATAE.

The INFERAE were further subdivided into the *Rubiales*,
with two or more ovary-loculi and the stamens inserted
on the corolla, the *Asterales* with one ovary-loculus and
similarly placed stamens, and the *Campanales*, with the
stamens mostly free from the corolla.

This classification, based on one or two characters,
was no doubt convenient but very artificial, and brought
into proximity families which now seem to show little real
affinity, particularly with *Compositae*. These families
are *Valerianaceae*, *Dipsacaceae*, and the exotic *Calycera-
ceae*.

Although the flowers of most *Dipsacaceae* are arranged

in heads almost as in *Compositae*, the resemblance seems to end there. Each flower of the *Dipsacaceous* head is surrounded by an involucel composed of two or more bracteoles. There is nothing like this in *Compositae*. In addition the ovule in *Dipsacaceae* is pendulous, not erect as in *Compositae*, and the seed contains endosperm. The stomata of **Valerianaceae** possess no special subsidiary cells. The indumentum consists of simple and glandular hairs, the former generally being unicellular, but sometimes multicellular with delicate transverse walls. The glandular hairs have a multicellular head.

It seems probable that these three families have had a very different phylogenetic history from *Compositae*, and that the supposed affinity is due to convergent evolution. I believe, therefore, that *Valerianaceae* have been evolved from the same stock as the *Scrophulariaceae*, i.e., the *Saxifragaceae*. They are little more than inferior-ovaried *Saxifragaceae* with a sympetalous corolla. This problem will be more fully dealt with in another work, however, and we need only consider here the British genera of *Valerianaceae*, which may be keyed out as follows in phylogenetic sequence :—

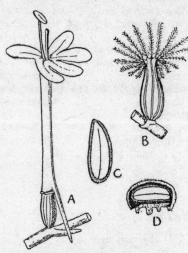

Fig. 109.—*Centranthus ruber* L. (Valerianaceae).

A, flower. B, achene. C, longitudinal section of same. D, transverse section of same. (From Hutchinson, *Families of Flowering Plants*).

Stamens 3; corolla not spurred :
 Perennials; fruit crowned by a plumose pappus. . . . Valeriana
 Annuals; fruit crowned by a small cupshaped rim . Valerianella
Stamen 1; corolla spurred at the base; fruit crowned by a plumose
 pappus . . . . Centranthus*

In general, it will be observed that reduction and specialisation has proceeded very much as in *Scro-*

phulariaceae, the spurred corolla bringing to mind that of *Linaria*.

The study of exotic genera has assisted me to this conclusion of the close affinity of *Saxifragaceae* and *Valerianaceae*. Opposite exstipulate leaves are constant in the latter family, whilst the East Asiatic genus *Triplostegia* (*Dipsacaceae*) has the habit and glandular hairs of some species of *Saxifraga*, but it has a double involucel and its seeds abundant endosperm with a small embryo.

These ideas are crystallised in the following diagram. At the best they may only be instinctive speculation, but who can say they are either right or wrong?

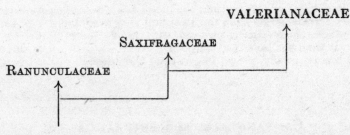

There are four genera of **Dipsacaceae** represented in Britain. These are *Dipsacus*, *Succisa*, *Scabiosa*, and *Knautia*. In the first the scales or bracts of the receptacle between the flowers are prickly, and the plants are either prickly or clothed with stiff hairs; in the remainder the scales of the receptacle as well as the plants themselves are not prickly. They are keyed out below. *Dipsacus sylvestris* Linn., the Teasel, is common on roadsides and waste places.

Usually the stomata have no special subsidiary cells, but sometimes, though rarely, there are three as in *Cruciferae*, one cell being smaller than the other two. The indumentum consists of clothing and glandular hairs, the former being unicellular, and the latter with a head composed of few or many cells. As shown in the following table, the family, taken as a whole, is a stage higher than the *Valerianaceae*, and mimics the *Compositae*.

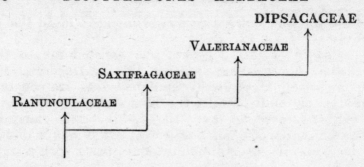

Key to genera.

Floral bracts and leaves not prickly :
  Receptacles elongated, covered with bracts :
    Outer corollas not larger than the inner, the lobes subequal SUCCISA
    Outer corollas larger than the inner and very irregular.   . SCABIOSA
  Receptacles hemispheric, covered with hairs; outer flowers much
    larger than the inner and 2-lipped . . . . KNAUTIA
Floral bracts prickly, protruding beyond the flowers. . . DIPSACUS

CAMPANULALES and ASTERALES.

78. Campanulaceae.   79. Lobeliaceae.   80. Compositae.

The family **Campanulaceae,** and its closely allied derived family *Lobeliaceae,* have sometimes been regarded as the basic stock for *Compositae. Campanulaceae* have perhaps been derived from the early *Gentianales,* one exotic genus, *Cyananthus,* having a *superior* ovary. All other *Campanulaceae* have an inferior or nearly completely inferior ovary. A rather primitive feature is the insertion of the stamens, which are free or placed very low down in the corolla-tube, showing only partial adhesion, perhaps a survival character from the Saxifragaceous stock.

Solereder calls attention to the anatomical similarity of *Campanulaceae* and *Compositae* through the presence of inulin and laticiferous vessels, particularly with the *Cichorieae,* which the *Campanulaceae* resemble in other respects. The stomata are not surrounded by any

Fig. 110.—The Devil's-Bit, *Succisa
pratensis* Moench (Dipsacaceae),
bears only a superficial resemblance
to some members of the *Compositae*;
its flower-structure is very different.

A, flower opened out. B and C,
flowers. D, anthers. E, fruit.

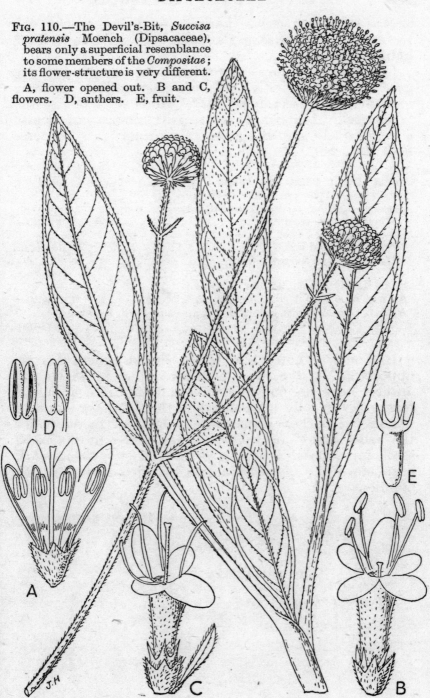

special subsidiary cells.   Large water pores occur on the leaf-teeth.   There are no glandular hairs, and the clothing hairs are one-celled.

Campanulaceae are represented in Britain by five genera, and the individuals of some species are very numerous, for example, the " Harebell " or Scotch " Blue bell ", *Campanula rotundifolia* Linn., which is also a very widely spread species.   Its fruits open by pores near the base.

Corolla shortly lobed (not below the middle); flowers in panicles,
 racemes or spikes or rarely solitary :
 Capsule opening within the calyx-lobes; pedicels leaf-opposed;
  stems slender, creeping . . . . WAHLENBERGIA
 Capsule opening at the side, below the calyx-lobes :
 Ovary short and broad. . . . . CAMPANULA
 Ovary long and narrow . . . . SPECULARIA
           (*Legousia*)
Corolla deeply lobed; flowers in heads :
 Anthers separate; heads elongated or globose . . . PHYTEUMA
 Anthers united in a ring at the base; heads small, hemispherical
           JASIONE

It should be noted that of the British genera *Jasione* appears to be the most advanced type in which the anthers have become united at the base into a ring, a feature more fully carried out in the *Lobeliaceae* and in *Compositae*.   There seems some foundation, therefore, for the belief that *Campanulaceae* may represent the basal stock for at least a part of or even all the *Compositae*, particularly the *Liguliflorae*.   Milky juice occurs in both families.

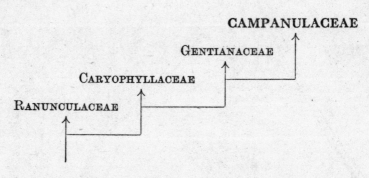

CAMPANULACEAE TO COMPOSITAE

The natural, i.e. *homogeneous*, families of flowering plants are usually very sharply cut off from others, intermediate stages having disappeared. Among British examples are the UMBELLIFERAE, COMPOSITAE and LABIATAE, ORCHIDACEAE, CYPERACEAE and GRAMINEAE. The true affinities of COMPOSITAE have long exercised the minds of botanists, some favouring RUBIACEAE and some CAMPANULACEAE, or even UMBELLIFERAE. A striking feature of the RUBIACEAE is the inter- or intrapetiolar stipules, and woody habit, except for one or two tribes. There are no stipules in COMPOSITAE, and they share this deficiency with CAMPANULACEAE. The plants illustrated have been selected to show how the Composite inflorescence, the capitulum, may have been gradually evolved, beginning at the base with a native species of *Campanula* (*C. latifolia*) with single flowers in the axil of a bract or leaf, and with another species, *C. glomerata*, in which part of the flowers are crowded together into a bunch. Indeed in CAMPANULACEAE the head is actually attained in *Jasione* (left, middle), and it is not a far step from this genus into COMPOSITAE at the top (left, *Cichorium*; right, *Pulicaria*), whilst a parallel family, LOBELIACEAE (*Lobelia*), is shown on the right hand side.

The plants illustrated in the coloured plate are: Bottom, left, Campanula latifolia *Linn.*; right, Campanula glomerata *Linn.* Middle, left, Jasione montana *Linn.* Top, left, Cichorium intybus *Linn.*; middle, Pulicaria dysenterica (*Linn.*) *Bernh.*; right, Lobelia dortmanna *Linn.*

To face p. 208.

Lobeliaceae are more advanced than *Campanulaceae*. *Lobelia* is the only genus in Britain. The corolla is zygomorphic and split open on the upper side, and the anthers are united into a tube around the style as in *Compositae*.

The two British species of *Lobelia* have an interesting distribution. *L. dortmanna* Linn. is an aquatic perennial with radical hollow cylindrical leaves which form a dense carpet at the bottom of the water, the flowering stems arising above the water. It occurs in the lakes of Scotland and Ireland, in the west of England and Wales, and elsewhere in northern Europe and America. *L. urens* Linn. is found only in Dorset and Cornwall, on moist heaths, and elsewhere only in western Europe.

Numerous species of *Lobelia* occur in South Africa, where some are quite woody; and giant Lobelias are a well-known feature of the landscape of the mountains of tropical East Africa. The common blue bedding-Lobelias are forms of *Lobelia erinus* Linn., a native of South Africa. The brilliant scarlet species, also used for bedding, is *L. cardinalis* Linn., from North America.

LOBELIACEAE

CAMPANULACEAE

GENTIANACEAE

CARYOPHYLLACEAE

RANUNCULACEAE

The vast family **Compositae** furnishes ample material for the study of phylogeny, and on broad lines the evolutionary history may be followed by a study of the tribes and principal genera. These fall into two main groups, the one much more primitive than the other. The first, *Tubuliflorae*, have the disk flowers tubular and actinomorphic (" regular "), with frequently ligulate ray and entirely female flowers, and with a *watery juice*; in the second and much more advanced group, the *Liguliflorae*, the flowers are all ligulate and hermaphrodite (Fig. G, p. 212), and the juice is usually *milky*.

In Britain over forty genera of *Compositae* are represented, and some idea as to the general development of the family may be gleaned from them. The tribe *Helianthoideae* is probably the most primitive of the *Tubuliflorae*. In some exotic genera of this tribe, such as *Rudbeckia* and related genera, the inflorescence approximates most closely to an ordinary spike, the axis is

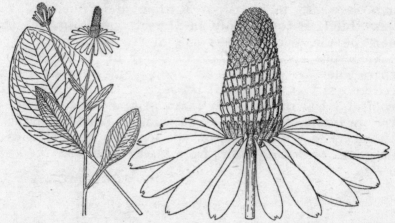

FIG. 111.—*Rudbeckia maxima* Nutt., a North American species representing a primitive type of *Compositae*; note the spike-like inflorescence, each flower subtended by a bract.

elongated, there is a *bract below each flower*, and the "pappus" is more calyx-like than in most other tribes. Unfortunately, there is only one indigenous genus in our islands, *Bidens*, and that is a very advanced member of the tribe, being a weed with a specially modified pappus to aid dispersal by animals. But there are plenty in cultivation, such as *Helianthus*, *Rudbeckia*, etc., most of them with yellow flowers. *Yellow* is the basic colour of the *Helianthoideae*, and *yellow is probably a primitive colour*, being little removed from green. The style-arms are truncate and papillous at the tip (as in Fig. 113, A) in tribe *Helianthoideae*.

From *Helianthoideae* it is not a far step to the next tribe *Senecionideae*, quite abundantly represented by species of *Senecio*, and particularly numerous individuals of certain species, such as the ragwort, *Senecio jacobaea* Linn., and the groundsel, *S. vulgaris* Linn. The several rows of involucral bracts of *Helianthoideae* have been reduced to a single row in *Senecio*, and are sometimes coherent, but the bracts subtending the flowers on the receptacle have been completely reduced. The style-arms are similar to those of *Helianthoideae* (Fig. 113, A), and the yellow flower-colour is general. *Petasites* and *Tussilago* are very near *Senecio*.

Tribes also derived immediately from the *Helianthoideae* are *Inuleae* and *Asteroideae*, and in the latter tribe there is frequently a colour change to blue. But the numerous involucral bracts of the *Helianthoideae* are maintained. *Inula* has club-shaped smooth style-arms and long-tailed anther-bases (Fig. 113, J. K). *Gnaphalium*, *Filago*, and *Antennaria* are reduced relatives of *Inula*, in *Antennaria* the flowers being mostly unisexual. *Asteroi-*

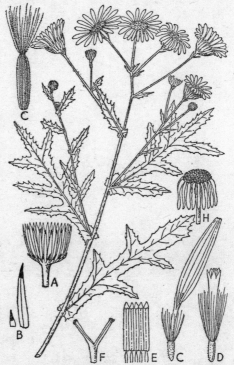

FIG. 112.—From time to time our flora has been invaded by various aliens with which native species have to contend. Here is one of them, though it interferes little with others, the so-called "Oxford Ragwort," *Senecio squalidus* L. (Compositae), from South Europe. It occurs in great quantity on walls and embankments near railway sidings.

A, involucre. B, bract from the same. C, ray-flower. D, disk-flower. E, stamens. F, style-arms. G, achene and pappus. H, old flower-head.

deae are represented by several genera, *Aster*, *Erigeron*, *Solidago* (Golden Rod), *Linosyris*, and *Bellis* (Daisy). The last-mentioned is an aggressive and successful type,

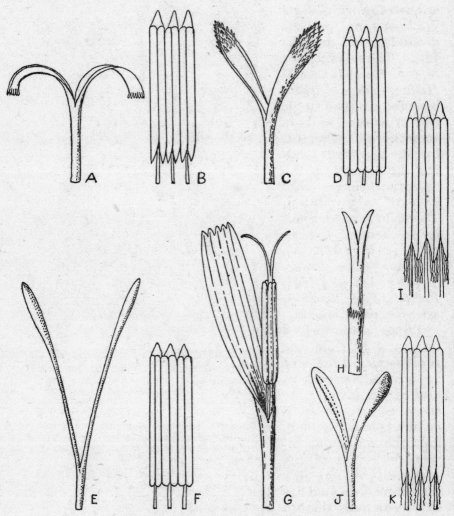

FIG. 113.—Tribal characters in the *Compositae*.

A and B, style-arms and anthers of *Helianthoideae*, *Senecionideae*, and *Anthemideae*. C and D, *Asteroideae*. E and F, *Eupatorieae*. G, corolla, stamens and style-arms of *Cichorieae*. H and I, *Cynaroideae*. J and K, *Inuloideae*.

although there is no pappus to aid its distribution (Fig. 117, C. D). A pappus has probably been somewhat over-rated as a means of dispersal.

This leaves us now with tribes *Anthemideae* and *Eupatorieae*. The former is not far removed from *Helianthoideae*, without or with a very *reduced pappus*, represented in Britain by the genera *Anthemis*, *Achillea*, *Diotis*, *Matricaria*, *Chrysanthemum*, *Tanacetum*, and *Artemisia*. All these are highly evolved genera, often with strongly scented leaves due to the presence of volatile oil glands. The rayless *Matricaria matricarioides* is a remarkable alien established on garden paths and farmyards in many parts of the country.

The most advanced tribe of this group is probably the *Cynaroideae*, which contains the Knapweeds (*Centaurea*) and other genera, and is distinguished from all the other groups by the ring of hairs below the base of the style-arms (Fig. 113, H). Three genera have tailed anthers (Fig. 113, I) (*Arctium*, *Carlina*, and *Saussurea*), the others have no tails (*Centaurea*, *Serratula*, *Carduus*, *Onopordon*).

We may now consider the second and more advanced group, the *Liguliflorae* represented by tribe *Cichorieae* (Fig. 113, G). It contains several troublesome garden weeds, showing it to be a highly successful type, and the genera differ little from one another. Common weeds are *Lapsana communis* Linn., *Taraxacum officinale* Wigg., the Dandelion, and *Crepis capillaris* (L.) Wallr. Some genera have a pappus of simple hairs (*Lactuca*, *Sonchus*, *Crepis*, and *Taraxacum*), others a plumose pappus (*Hypochaeris*, *Helminthia*, *Tragopogon*, *Picris*, and *Leontodon*), whilst *Cichorium* has a pappus of broad short scales, *Arnoseris* a coriaceous raised rim, and *Lapsana* no pappus at all.

In the subfamily *Tubuliflorae* schizogenous resin-canals are widely distributed and distinctive, whilst in the *Liguliflorae* lacticiferous vessels are characteristic. The indumentum may be of simple, two-armed, stellate, or scale-like hairs. The hairs are uniseriate or of two or more rows of cells. One-celled hairs are not recorded. Glandular hairs are widely distributed. The stomata are surrounded by ordinary epidermal cells, and not by special cells as in *Rubiaceae*, near which *Compositae* have usually been placed.

FIG. 114.—The limit of reduction in the Composite flower-head is reached in *Echinops*, in which each separate head is reduced to a single flower, the whole being collected into a globose compound head.

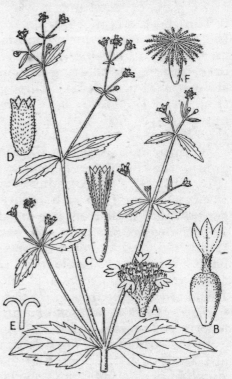

FIG. 115.—Because of its interesting botanical features and history, the "Kew Weed," *Galinsoga parviflora* Cav. (Compositae) is beloved by botanists, but not by gardeners.

A, flower-head which mimics an ordinary flower by having only 5 rays. B, ray-flower. C, disk-flower. D, corolla of disk. E, style-arms. F, fruit with spreading pappus.

Compositae is a very wonderful family, found all over the world, and a climax development in epigynous floral structure in the Dicotyledons. Amongst the most advanced genera are those in which the individual flower-

heads are again collected into heads, each separate head
being reduced to a single flower, as in *Echinops* (Fig. 114);
an exotic genus which may be seen in many gardens and
which is much visited by bees.

About the origin of *Compositae* I can say very little.
In many of the higher families, i.e., families approaching
a climax in floral structure, there is a strong tendency to
bunch the flowers into a head (capitulum). It may be
that the family is of mixed descent from the Rubiaceous,
the Umbelliferous, and the Campanulaceous stocks, but
real connecting links are not very evident. The
Rubiaceous type of stoma is not found in *Compositae*.
I favour the Campanulaceous origin, as adopted in the
present book.

Table of the tribes of Compositae showing their relationships and
probable evolution.

Compared with the great size of the family, economic plants are few. The most important are the Jerusalem Artichoke (*Helianthus tuberosus* Linn.), the Globe Artichoke (*Cynara scolymus* Linn.), Lettuce (*Lactuca sativa* Linn.), Santonin (*Artemisia cina* Berg.), Chicory (*Cichorium intybus* Linn.), besides numerous medicinal products and dyes. During the Second World War interest was revived in the Mexican Guayale Rubber plant (*Parthenium argentatum* A. Gray). A recent addition to rubber-producing plants is the Russian Dandelion, *Taraxacum kok-saghyz*. There is, of course, a multitude of ornamental garden plants, such as the *Dahlia, Chrysanthemum, Ageratum, Aster*, etc.

Key to Subfamilies and Tribes of *Compositae*.

Heads with all the flowers hermaphrodite and tubular, or the marginal flowers female, with or without a ligulate limb
                    Subfamily I. TUBULIFLORAE
Style without a ring of hairs below the base of the branches :
  Receptacle with scales between the flowers :
    Pappus present, sometimes bristly :
      Anthers not tailed at the base (Fig. 113, B) .   HELIANTHOIDEAE
      Anthers tailed at the base (Fig. 113, K) . . . . INULOIDEAE
    Pappus none or very minute . . . . . . ANTHEMIDEAE
  Receptacle without scales between the flowers :
    Anthers not tailed at the base :
      Style branches truncate and penicillate at the apex (Fig. 113, A) :
        Pappus present. . . . . SENECIONIDEAE
        Pappus none or very minute . . . . . ANTHEMIDEAE
      Style branches not truncate at the apex :
        Style branches flattened and pointed, comparatively short (Fig. 113, C) . . . . ASTEROIDEAE
        Style branches club-shaped and slender (Fig. 113, E)
                    EUPATORIEAE
    Anthers tailed at the base; style branches club-shaped, smooth (Fig. 113, J, K). . . . . INULOIDEAE
Style with a ring of hairs below the base of the branches (Fig. 113, H)
                    CYNAROIDEAE
Heads with all the flowers hermaphrodite and ligulate (Fig. 113, G)
                    Subfamily II. LIGULIFLORAE
One tribe . . . . CICHORIEAE

Subfamily I. TUBULIFLORAE.
Tribe HELIANTHOIDEAE.
Pappus bristles with reflexed hairs . . . . BIDENS
Pappus bristles with soft spreading hairs . . . . . ⸳ GALINSOGA*

Tribe SENECIONIDEAE.

All the flowers with a pappus :
  Flowers appearing before the leaves :
    Flower-heads solitary, bisexual . . . . TUSSILAGO
    Flower-heads racemose, dioecious . . . . . . PETASITES

  Flowers and leaves appearing together; flower-heads bisexual
                                 SENECIO
Ray-flowers without a pappus . . . . DORONICUM*

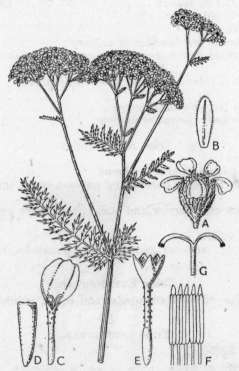

FIG. 116.—The " Yarrow " or " Milfoil,"
Achillea millefolium L. (Compositae), like
the Daisy, could tell a tale of competition
and strife whereby it has been evolved
to compete with grasses and other rough
herbage in pastures, meadows and waste
places. But it has gone even farther
than the Daisy in reducing the number
of its ray-flowers to five, thus simulating
an ordinary flower with five petals.

A, flower-head. B, bract. C, ray-flower.
D, achene. E, disk-flower. F, stamens.
G, style-arms.

P

Tribe CYNAROIDEAE.

Tips of the involucral bracts not hooked :
Pappus well developed, of slender hairs or bristles :
Pappus-hairs or bristles smooth or slightly rough :
Bracts not divided at the tip :
Stems not winged :
Leaves without spines . . . . SERRATULA
Leaves very spiny . . . . SILYBUM*
Stem with prickly wings . . . . ONOPORDON
Bracts divided and very prickly at the top . . . CARDUUS
Pappus-hairs or bristles plumose (with slender side-hairs) :
Tips of bracts not divided :
Anther-loculi long-tailed; bracts not spiny . . . SAUSSUREA
Anther-loculi not or only shortly tailed; bracts spiny-tipped
CIRSIUM (Cnicus)
Tips of the bracts toothed or branched, the inner bracts long and
linear, like ray flowers, outer very prickly . . . . CARLINA
Pappus very short or scale-like or absent; bracts often toothed or
jagged at the apex like a comb . . . . CENTAUREA
Tips of involucral bracts hooked; pappus short, barbellate, caducous
ARCTIUM

Subfamily II. LIGULIFLORAE.

Tribe CICHORIEAE.

*Achenes with a pappus of numerous long hairs :
Pappus hairs at most barbellate :
Achenes flattened; leaves often prickly :
Achenes beaked :
Stems leafy . . . . LACTUCA
Stems absent, leaves all radical . . . . . . TARAXACUM
Achenes not beaked; stems leafy :
Flowers yellow . . . . SONCHUS
Flowers blue . . . . MULGEDIUM
Achenes cylindrical or angular :
Achenes beaked :
Peduncles solitary, radical . . . . TARAXACUM
Peduncles several, branched . . . . CREPIS
Achenes not beaked :
Achenes very striate . . . . CREPIS
Achenes slightly striate :
Leaves toothed or entire . . . . HIERACIUM
Leaves pinnatifid . . . . LACTUCA
Pappus hairs plumose (with long side hairs) :
Involucral bracts gradually longer from the base upwards :
Outer bracts broadly ovate, cordate at the base . . HELMINTHIA
Outer bracts small, narrow and unequal :
Receptacles scaly between the flowers . . . HYPOCHAERIS
Receptacles not scaly between the flowers :
Stem leafy, clothed with hooked hairs; achenes without a beak
PICRIS

SOLANACEAE AND CONVOLVULACEAE

The families shown here are in themselves considerably advanced, and are climax groups more or less midway between the more primitive CRASSULACEAE and SAXIFRAGACEAE and the more advanced, such as SCROPHULARIACEAE, GESNERIACEAE, ACANTHACEAE and LABIATAE. Indeed some of them are quite woody, and no doubt critics of the system here outlined will fasten on them to try and prove the fallacy of dividing the Dicotyledons into two main subphyla, the one fundamentally woody, the other fundamentally herbaceous. The author would wriggle out of the difficulty by suggesting that the two families shown, SOLANACEAE and CONVOLVULACEAE, are mostly herbaceous, and that they may contain elements of both groups. Who can say? At the bottom, right, is *Solanum*, left, *Atropa*, and top left, *Hyocyamus* (belonging to SOLANACEAE), and the Common bindweed, *Convolvulus* (CONVOLVULACEAE).

The plants illustrated in the coloured plate are: Bottom, left, Atropa belladonna *Linn.*; right, Solanum dulcamara *Linn.* Top, left, Hyoscyamus niger *Linn.*; right, Convolvulus arvensis *Linn.*

To face p. 220.

Stem leafless or almost so; achenes shortly beaked :
Leaves with one main longitudinal nerve, coarsely toothed or
   lobulate; involucre composed of an inner long series of bracts
   and of a few much shorter bracts at the base; pappus-bristles
   plumose to the apex or nearly so . . . . . LEONTODON
Leaves with about 5 longitudinal nerves, entire; involucre
   composed of a series of bracts gradually increasing in length
   from the base upwards; pappus-bristles not plumose to the
   apex . . . . SCORZONERA
Involucral bracts of equal length. . . . . . . TRAGOPOGON

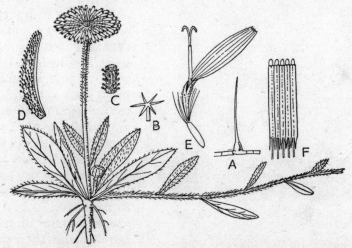

FIG. 119.—The "Mouse-Ear Hawkweed," *Hieracium pilosella*
L. (Compositae), is the least difficult to recognise in this
unstable genus.

A, hair from leaf. B, star-shaped hair from the same. C,
glandular hairs on the flower-head stalk. D, bract. E, flower.
F, stamens.

*Achenes without a pappus or with only a short cup :
Flowers blue; pappus a short cup . . . . CICHORIUM
Flowers yellow; pappus absent :
Stem leafy, up to 2 feet or more high; peduncles not swollen
                                        LAPSANA
Leaves all radical; peduncles swollen below the heads. ARNOSERIS

SOLANALES.

81. Solanaceae.   82. Convolvulaceae.

THE family **Solanaceae** is an important one.   Many are
medicinal, and some are of great economic importance as

food, such as the Potato, *Solanum tuberosum* L., and the Tomato, *Lycopersicum esculentum* Mill.   Tobacco is made from the dried leaves of *Nicotiana tabacum* L.

All *Solanaceae* are distinguished by the possession of intraxylary phloem. The stomata, with one or two exceptions, are surrounded by undifferentiated epidermal cells. The hairy covering is very varied. Clothing hairs are usually simple and uniseriate, but branched hairs are found in many genera, such as *Solanum*, and even peltate hairs. Glandular hairs are common.

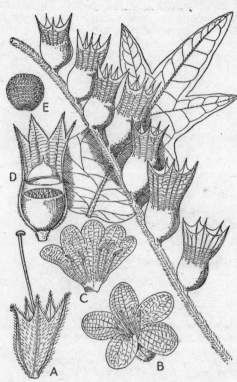

From the few genera represented in Britain alone we cannot learn much about their phylogeny. In *Hyoscyamus niger* Linn., the Henbane, the corolla-lobes are imbricate, and the fruit a capsule, like that of the introduced *Datura*. In *Atropa belladonna* Linn., the Deadly Nightshade, the corolla-lobes are also imbricate, but the fruit is a berry, as it is also in *Lycium*, a berry being more advanced than a capsule, as a rule. *Solanum*, of which there are two indigenous species, has plicate corolla-lobes (characteristic of the next family, *Convolvulaceae*), and the fruit is also a berry.   Moreover,

Fig. 120.—The medicinal and poisonous properties of the "Henbane," *Hyoscyamus niger* L. (Solanaceae) are betrayed by its unpleasant odour.

A, calyx and style.   B, corolla and stamens.   C, opened corolla.   D, fruit opening by its lid.   E, seed.

the anthers open by a terminal pore, which is rather an advanced character (see *Ericaceae* p. 105).

Solanaceae are on the whole more primitive than *Convolvulaceae*, because of their numerous ovules and their seeds with copious endosperm.

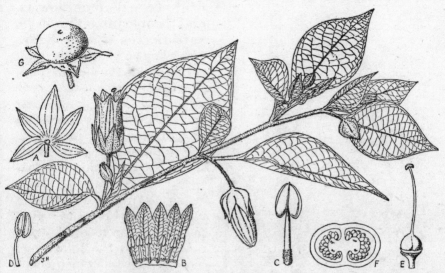

FIG. 121.—*Atropa belladonna* Linn. (Solanaceae); flowering shoot.

A, calyx, laid open. B, corolla, laid open. C, young stamen. D, older stamen. E, pistil and disk. F, cross-section of ovary. G, fruit.

Here is a key to the British genera :—

Fruit a capsule; anthers opening by slits :
  Corolla-lobes imbricate; tube short . . . . . . HYOSCYAMUS
  Corolla-lobes plicate, tube elongated . . . . DATURA*
Fruit a berry :
  Anthers opening by slits; corolla subcampanulate :
    Calyx leafy, deeply 5-lobed; herb with broad ovate leaves ATROPA
    Calyx toothed; shrub with slender branches and narrow leaves
                                       LYCIUM*
  Anthers opening by terminal pores; corolla rotate . . . SOLANUM

Convolvulaceae is a very natural family, and mainly found in the tropics. It includes some very beautiful climbers (*Ipomoea*, etc.). Useful products are the Sweet

Potato (*Ipomoea batatas* Poir.), Jalap (*Ipomoea purga* Hayne), and Scammony (*Convolvulus scammonia* Linn.). There are three genera in Britain, *Convolvulus*, *Calystegia*, and *Cuscuta*, the first two twiners or prostrate, *Convolvulus arvensis* Linn., with pink flowers, a troublesome weed, and *Calystegia sepium* (Linn.) R.Br. climbing, with large white or pale pink flowers, and the maritime *Calystegia soldanella* (Linn.) R.Br., prostrate with thick rounded leaves and pink flowers. *Cuscuta* is a very advanced type, and its species are leafless parasites on various other plants.

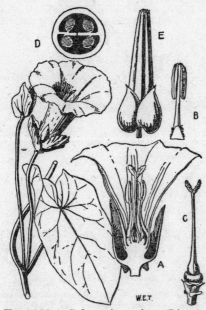

FIG. 122.—*Calystegia sepium* (Linn.) R. Br. (Convolvulaceae).

A, vertical section of flower. B, stamen. C, ovary. D, transverse section of same. E, bud. (From Hutchinson, *Families of Flowering Plants*.

Solereder notes " a whole series of anatomical features characterising this family in an excellent manner ". For our purposes we need only draw attention to the following: intraxylary phloem (except *Cuscuta*), the prevalence of a stomatal type with two subsidiary cells placed parallel to the pore, and the uniform structure of the clothing hairs. The last usually consist of two cells, (*a*) a suberized stalk cell, and (*b*) a terminal cell of variable shape. Frequently the terminal cell is two-armed or stellate. Glandular hairs mostly have a short one-celled stalk and a variously shaped head, the latter divided by vertical walls only, or by horizontal walls, or by both.

Convolvulaceae differ from *Solanaceae* mainly by the plicate corolla-lobes, the few ovules, and the scanty endosperm of the seeds.

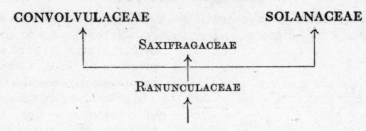

Key to genera of *Convolvulaceae*.

Twining or prostrate herbs with well-developed green leaves; flowers
  large and conspicuous; style single, divided above :
  Bracts remote from the calyx, small; stigmas narrow Convolvulus
  Bracts close up to the calyx, large and leafy; stigmas thick, ovate or
  oblong in outline . . . . Calystegia
Parasitical, leafless, twining herbs; styles two, free from the base
                                                    Cuscuta

PERSONALES.

83. Scrophulariaceae. 84. Orobanchaceae.
85. Lentibulariaceae.

As already stated on p. 188 it seems a reasonable hypothesis that **Scrophulariaceae** have been derived direct
from an Archichlamydeous stock, i.e., from *Saxifragaceae*,
and not through some intermediate or less advanced
sympetalous group. This seems probable because the
reduction to two carpels, as found in *Scrophulariaceae*, is
already general in *Saxifragaceae*. *Solanaceae* may be the
intermediate stock, however, and it may even have
branched off from below the *Saxifragaceae*.

Although the habit of the family, as we know it by our
native species and in our gardens, is herbaceous, it is not
a little surprising when one meets—for example, in South
Africa—a few trees and shrubs of considerable size with
quite hard wood (*Halleria*, etc.).

Although the ovules are usually numerous, there is
greater economy in the number of stamens, which are
mostly reduced to four or even two (*Veronica*). And the
corolla becomes increasingly zygomorphic except for the

more primitive types such as *Verbascum*, which has retained five stamens. Frequently where there are four or two stamens there are vestiges of those which have been dispensed with.

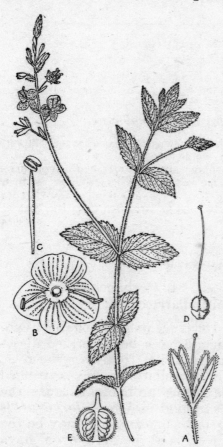

Anatomical characters of importance are the absence of intraxylary phloem, and the possession of external glands in which the head is divided by vertical walls only. The hairs are simple and unicellular or uniseriate and sometimes contain bodies resembling cystoliths, or they are branched and multicellular; or they may be glandular and of peltate form, and there are sometimes peltate glands as in *Euphrasia*. The stomata are usually surrounded by ordinary epidermal cells, but they are sometimes of the Cruciferous type.

In *Verbascum thapsus* the hairs are candelabra-like, and consist of an erect one-celled main axis, from which whorls of from two to eight ray-cells arise at certain points and at the tip.

Fig. 123.—The "Germander Speedwell" or "Bird's-Eye," *Veronica chamaedrys* L. (Scrophulariaceae), gets along with only two stamens.

A, calyx and pistil. B, corolla from above. C, stamen. D, disk and pistil. E, fruit.

Scrophulariaceae are fairly well represented in our flora by about a dozen genera. Of these *Verbascum*, the Mullein, shows the most primitive characters; the leaves are alternate, the corolla is actinomorphic (regular), and there are five stamens. *Digitalis* should perhaps come next, still with alternate leaves, the corolla tubular and only slightly zygomorhpic, but the stamens reduced to four or even two.

The stock, as represented by the British genera, seems to branch out on different lines, one producing a saccate or spurred corolla, *Antirrhinum* and *Linaria* respectively, retaining four stamens and often with a fifth rudimentary stamen; another represented by *Sibthorpia*, *Veronica*, and *Limosella*, retaining the actinomorphic corolla and with four or two stamens; and a third, the tribe *Euphrasieae*, with usually opposite leaves and a bilabiate corolla as in *Labiatae*, and all of them have become parasitic or semi-parasitic on the roots of other plants. These characters combined carry the *Euphrasieae* quite up to the evolutionary level of the *Labiatae*.

Apart from the Foxglove (*Digitalis purpurea* Linn.) the

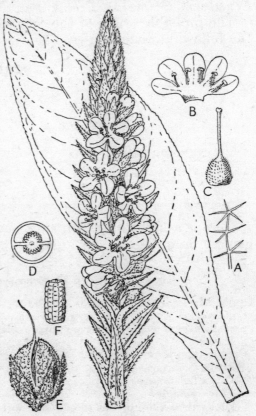

Fig. 124.—One of the most striking of our wild flowers, the "Great Mullein," *Verbascum thapsus* L. (Scrophulariaceae), unlike most of its relatives, has retained an almost regularly lobed corolla and five stamens providing a link with its past evolutionary history. Its indumentum (hairy covering) is interesting.

A, tree-like hair. B, corolla opened out. C, pistil. D, cross-section of ovary. E, fruit. F, seed.

family is of little economic importance, except for horticultural purposes, such as *Calceolaria, Antirrhinum,
Penstemon, Mimulus, Rehmannia, Veronica, Hebe,* etc.

The probable origin of the *Scrophulariaceae* is shown in
the following diagram :—

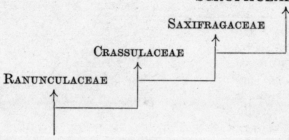

Here is a key to the British genera arranged on phylogenetic lines :—

Key to genera of *Scrophulariaceae.*

Upper lobe or lip of the corolla outside the others in bud :
  Corolla-tube very short or open and concave, shorter than the lobes;
    stamens 5, woolly; tall coarse plants often with a rosette of larger
    leaves . . . . VERBASCUM
  Corolla-tube appreciably long, as long or longer than the lobes :
    Corolla-tube not spurred at the base, the mouth usually open :
      Calyx not 5-angled . . . . SCROPHULARIA
      Calyx 5-angled . . . . MIMULUS *
    Corolla-tube more or less saccate or spurred at the base, the mouth
      closed by a projecting palate :
      Corolla-tube at most saccate at the base . . . ANTIRRHINUM
      Corolla-tube spurred at the base . . . . . . LINARIA
Upper lobe or lip of the corolla entirely or partly inside the others in
  bud :
  Corolla with a very short tube :
    Stamens 4, glabrous :
      Leaves alternate, orbicular; slender creeping plants; flowers
        axillary, very small; anthers sagittate, 2-locular SIBTHORPIA
      Leaves radical; glabrous almost stemless plants; flowers clustered,
        very small; anther loculi confluent into one . . . LIMOSELLA
    Stamens 2; corolla 4-lobed, never yellow . . . . . VERONICA
  Corolla-tube appreciably long :
    Flowers reddish or white, in a long terminal spike from a rosette
      of leaves . . . . DIGITALIS

SCROPHULARIACEAE TO LENTIBULARIACEAE

In this illustration only three families are represented, SCROPHULARIACEAE, by *Verbascum* (Mullein), *Digitalis* (Foxglove), and *Veronica* (Speedwell), OROBANCHACEAE, by *Orobanche*, and LENTIBULARIACEAE, by *Utricularia*. The range of floral structure and habit, however, is considerable. *Verbascum* is a primitive example of the large family SCROPHULARIACEAE, because in it are retained five stamens, whilst in most of the other members one or more are completely reduced. In *Digitalis* there are four, and in *Veronica* only two. The most advanced tribe is *Euphrasieae*, not shown in the picture, with markedly two-lipped corolla (this being a parallel of LABIATAE), some of them having become parasites, such as *Bartsia, Euphrasia, Rhinanthus, Pedicularis, Melampyrum,* and *Lathraea*. Only the last is devoid of green leaves. This habit is even more fixed in OROBANCHACEAE, which are root-parasites, with the leaves reduced to scales and destitute of chlorophyll. The climax development in this group of families is found in LENTIBULARIACEAE, which are aquatic or marsh plants. A tropical family closely allied to this group is GESNERIACEAE, of which *Streptocarpus* is a well known cultivated example.

The plants illustrated in the coloured plate are: Bottom, left, Digitalis purpurea *Linn.*; right, Verbascum thapsus *Linn.* Middle, Orobanche elatior *Sutton.* Top, left, Veronica chamaedrys *Linn.*; right, Utricularia vulgaris *Linn.*

To face p. 228.

Flowers not as above :
  Seeds not winged :
    Seeds numerous or several in each loculus of the fruit :
      Upper limb of the corolla 2-lobed, spreading . . EUPHRASIA
      Upper limb of the corolla nearly entire, arched or concave
                                          BARTSIA
      Upper limb of the corolla laterally compressed, entire or with
        a small tooth in front on each side . . . . PEDICULARIS
    Seeds 1–2 in each loculus of the fruit; calyx tubular or cam-
      panulate, with 4 teeth . . . . . MELAMPYRUM
  Seeds winged, compressed; semi-parasitical herbs; calyx
    inflated, with 4 small teeth . . . . . . RHINANTHUS

Orobanchaceae is a very small family of leafless root-parasites derived from the *Scrophulariaceae*, the same mode of growth being already developed in the *Euphrasieae* tribe of that family. There is no chlorophyll. The family differs from the *Scrophulariaceae* mainly by the one-locular ovary with parietal placentas. Anatomical characters have points in common with the *Scrophulariaceae* (p. 226), the glandular hairs being divided by vertical walls only.

There are about a dozen genera in the whole family, and of these only two are represented in Britain, *Orobanche* and *Lathraea*, which are very closely related. In the former the calyx is deeply divided, in the latter it is broadly campanulate with short lobes. There is only one species of *Lathraea*, *L. squamaria* Linn., in our flora, but there are several of *Orobanche*, and all are difficult to distinguish.

The path of evolution of these highly developed families is shown as follows :—

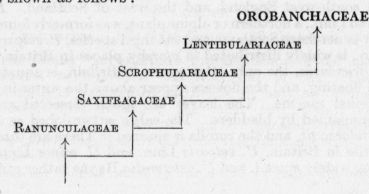

                                OROBANCHACEAE

                   LENTIBULARIACEAE

            SCROPHULARIACEAE

        SAXIFRAGACEAE

RANUNCULACEAE

The cells surrounding the stomata are not specially differentiated in the family. The indumentum consists of simple unicellular or uniseriate hairs, of bladder-hairs, and of glandular hairs with a uniseriate stalk and unicellular head. Interesting anatomical features of the family include the widely spaced vascular bundles of the axis, and a distinctive type of ring of mechanical tissue to which the bundles are often connected.

Although represented in Britain by only one species, the " Wood-Sorrel ", *Oxalis acetosella* Linn., the family **Oxalidaceae** is quite extensive, containing about 800 species, according to the latest monograph.[1] Most of these belong to the largest genus *Oxalis*, and to *Biophytum*. About 200 species of *Oxalis* occur at the Cape of Good Hope, where they grow like Primroses and add greatly to the beauty of the spring flora. An even greater number of species occurs in South America, especially in Chile and Peru, and in Brazil. So that on the whole of the family is mainly *austral* in distribution and probably also in origin, and of which we have only a few stragglers in the northern hemisphere, as in the case of *Erica*. Several quite shrubby species occur in the South American tropics. But for some reason there are very few species in *tropical* Africa.

Whilst the family is mainly herbaceous, there is one arborescent genus, *Averrhoa* Linn., widely cultivated in the tropics for its baccate fruit.

The " Wood-Sorrel ", *Oxalis acetosella* Linn., is one of the very few British plants with cleistogamous flowers; and the leaves droop at night. This seems to be a habit of many of the exotic species also.

Of the Geranial alliance we have now left only the family **Balsaminaceae**. It is poorly represented in Britain by only one native species, *Impatiens noli-tangere* Linn., the " Touch-me-not ", a name applied on account of the ripe capsules, which burst on being touched.

The genus *Impatiens* represents a complete climax type of development in its own alliance—that is to say, there are no plants on a higher plane which are related to it.

[1] Knuth in Engler, Das Pflanzenreich, *Oxalidaceae*, 1930.

GERANIACEAE TO LABIATAE

This design shows a fairly logical phylogenetic sequence of families from the GERANIACEAE, at the base, right up to the climax family, LABIATAE. The latter, in the writer's opinion, with its bilabiate corolla and deeply lobed ovary, represents the highest degree of floral evolution amongst British flowering plants. An equally advanced family in warmer parts of the world is ACANTHACEAE. In this the corolla has developed more or less on parallel lines, though the ovary is not vertically lobed as in LABIATAE. *Geranium* is shown to represent the GERANIACEAE, which, as indicated in the text, may have been directly derived from the *Ranunculaceous* stock. OXALIDACEAE (*Oxalis* shown) are closely related, but lack the glands characteristic of *Geraniaceae*, and have a different capsule. BALSAMINACEAE (*Impatiens*) are easily recognised by their zygomorphic corolla. The flowers of *Polemonium* (POLEMONIACEAE) are very similar to GERANIACEAE, except that the corolla is sympetalous, a character not regarded as very important in this system. There is a considerable gap between the families mentioned and BORAGINACEAE (*Myosotis*), with its alternate leaves and its gynobasic style on a deeply lobed ovary, a feature also common to the more climax LABIATAE (p. 237), with opposite or verticillate leaves.

The plants illustrated in the coloured plate are : Bottom, Geranium sanguineum *Linn.*; above, Oxalis acetosella *Linn.* Middle, left, Polemonium caeruleum *Linn.*; right, Impatiens noli-tangere *Linn.* Top, left, Myosotis palustris *Linn.*; middle, Lamium purpureum *Linn.*; right, Stachys sylvatica *Linn.*

To face p. 234.

Its species are found mainly in India and tropical Africa, being very numerous in the former region. Sir Joseph Hooker, the famous Kew botanist and for many years Director of Kew, was still working at this genus up to the time of his death at the age of 95.

As already stated (p. 231), Engler placed the *Balsaminaceae* in the *Sapindales,* far away from the *Geraniales.*

The origin of the *Geraniales* is suggested in the following table :—

BALSAMINACEAE
OXALIDACEAE   } Geraniales
GERANIACEAE
RANUNCULACEAE

POLEMONIALES to LAMIALES.

89. Polemoniaceae.   80. Boraginaceae.   91. Labiatae.

The family **Polemoniaceae** is represented in Britain by one species, *Polemonium caeruleum* Linn., a perennial widely distributed in the cooler parts of the northern hemisphere. *Polemonium* has pinnate leaves, and the flowers, but for their sympetaly, are very similar to some *Geraniaceae* and *Oxalidaceae*, whence the family may have been derived. On the other hand the familiar *Phlox* of

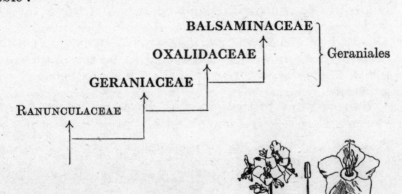

FIG. 127.—*Polemonium coeruleum* L. (Polemoniaceae).

A, flower. B, vertical section of same. C, stamen. D, ovary. E, fruit. F, seeds. (After Le Maout and Decne, from Hutchinson, *Families of Flowering Plants*).

our gardens might be a sympetalous representative of the *Caryophyllaceae*, especially of tribe *Sileneae*. Other common Polemoniaceous plants of our gardens are *Gilia*, with a wide range in species mimicking several families, and a common greenhouse climber is *Cobaea scandens*, with pinnate leaves, the upper leaflets being modified into tendrils as in *Lathyrus*.

There is rather a wide gap between the **Boraginaceae**, a family quite richly represented in Britain, and the more primitive stock from which it may have been derived. This I consider to be the *Geraniales*. In the latter group it should be noted that the character of the gynobasic style is already present in *Limnanthaceae*. And the gynobasic style is a very marked feature of *Boraginaceae*, from which, as noted on p. 129, the *Ehretiaceae* are excluded. On this account *Boraginaceae* is considered to be the basic group for the *Labiatae*, wherein this character has become very general.

Here is a key to the genera of *Boraginaceae* :—

Flowers axillary, solitary ; calyx enlarging in fruit and becoming 2-lobed
                                             ASPERUGO*
Flowers several together in an inflorescence, mostly in a one-sided
   (scorpioid) cyme :
  Corolla open at the mouth, neither contracted nor closed by anthers
    or scales :
   Stamens exserted beyond the corolla:
    Corolla with a straight tube ; nutlets smooth . . MERTENSIA
    Corolla curved and slightly zygomorphic, reddish or blue ;
      flowers bracteate ; nutlets rugose . . . . . ECHIUM
   Stamens included in the tube of the corolla :
    Calyx lobed to the base ; nutlets smooth or foveolate
                                  LITHOSPERMUM
    Calyx lobed to the middle ; nutlets smooth . . PULMONARIA
  Corolla closed at the mouth either by scales or anthers :
   Corolla-tube with an erect limb (i.e., the lobes continued in the same
    plane as the tube) ; nutlets slightly wrinkled . . SYMPHYTUM
   Corolla with an abruptly spreading limb :
    Anthers not conniving in a cone at the mouth of the corolla :
     Corolla-tube straight :
      Nutlets smooth or at most wrinkled, erect :
       Flowers subtended by leafy bracts ; nutlets wrinkled
                                ANCHUSA *
       Flowers without bracts ; nutlets smooth . MYOSOTIS
      Nutlets muricate, spreading or reflexed . CYNOGLOSSUM
     Corolla-tube slightly bent ; limb oblique and spreading
                                LYCOPSIS
    Anthers conniving in a cone at the mouth of the corolla ; fila-
    ments bifid ; nutlets grooved, with a white pulvinus at the
    base . . . . BORAGO *

The path of descent of *Boraginaceae* has probably been more or less as follows :—

BORAGINACEAE

[LIMNANTHACEAE]

GERANIACEAE

RANUNCULACEAE

And now we have reached the complete climax family of the herbaceous phylum, the **Labiatae**. It is perhaps the most homogeneous or " natural " family of dicotyledonous Flowering Plants, and there are quite a number of genera in Britain, representing as many as five of the eight tribes into which the family is classified in the Bentham and Hooker system.

A very characteristic feature of *Labiatae* is the possession of ethereal oil, which is excreted mainly beneath the cuticle in various kinds of capitate hairs, and especially in the shortly stalked, bladder-like integumental glands. In the capitate hairs the head is either one-celled or divided by vertical walls only. The stomata are usually accompanied by two or more subsidiary cells arranged *transversely* to the pore. The clothing hairs are usually uniseriate, sometimes only of two cells, but often of many cells.

Because we believe *Labiatae* to be the culmination of evolution in the sympetalous families, we must try and indicate its point, or points, of contact with less advanced groups. As they are mostly herbs it seems probable that we shall find the most nearly related family or families to be herbaceous. And from this point of view there is only one family showing a strong tendency towards the evolution of the Labiate type of flower-structure. This is *Boraginaceae*, excluding the tribes *Cordieae* and *Ehretieae* (see p. 236). In *Boraginaceae* (sensu stricto) the ovary of

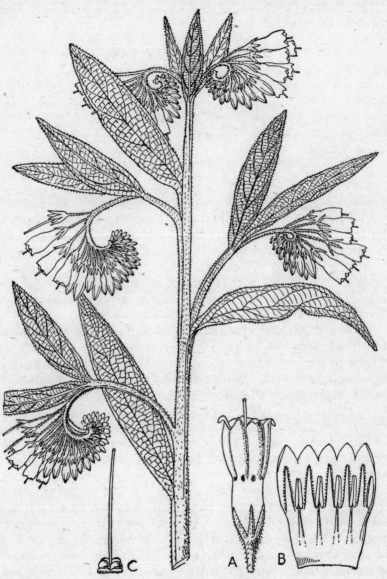

FIG. 128.—The family *Boraginaceae* (sensu stricto) is usually recognised by the coiled (scorpioid) inflorescence. *Symphytum officinale* L.

A, flower.   B, corolla laid open.   C, pistil.

the more advanced genera is usually deeply four-lobed, as in *Labiatae*.

As in the case of most natural families, i.e., families in which the flowers have evolved into very similar forms, the genera of *Labiatae* are difficult to distinguish and are separated by small and what appear to be trivial characters. Indeed, in many other families these characters would often be regarded as little more than specific. This is particularly the case in *Labiatae*. The stem is always four-sided ("square"), and the flowers often axillary and verticillate. The calyx throughout is tubular and variously toothed, the corolla is sympetalous and usually zygomorphic (two-lipped) and the stamens may be either four or two. The ovary furnishes little of a generic character, being always deeply vertically four-lobed with the style inserted between the lobes

FIG. 129.—The "Wood-Sage", *Teucrium scorodonia* L. (Labiatae), has a singular (yellow) corolla with the five lobes merged into one lip, forming an efficient platform for insects.

A, flower. B, calyx opened out. C, corolla. D, anther. E, nutlet. F, hair from inside calyx.

(gynobasic). Each lobe of the ovary becomes in fruit a separate nutlet, and there is one erect ovule in each lobe.

The genera represented in Britain show a considerable range in structure, and they are arranged in the key in an ascending series. The most advanced genus seems to be *Salvia*, always to be recognised by its two stamens, the anther-cells of which are widely separated. Only one other British genus, *Lycopus*, has but two stamens. Then *Galeopsis* also occupies a high place in the key because of the transverse dehiscence of the anthers.

Mentha seems to have the most primitive type of corolla, which is actinomorphic or nearly so. Then the majority of the genera have a bilabiate corolla, as compared with the two genera *Teucrium* and *Ajuga*, in which

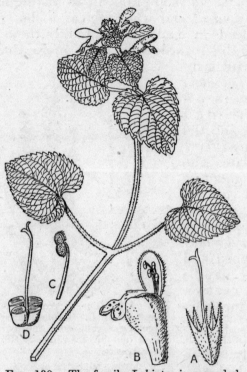

Fig. 130.—The family *Labiatae* is regarded in the present systematic arrangement as being at the very top of the family "tree" of the *Herbaceae* (see p. 237). This is the "Red Dead Nettle," *Lamium purpureum* L.

A, calyx and style. B, corolla. C, stamen. D, nutlets and style.

the corolla is more or less one-lipped with an oblique limb. The calyx is then employed, those with a more or less actinomorphic and equally toothed limb preceding those with a zygomorphic limb. *Scutellaria* seems to be at the top of these with a calyx of two entire lobes, the upper one with a concave dorsal scale.

The family is very widely spread all over the world like most other natural and climax families, such as *Papilion-aceae*, *Umbelliferae*, *Compositae*, and *Gramineae*.

Key to genera of *Labiatae*.

Anther-cells more or less parallel or contiguous though sometimes divergent; stamens usually 4, rarely 2 :
Stamens 4 :
Anthers opening by slits lengthwise :
Corolla actinomorphic or nearly so, 4-lobed with more or less equal lobes; calyx equally 5-toothed; flowers in terminal spikes or axillary clusters; nut smooth . . . . MENTHA
Corolla more or less zygomorphic :
Corolla 2-lipped, with distinct upper and lower lips :
Stamens longer than the upper lip of the corolla, with the anthers exserted :
Low and procumbent with small leaves fringed with long hairs towards the base; calyx 2-lipped, the upper lip 3-toothed, the lower 2-lobed, the mouth closed with hairs after flowering
THYMUS
Erect; flowers in heads in a terminal panicle; calyx actinomorphic or nearly so . . . . ORIGANUM
Stamens with the anthers close under the upper lip of the corolla :
Calyx actinomorphic and equally 5-toothed :
Calyx with 15 parallel ribs; upper pair of stamens the longer; flowers blue to nearly white . . . . NEPETA
Calyx with 10 or 5 ribs :
Lower leaves deeply divided rather like those of *Artemisia*; flowers in close axillary whorls forming long leafy spikes; nut flat, triangular at the top; corolla pink or nearly white, with a very hairy upper lip . . . . . . LEONURUS*
Lower leaves at most coarsely toothed :
Nuts flat and angular at the top; anthers usually hairy; flowers white, purplish red or yellow, in close axillary whorls . . . . LAMIUM
(*Galeobdolon*)
Nuts rounded at the top :
Calyx funnel-shaped, with ovate finely pointed teeth, 10-ribbed . . . . BALLOTA
Calyx tubular or campanulate, with narrow pointed teeth, 5- or 10-ribbed. . . . . STACHYS
Calyx actinomorphic, with 10 recurved teeth; upper lip of corolla narrow, erect, 2-lobed; flowers dull white; nuts rounded at the top . . . . MARRUBIUM
Calyx zygomorphic and distinctly 2-lipped :
†Calyx with the upper lip more or less toothed or lobed, the lower split to the base into 2 segments :

Calyx broadly campanulate, nervose, with 4 or 5 obtuse lobes
or teeth; flowers in axillary whorls separated by the
internodes . . . . MELITTIS
Calyx upper lip flat and angular, with 3 small teeth; filaments
with a small tooth below the anther; flowers collected into
dense terminal heads with broad leafy bracts   PRUNELLA
Calyx upper lip 3-toothed, the tube 13-nerved :
Calyx hairy inside at the top; flowers in axillary clusters
CALAMINTHA (*Clinopodium*)
Calyx not hairy inside at the top; flowers few, axillary
MELISSA *
†Calyx of 2 entire lobes, the upper one with a concave scale on
the back; flowers dingy blue or pink . . . SCUTELLARIA
Corolla more or less 1-lipped, the upper lobes very short and
tooth-like, the lower elongated, making the limb oblique :
Short upper lip of corolla deeply cleft into 2 teeth between which
the stamens protrude . . . . TEUCRIUM
Short upper lip of corolla entire or notched behind the stamens
AJUGA
Anthers opening by a transverse slit bordered by hairs; flowers in
dense whorls in the upper leaf-axils; calyx with 5 subequal teeth
GALEOPSIS
Stamens 2; leaves pinnately lobulate or coarsely toothed; flowers
very small and numerous in dense axillary whorls; corolla only a
little longer than the calyx; nutlets surrounded by a thickened
border . . . . LYCOPUS
Anther-cells remote from each other or reduced to one; stamens 2,
ascending; corolla blue, very zygomorphic, 2-lipped; calyx 2-lipped,
the upper lip entire or nearly so, the lower 2-fid. . . . SALVIA

Monocotyledones.

Systematic Anatomy of Monocotyledons.

HERE and there in the foregoing account of the Dicotyledons notes have been given on certain of the more macroscopic anatomical characters of many of the families which might aid the student in the identification of sterile specimens. These have been culled from the English edition of Solereder's *Systematic Anatomy of the Dicotyledons* (1908). Although the anatomy of some of the families of Monocotyledons has been described in German by Solereder and Meyer (*Systematische Anatomie der Monocotyledonen*, parts 3, 4 and 6 ; Berlin, 1928–1930), no complete work for the Monocotyledons as a whole is yet available. I am, therefore, much indebted to a colleague [1] for the following notes :—

The systematic anatomy of the Monocotyledons has not been so thoroughly investigated as that of the Dicotyledons, except in a few families. The Monocotyledons also present comparatively few diagnostic characters. This is partly due to the predominance of herbs and the suppression of the stem especially in species with corms or bulbs. Where secondary thickening occurs in the axis, it is often confined to the basal region as in the Elephant's Foot (*Testudinaria elephantipes* Salisb.) and *Nolina*, both of which are commonly cultivated in botanic gardens. In the Palms, on the other hand, the trunk increases in girth throughout its length, the scattered bundles being supported by interfascicular fibres which give rigidity to the axis. The comparative rarity of an indumentum of distinct kinds of trichome and the lack of true secondary wood, also present difficulties to the systematic anatomist. In the few arboreal families such as the Palms there are more structural features to be investigated, and consequently the possibility of using anatomical characters in taxonomy is greater. Growth in thickness—for example, in *Dracaena*—is due to the activity of a meristematic zone outside the central region containing the primary scattered bundles. The meristematic tissue gives rise to additional discrete bundles which remain separated from one another by the intervening secondary parenchyma. The scattered bundles usually possess no cambium except when very young. They are generally

---

[1] Dr. C. R. Metcalfe, Keeper of the Jodrell Laboratory, Royal Botanic Gardens, Kew.

collateral, but often with the phloem partly surrounded by the xylem. Where the xylem completely encloses the phloem the bundles become centric. This structure recalls that of the Ranunculaceae and other related families of the Dicotyledons which are generally accepted as having affinities amongst the Monocotyledons with the Alismataceae. Variations in the structure and distribution of the fibro-vascular bundles, as seen in transverse sections, are of considerable taxonomic value in some instances, e.g., in plants with the gramineous habit, the difficult genus *Agave*, which seldom flowers, and in arboreal types like the Palms. The arrangement of the fibres around the bundles, as well as the presence or absence of epidermal papillae, have also been used for the identification of certain closely related species of *Iris*.

The mesophyll of the leaf in the Monocotyledons is less frequently differentiated into well-defined palisade and spongy portions than in the Dicotyledons, the blade being composed of roundish cells. Leaves with a well-developed median bundle are also uncommon in the Monocotyledons, where a system of parallel veins is more characteristic. The Dioscoreaceae, represented in the British Flora by *Tamus communis*, and *Arum maculatum*, of the family *Araceae*, are exceptional in exhibiting a network of veins.

Preliminary phylogenetic studies of the Monocotyledons based on anatomical work have recently been made in the U.S.A. by Cheadle.[1] This author regards the following characters as primitive : (1) A large amount of secondary thickening. (2) The replacement of vessels by tracheids. (3) The larger girth of the upper than of the lower part of the axis. (4) The occurrence of less specialized sieve tubes in the roots. Cheadle has made certain suggestions, based on these and other associated characters, concerning possible lines of phylogenetic development in the Monocotyledons. While this line of investigation is yielding interesting results, it is early as yet to assess their full implications.

The following is a short list of families of Monocotyledons in which distinctive anatomical characters have been recorded or in which it has been shown that the microscopical structure is valuable in the identification of species.

Butomaceae.—Schizogenous laticiferous canals present except in *Butomus*.

Alismataceae.—Schizogenous laticiferous canals generally present. Hydathodes common in the upper part of the leaf towards the apex. The form and structure of the leaf are strongly influenced by environment.

Potamogetonaceae.—The leaves of *Potamogeton* are frequently covered with a calcareous deposit.

---

[1] Cheadle, V. I., " The Rôle of Anatomy in Phylogenetic Studies of the Monocotyledoneae ", *Chronica Botanica*, 1942, **7**, 253, and other papers in *Amer. Journ. Bot.*, vols. 26 (1939), 28 (1941), 29 (1942), and 30 (1943),

Liliaceae.—The work of Zweigelt [1] and others on the comparative anatomy was claimed by the authors to indicate that the Liliaceae should be divided into several sub-families.

Ruscaceae.—The vascular bundles are approximately triangular in transverse section, and have U-shaped xylem groups. This structure recalls that of the bundles in the Ranunculaceae amongst the Dicotyledons.

Alstroemeriaceae, etc.—The leaves of *Alstroemeria* and *Bomarea* are inverted by a basal twist. A somewhat similar arrangement occurs in *Allium ursinum* and a few of the Gramineae, including the seedling leaves of our common cereals. These plants exhibit anatomical peculiarities which compensate for the twisting.

Araceae.—Laticiferous elements, resin canals, sclerenchymatous idioblasts (the so-called internal hairs) and groups of mucilaginous cells are commonly but not universally present in the family. The occurrence and distribution of these elements, and particularly the laticiferous system, provide characters of importance in subdividing the family. The cauline vascular bundles in the rhizomes of *Acorus calamus* are centric with central phloem, whereas the adjacent leaf trace bundles are collateral.

Iridaceae.—Variations in the fibrous girdles associated with the vascular bundles and the presence or absence of epidermal papillae have been used to distinguish certain closely related species of *Iris.*

Dioscoreaceae.—The young stem of *Tamus communis* is exceptional amongst the Monocotyledons in having the vascular bundles arranged in a ring instead of being scattered. The network of veins in the leaf has already been mentioned above.

Orchidaceae.—The outer part of the aerial roots consists of a spongy tissue, the velamen, which is generally believed to serve for the storage of water and the exchange of gases between the root and the surrounding atmosphere.

Juncaceae.—In *Juncus* the pith is frequently composed of stellate cells with abundant intercellular spaces.

Cyperaceae and Gramineae.—Members of the *Gramineae* can generally be distinguished from those of the *Cyperaceae* by microscopical examination of the incinerated leaf. This method has also been used by Japanese workers for identifying Bamboos. In the *Cyperaceae* the epidermis includes a proportion of conical silicified cells, whilst in the *Gramineae* some of the epidermal cells are distinguishable from the remainder by being shorter and silicified as seen in surface view. Both families are characterised by having stomata whose guard cells appear to be shaped like dumb-bells as seen in surface view. The anatomical structure of the leaf of the grasses and sedges provides characters of considerable diagnostic value which should be much more widely known and used.

---

[1] Zweigelt, F., *Vergl. Anat. d. Asparag. Opiopog.,* etc., *Denkschr. Ak. Wiss.,* Wien 1912, **88**.

Calyciferae.

Butomales to Eriocaulales.

92. Butomaceae. 93. Hydrocharitaceae. 94. Alismataceae. 95. Scheuchzeriaceae. 96. Zosteraceae. 97. Juncaginaceae. 98. Potamogetonaceae. 99. Ruppiaceae. 100. Zannichelliaceae. 101. Najadaceae. 102. Eriocaulaceae.

Our first family of Monocotyledons is **Butomaceae**, formerly part of the *Alismataceae*. The character of the carpels seems to indicate a very ancient type. They are free from one another, and the ovules are numerous and *scattered on the reticulately branched parietal placentas*. A similar arrangement is found in the exotic family *Cabombaceae*, near the beginning of the herbaceous Dicotyledons. It is interesting to note also that we have already in *Butomus* an *umbellate* inflorescence, with an *involucre of bracts*, such as is found throughout the higher family *Amaryllidaceae*.

Butomus umbellatus Linn. is the only British representative of this small family. The diagram below shows the connection with *Ranunculaceae*.

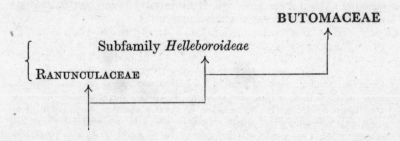

BUTOMACEAE

Subfamily *Helleboroideae*

Ranunculaceae

Hydrocharitaceae are clearly related to the *Butomaceae*, but with an inferior ovary, and often with unisexual, even dioecious flowers. These two families were widely separated in Bentham and Hooker's system. The peculiar

BUTOMACEAE TO ERIOCAULACEAE

The families of Monocotyledons shown here belong to the group called in this system the *Calyciferae*. This group is characterised by the presence of a distinct *calyx and corolla*, the former often green, as in HYDROCHARITACEAE (*Hydrocharis*, bottom, right hand). In BUTOMACEAE (bottom, left) both the sepals and corolla are coloured, but they are in two distinct series, though in ALIS-MATACEAE the sepals are green. In these two more primitive families the carpels are free, just as in RANUNCULACEAE, and there is quite a close relationship with that family. It is in these families that Dicotyledons and Monocotyledons approach each other most closely, and in no others. The large family COMMELINACEAE, almost entirely tropical, has always a very distinct calyx and corolla. ERIOCAULACEAE is a very advanced family in the group, but there is only one genus, *Eriocaulon*, and species, in Britain. This is shown at the top, and in a way is a parallel or equivalent of the COM-POSITAE in the Dicotyledons, with the flowers much reduced and collected into heads. Some of the families with very reduced flowers have become marine, such as *Najas* shown at the top (right).

The plants illustrated in the coloured plate are : Bottom, left, Butomus umbellatus *Linn.*; right, Hydrocharis morsus-ranae *Linn.* Middle, Alisma plantago-aquatica *Linn.*; left (with spike), Potamogeton natans *Linn.* Top, left, Eriocaulon septangulare *With.*; right, Najas marina *Linn.*

To face p. 246.

placentation of the ovules shared by them is unique in the Monocotyledons, and seems to be a strong mark of affinity, together with the *umbellate* inflorescence. The ovary is one-locular with *intrusive parietal placentas*, and the ovules are spread over the placentas.

The indigenous British genera are *Hydrocharis*, *Stratiotes*, and *Hydrilla*. They are all fresh-water aquatics, and each is represented by a single species. *Hydrocharis morsus-ranae* Linn. is a herb with petiolate cordate-orbicular floating leaves, which have stomata only on the upper surface as in *Nymphaea*. The flowers are white and dioecious, the males two to three in an umbel subtended by two spathaceous bracts. The female flowers are solitary and longer-stalked than in the male. There is a distinct calyx of three green sepals and three large white petals, with twelve stamens in the male, and in the female the ovary is inferior. *Stratiotes aloides* Linn., the " Water Soldier ", is a herb which sinks to the bottom of the water in autumn, where it passes the winter safe from frost, suckers rising from it to the surface in spring. The flowers are subdioecious and are submerged when in bud, but they appear on the surface when open. The leaves are not differentiated into petiole and blade, and are, as the name implies, similar to those of a small *Aloe*, with serrate margins. Another water plant, *Hydrilla verticillata* (Linn. f.) Royle, has in recent years been found in Eastwaite Water in Lancashire, and in the west of Eire. It has slender leafy stems and is widely spread in the warmer parts of the Old World. The flowers are hydrophilous.

Two other genera have become naturalised. These are *Elodea* (*E. canadensis* Michx.) and *Vallisneria* (*V. spiralis*). *Elodea canadensis* L., " Water-Thyme ", was introduced from America in the first half of last century and spread so rapidly as often to choke streams and canals with its rank growth. The flowers are dioecious, and it is mainly from the female plant that vegetative propagation has taken place. Male plants are very rare in Britain. The stem is elongated and slender, closely beset with whorls of narrow leaves.

Vallisneria spiralis also has dioecious flowers, the males with short stalks, three unequal sepals, three minute petals, and only two of the three stamens fertile. The female flowers are solitary within the spathe supported on a long spirally coiled peduncle; there are no vestiges of stamens, and the small perianth is sessile on the one-locular inferior ovary, which has three broad styles, with numerous ascending ovules. The method of pollination is interesting and has been described in many text-books.

Key to the genera of *Hydrocharitaceae* :—

Spathes composed of 1 or 2 free bracts :
  Leaves differentiated into blade and petiole, blade rounded, cordate
    at the base; female flower and fruit pedicellate within the bracts
                                                          HYDROCHARIS
  Leaves not differentiated into blade and petiole, oblong-lanceolate;
    female flower sessile or subsessile within the bracts . STRATIOTES
Spathes composed of two bracts connate into a tube :
  Perianth double, with the petals well developed and subequalling or
    larger than the sepals; leaves small, in whorls :
    Flowers hydrophilous; petals narrower than the sepals; male
      spathes 1-flowered . . . . HYDRILLA
    Flowers entomophilous; petals much longer and broader than the
      sepals; male spathes 2- or more-flowered. . . . . ELODEA *
  Perianth of the male flowers single and with 1–3 stamens; female
    flowers with a double perianth, the petals very small; leaves
    elongated and strap-like . . . . VALLISNERIA *

Our next family, **Alismataceae,** is closely connected with *Butomaceae,* and their general resemblance to RANUNCULACEAE is obvious, especially to the second sub-family of that group, the *Ranunculoideae.*

Here is a key to the British genera for the student to appreciate some of the characters.

Carpels free from one another :
  Carpels spirally arranged in several series on a large globose or oblong
    receptacle :
    Flowers hermaphrodite . . . . . BALDELLA (*Echinodorus*)
    Flowers unisexual . . . . SAGITTARIA
  Carpels arranged on a very small receptacle :
    Flowers subsolitary; leaves floating; carpels capitate. LURONIUM
                                                          (*Elisma*)
    Flowers several to numerous; leaves erect; carpels in a single whorl,
      laterally compressed. . . . . ALISMA
Carpels united at the base, in a single whorl and spreading stellately
                                          DAMASONIUM (*Actinocarpus*)

We find the most primitive genera amongst those with free carpels, particularly those in which they are arranged in several spirals after the manner of *Ranunculus*. First place falls to *Baldella* (*B. ranunculoides* (Linn.) Parl., the *Alisma ranunculoides* of Linnaeus), with *hermaphrodite* flowers. *Sagittaria* is more advanced with *unisexual* flowers. There is only one species in Britain, *S. sagittifolia* Linn. *Luronium* (*L. natans* (Linn.) Raf.) comes next with capitate carpels, and *Alisma* (*A. plantago-aquatica* Linn.), with the carpels in a single whorl, and finally the most advanced genus *Damasonium* (*D. alisma* Mill), also with the carpels in a single whorl but united at the base, and spreading star-like.

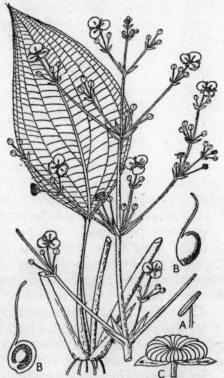

FIG. 131.—A close relationship between the Dicotyledons and Monocotyledons is shown by the *Ranunculaceae* and *Alismataceae* respectively. This is the "Water Plantain", *Alisma plantago-aquatica* L. (Alismataceae), which has numerous free carpels as in many *Ranunculaceae*.

A, stamen. B, single young carpel, and vertical section. C, carpels in fruit.

Very closely allied to the ALISMATACEAE is the small monotypic family **Scheuchzeriaceae**, genus SCHEUCHZERIA. This appears to be another ancient relict which grows in bogs amongst sphagnum in the colder parts of the north temperate zone. The leaves sheath at the base like a grass, and there is a ligule at the junction with the blade. There are six to three carpels nearly free from one another, and there are two ovules in each. The fruiting carpels are divaricate like those of a *Paeonia*. *Scheuchzeria*

R

palustris Linn. is widely spread across the northern hemisphere.

SCHEUCHZERIACEAE

ALISMATACEAE

Subfamily Ranunculoideae

RANUNCULACEAE

Zosteraceae are unique for the British flora in their habitat. They are submerged grass-like *marine* perennials with creeping rhizomes and compressed stems, and leaves sheathing at the base with stipule-like margins. There are two species of *Zostera* around our coasts, *Z. marina* Linn., the " Grass-wrack ", and *Z. nana* Roth. There is only one other genus of this family as recognised here, the exotic *Phyllospadix*, which is found in the seas of western North America and of Japan.

The small family **Juncaginaceae** (not to be confused with *Juncaceae*) is most abundantly represented by the number of species in Australia. The flowers are protogynous and wind-pollinated. There are no bracts.

In Britain there is one genus, *Triglochin*, the " Arrowgrass ", with two species, *T. palustre* Linn., in fresh water marshes and wet meadows, and *T. maritimum* Linn., in salt marshes.

The family seems to be closely connected with tribe *Narthecieae*, an early group of *Liliaceae* (see p. 255).

The family **Potamogetonaceae** is here limited to the type genus *Potamogeton*, because it is considered to represent the first step towards those higher evolved genera, which are even more completely aquatic and even marine, with a very much more reduced floral structure. Their exact relationships are, however, problematical, owing to the extreme reduction of the flowers, and there are many gaps amongst some very distinct types.

The flowers of *Potamogeton* are hermaphrodite and arranged in pedunculate axillary spikes, the peduncle being embraced by a sheath at the base; there are no bracts. There are four, clawed, valvate, free perianth-segments, with one stamen inserted on each claw; the anthers are extrorse, two-locular, and sessile. The gynoecium is composed of four, sessile, free, one-locular carpels, each containing one ovule. The fruits are indehiscent.

Ruppiaceae is a family of one genus, *Ruppia*, which grows in salt marshes, lagoons, shallow creeks, etc., nearly all over the world. There are two very closely allied species around the British Isles, *R. maritima* Linn., and *R. rostellata* Koch. They are slender floating herbs with narrowly linear leaves sheathing at the base.

The flowers are hermaphrodite, very small, and arranged in spikes at first enclosed by the sheathing base of the leaves, but at length exserted. There are no bracts and no perianth; stamens two, and gynoecium of four or more carpels, with a solitary pendulous ovule. A peculiar feature is the long-stipitate fruiting carpels, the peduncle at length often twisting spirally. The seeds are devoid of endosperm.

The affinity of this small family is undoubtedly with *Potamogetonaceae*, and probably derived from the same stock, though the floral structure is so reduced that there are few clues to point to its origin.

Zannichelliaceae are submerged aquatic herbs, either in fresh, brackish, or salt water. They are represented in Britain by a single genus of one species, the " Horned Pond-weed ", *Zannichellia palustris* Linn., which is distributed over a great part of the world. The flowers are monoecious and axillary, and the leaves narrowly linear. The four free carpels are sometimes accompanied by a single male flower consisting of a single stamen, or the latter in a separate leaf-axil. The ripe carpels are shortly stipitate and rugose on the back, and the seed is pendulous.

Najadaceae are also represented in Britain by a single genus, *Najas*, with two or three species. The flowers are much reduced and were regarded by followers of the Englerian system as being a very primitive type of flower. Here they are considered to be the reverse, and so much reduced that their relationship with others is difficult to trace. For a flowering plant the habitat—complete submergence in water even during flowering—is anything but primitive; the flowers are minute and dioecious, the male reduced to a small perianth and a single stamen, the female usually without a perianth and composed of one carpel with one erect ovule and without endosperm in the seed.

The family **Eriocaulaceae** appears to be one of the climax groups of the *Calyciferae*, and they are probably reduced advanced types of the more tropical order *Commelinales*, but with the flowers in heads subtended by bracts. They may be regarded as the " Compositae " of the Monocotyledons, and also something of a parallel development with the *Glumiflorae*, the third large group of Monocotyledons, which is the reduced climax group of the *Corolliferae*.

Besides being in heads, the flowers are *unisexual*, and there is only *one ovule* in the ovary.

The family is found most abundantly in swampy places in the tropics of both hemispheres, with a few in temperate regions. In Britain there is one genus and species, *Eriocaulon septangulare* With., the Pipe-Wort, which is only found on the coasts of the islands to the west of Scotland (Iona and Skye), and on the west coast of Ireland. It is also found in North America, and is therefore a plant of very great phytogeographical interest (see p. 17).

Corolliferae.

Liliales to Typhales.

103. Trilliaceae.   104. Liliaceae.   105. Ruscaceae.
106. Dioscoreaceae.   107. Araceae.   108. Lemnaceae.
109. Sparganiaceae.   110. Typhaceae.

One of the minor thrills of botanical collecting in woodlands in Britain is to find a plant such as " Herb

Paris ", *Paris quadrifolia* Linn. I have included this genus in **Trilliaceae**, together with *Trillium* (lovely

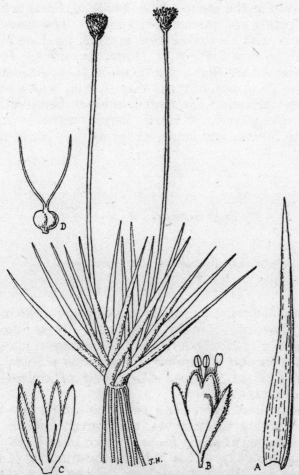

FIG. 132.—Of exceptional interest on account of its geographical distribution (see p. 252), *Eriocaulon septangulare* With. (Eriocaulaceae).   Whole plant.

A, bract. B, flower. C, calyx. D, pistil.

garden plants), *Scoliopus* (N. Amer.), and *Medeola* (N. Amer.).   In most systems *Trilliaceae* is treated as a tribe of *Liliaceae*.

The leaves of *Paris* are usually four and are whorled on the simple stem, and the venation is *reticulate* between the main nerves. In *Scoliopus* the leaves are paired and opposite along the stem. The sepals of *Paris* are green, and the petals are narrow and yellow. The stamens are six or more, and the connective is much produced beyond the loculi, a rare feature in Monocotyledons. It shows the comparatively slight modification these stamens have undergone from the original leaves from which stamens have been derived. The fruit is a black berry, at length bursting irregularly. "Herb Paris" extends through Europe to Siberia and south as far as the Caucasus.

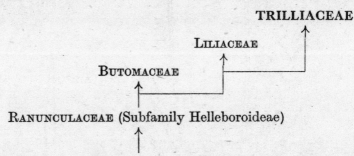

And now we must pause quite a while over the interesting and beautiful family **Liliaceae**. It is the third largest family of Monocotyledons and contains many very lovely garden and a number of economic plants. *Poker plants, Hyacinths, Tulips, Aloes,* and of course *Lilies,* belong to LILIACEAE.

I have treated *Ruscus* as a separate family (see p. 260) and have, as stated on p. 44, transferred *Allium* to the AMARYLLIDACEAE, whilst *Paris* ("Herb Paris") appears in *Trilliaceae* (p. 253). This reduces the number of genera indigenous in Britain to sixteen. Even from these we may gain some idea of the general evolutionary tendencies within the family.

In my larger classification the family is divided into two main series, (1) a generally more primitive group with the *rootstock a rhizome,* with fibrous or tuberous roots, and (2) a more advanced group with the rootstock a *bulb* or *corm.*

TRILLIACEAE TO TYPHACEAE

The families shown on this page should be compared with those on the previous coloured plate. The basic group, it may be noted, is more highly evolved than that at the bottom of the other picture. There the sepals and petals are quite separate. Here the sepals and petals have become merged into a single whorl, as in *Fritillaria*, shown on the left hand side. I have called the whole group or subphylum the *Corolliferae*. *Fritillaria* represents the great family LILIACEAE, from the stock of which several other families are traceable. In this connection, the humble and long-suffering *Aspidistra* behind urban window panes provides an important link, and especially certain genera closely related to it. These point to the evolution of the *Arum* family, ARACEAE (*Arum* shown in flower and fruit), in which the flowers are greatly reduced and arranged on a spadix within a spathe. The Butcher's Broom (shown on the right) is also a near relation of the Liliaceae and represents the RUSCACEAE (see general text), in which the real leaves are reduced to scales and the branchlets have become leaf-like and bear the flowers in the middle. *Tamus*, the Black Bryony (top left), represents the Yam family, DIOSCORE-ACEAE, with twining stems, and is abundant in the tropics. A very high stage of evolution is represented in the SPARGANIACEAE (*Sparganium*) shown at the top, with the unisexual flowers arranged in a panicle, and even still higher, perhaps, by the TYPHACEAE, with them arranged in a dense spike, the males at the top, the females below.

The plants illustrated in the coloured plate are : Bottom, left, Fritillaria meleagris *Linn.*; right, Paris quadrifolia *Linn.* Middle, red fruits and spathe and spadix of Arum maculatum *Linn.*; right, Ruscus aculeatus *Linn.* Top, left, Tamus communis Linn.; middle, Sparganium ramosum *Huds.*; right, Typha latifolia *Linn.*

To face p. 254.

In the first group *Narthecium*, *Simethis* and *Tofieldia* come very early and represent the tribe *Narthecieae*, an ancient group with a wide discontinuous distribution. In these the styles are sometimes free or nearly so and the

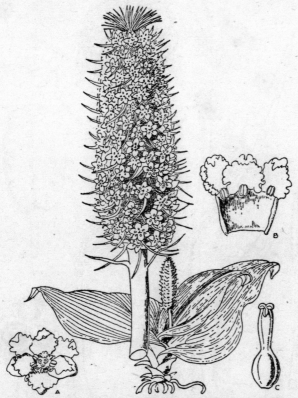

Fig. 133.—*Gonioscypha eucomioides* Baker, an advanced exotic genus of *Liliaceae*, tribe *Aspidistreae*, already shows an Aroid type of inflorescence; compare with the figure of *Lysichitum* (Araceae, p. 263). (From Hutchinson, *Families of Flowering Plants*).

anthers face outwards. The free styles seem to indicate a primitive type and the fruit is a capsule. These genera occur in bogs.

The tribe *Convallarieae* comes next and there is only one genus in Britain, *Convallaria*, the well-known " Lily of the

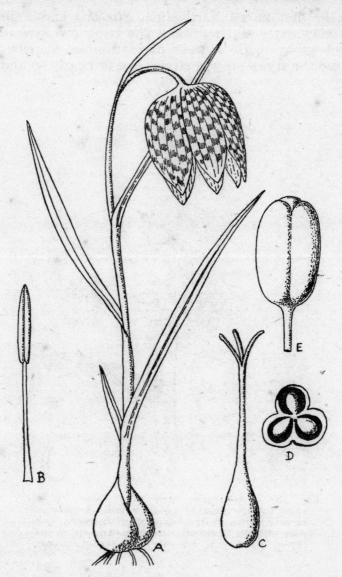

FIG. 134.—A lovely native species of *Liliaceae*, *Fritillaria meleagris* Linn.

A, whole plant. B, stamen. C, pistil. D, cross-section of ovary. E, fruit.

Valley ". The styles of this are united and the fruit is a berry.

In the genus *Polygonatum* (tribe *Polygonateae*) the stems are leafy and the flowers are axillary, and the fruit is again a berry. The familiar "Solomon's Seal" is *Polygonatum multiflorum* Moench. *Maianthemum bifolium* Schmidt also belongs to this tribe; it has a terminal raceme and the leaves are cordate, and the fruit is also a berry (*Smilacina bifolia* of some Floras).

A climax, rather isolated type is reached in *Asparagus*,

Fig. 135.—*Polygonatum officinale* All.
(Liliaceae).

A, perianth laid open. B, stamen. C, pistil.
D, cross-section of ovary. E, fruit. F, venation of leaf. G, rhizome (From Hutchinson,
Families of Flowering Plants.)

forming a tribe of its own, with clusters of fine short cladodes like subulate leaves borne in the axils of short membranous scales (the true leaves). The fruit is also a berry.

We have now to consider the *bulbous series*. Of the tribe *Tulipeae*, three genera are represented, *Fritillaria*, *Tulipa*, and *Gagea*, whilst *Lilium*, which belongs to the same tribe, is naturalised. *Lilium* differs from the others in having versatile anthers.

Tribe *Scilleae* embraces *Scilla* (" Squill "), *Muscari* (" Grape Hyacinth "), and *Ornithogalum* (" Star of Bethlehem ").

The single genus and species of the last tribe (*Colchiceae*) represented in Britain is *Colchicum autumnale* Linn. It is of very great interest because of its pollination and retarded development of the fruit. As the specific name

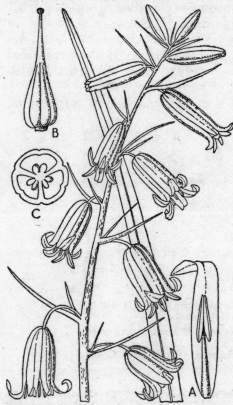

indicates, it flowers in the autumn, and the stigmas are usually mature before the stamens, but remain receptive until the latter are ripe.[1] If insects visit the flowers early, cross-pollination is ensured. Later, however, self-pollination is also possible, though rendered more difficult by the anthers turning their faces outwards whilst the stigmas increase in length. The nectar is concealed in furrows at the bottom of the free part of the filaments.

The most interesting point, however, is the fact that, whilst pollination takes place in the autumn, it is not until the following May that the embryo begins to form. Later the fruit develops with

Fig. 136.—There is no need in this book to sing the praises of the English Bluebell, *Scilla nonscripta* (L.) Hoffmgg. (Liliaceae).

A, perianth-segment and stamen. B, pistil. C, cross-section of ovary.

the leaves and is ripe in June or July.

The origin of *Liliaceae*, which itself has been a basal stock for much further evolution in the past, is shown in the diagram at the end of the book, and the characters of the tribes and genera are contrasted more clearly in the key below.

[1] See Knuth, *Handbook of Flower Pollination*, 3 : 471, Engl. ed., 1909.

LILIACEAE

↑

BUTOMACEAE

↑

RANUNCULACEAE (Subfamily Helleboroideae)

Key to the British genera of Liliaceae.

Rootstock a rhizome; roots fibrous or tuberous; perennials or rarely
 annuals :
Leaves well developed :
 Leaves radical :
  Anther-loculi facing outwards; fruit a capsule .Tribe *Narthecieae*
  Styles free; filaments glabrous . . . . . TOFIELDIA
  Styles partially or wholly united; filaments woolly :
   Flowers in a spike-like raceme . . . . . NARTHECIUM
   Flowers in a panicle . . . . SIMETHIS
  Anther-loculi facing inwards or lateral; flowers racemose; fruit a
   globular red berry . . . . . Tribe *Convallarieae*
  One genus . . . . CONVALLARIA
 Leaves cauline . . . . Tribe *Polygonatae*
  Flowers axillary; leaves numerous, not cordate . POLYGONATUM
  Flowers in a terminal panicle; leaves ovate, cordate at the base
                MAIANTHEMUM
Leaves reduced to scales, the branchlets cladodiform and green, like
 small acicular leaves; flowers very small; fruit a berry
                ASPARAGUS

Rootstock a bulb or corm; perennials :
Scape with one or more leaves . . . . . Tribe *Tulipeae*
 Fruits opening into the loculi; anthers basifixed :
  Perianth-segments with a nectariferous pits above the base
               FRITILLARIA
  Perianth-segments not pitted :
   Flowers large and solitary, the segments more or less connivent
             TULIPA
   Flowers small, 1–2 together with small spreading perianth-
    segments . . . . LLOYDIA
   Flowers small, more or less racemose or subumbellate . GAGEA
 Fruits opening by the walls of the loculi; anthers versatile LILIUM
Scape or flowering stem leafless or leafy only at the base :
 Flowers several to numerous, small . . . . Tribe *Scilleae*
  Perianth-segments free to the base or nearly so :
   Filaments not flattened; flowers blue or pink . . SCILLA
   Filaments flattened; flowers white or greenish . ORNITHOGALUM
  Perianth-segments more or less united in the lower part . MUSCARI
 Flowers solitary or paired, large, close to the ground; leaves and
  fruits produced during the second year . . . Tribe *Colchiceae*
 One genus . . . . COLCHICUM

The tendency at the present day is to regard many homogeneous outstanding groups as distinct families, and even my own classification may sometimes not go far enough in this direction to suit some botanists, especially younger botanists who are not troubled with tradition. **Ruscaceae** is a good example of such a group. Its geographical range is shown in the accompanying map, and it will be seen to occur only in a very restricted part of the

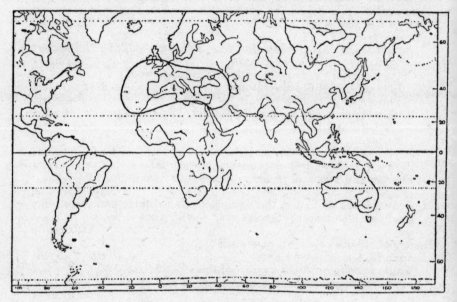

FIG. 137.—Range of Ruscaceae.

world, namely Western Europe and the Mediterranean region, from the Azores, Madeira, and the Canary Islands eastwards to the Caspian Sea.

Whilst no doubt a direct derivative from the Liliaceous stock, it differs from *Liliaceae* by its androecium of united stamens, besides its highly specialised morphology. The latter is very remarkable, the real leaves being reduced to small scarious scales which bear in their axils leaf-like modified branchlets (cladodes), the latter sometimes quite pungent at the tips and bearing on either surface or on their margins the small flowers. One genus is exceptional

as to the position of the flowers, which proclaims it to be
the most primitive in this respect. This is *Danae*, found
in the eastern part of the family's distribution, and which
has the flowers in terminal racemes free from the cladodes.

Ruscus is perhaps the most highly evolved, with dioecious flowers borne on the face of the cladodes. In this
genus the stamens are reduced to three, there being six in
the other two genera (*Danae* and *Semele*). The British
species, the " Butcher's Broom ", *R. aculeatus* Linn., is
the most widely spread of the family. The fruit is a
bright red berry.

Dioscoreaceae is a small family almost confined to the
tropics and warm temperate regions. In Britain there is
only one species, *Tamus communis* Linn., the " Black
Bryony ". It differs from the other genera in its fruits,
which are *baccate*. All the remainder have capsules, and
either they or the seeds are often winged, so the distribution is effected by mechanical means, either by the
wind or by birds eating the fruits. There is a small
isolated genus, *Borderea*, in the central Pyrenees, in which
the seeds are not winged.

The " Black Bryony " is not found in Scotland and is
rare in Eire, but very common in hedges and open
woods, etc., in England, and it is very widely spread as far
east as the Caucasus. The flowers are unisexual, the
males in axillary racemes, the females similarly disposed
but shorter and fewer flowered. The ovary is inferior
and three-locular. The berries are scarlet and very
attractive. The " White Bryony ", *Bryonia dioica* Jacq.,
is, of course, a very different plant, and belongs to *Cucurbitaceae*.

The *Dioscoreaceae* include the Yams, a valuable food in
warm countries, and a remarkable genus is *Testudinaria*,
the " Elephant's Foot ", found in the dry regions of
South-eastern Africa, with massive woody rootstocks.

Our next family, **Araceae**, the Arum family, has been
the subject of some discussion. Lotsy, a German
botanist, considered Monocotyledons to have had a
diphyletic origin, and he believed the Aroids, Palms, etc.,
to have been derived from the Peppers, and the remainder

from the *Ranales*.   I consider this to be highly improbable, because I have searched for proof amongst the plants themselves and found none to support it.   We should remember also that even Linnaeus in one of his classifications associated the Aroids and Peppers in one group.

The Aroids are clearly connected with the *Liliaceae* through the tribe *Aspidistreae*, which, of course, includes *Aspidistra*, beloved of Bayswater landladies.   In that tribe some exotic genera, such as *Gonioscypha*, have densely spicate inflorescences rather like those of certain Aroids.   A picture of this is included to show these points (see Fig. 133).

The most primitive Aroids have *no spathe*, the large bract, which encircles and protects the inflorescence, or spadix, for the spathe is only *a modified foliage-leaf* whose stalk has become concrescent with the peduncle.

The tribe *Acoreae* seems to be the most ancient of the Aroids, and there is one genus belonging to it in Britain, *Acorus calamus* Linn., the " Sweet Flag ".   In this tribe the leaf subtending the inflorescence is not modified into a spathe.   A genus often seen in gardens shows a stage a little farther advanced.   This is *Lysichitum*.   In this the modified leaf is coloured and its petiole embraces the peduncle of the spadix very loosely.   The origin of the spathe may thus be studied in this country from living specimens.   In addition the flowers of these two genera are all bisexual, the axis of the inflorescence bears flowers right to the top, and there is a perianth in each flower. More advanced Aroids have the upper part of the spadix barren, the flowers unisexual, and no perianth.

The second British genus and species belongs to the most advanced tribe, the *Areae*.   This is *Arum maculatum* Linn., the " Cuckoo Pint " or " Lords and Ladies ".   In this the flowers have become unisexual and the terminal part of the axis has become barren;   there is no perianth; the female flowers are borne at the base of the spadix, and the males above them.   The fruit is an attractive red berry.   *Arum* is nearly at the top of the Aroid family tree, but not quite.   Naturalised in one or two lakes in the south of England is the genus *Calla* (*C. palustris* L.).   The

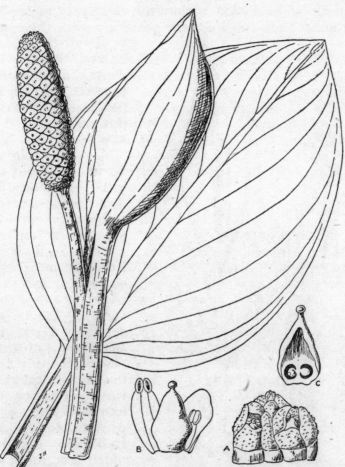

FIG. 138.—*Lysichitum camtschaticum* Schott (Araceae), one of
   the most primitive genera of the family ; grows in Eastern
   Asia ; the flowers are bisexual, and the spathe is little
   modified from an ordinary foliage leaf, its stalk only
   loosely encircling the peduncle ; to be compared with
   Gonioscypha (fig. 133), in the *Liliaceae*.

   A, portion of spadix, showing the hermaphrodite flowers.
B, pistil, stamens and segments.   C, vertical section of ovary.
(From Hutchinson, *Families of Flowering Plants*).

spathe is accrescent and persistent, and the spadix is
long-stipitate and much shorter than the spathe. All
the flowers are hermaphrodite and without a perianth.

The peak of evolution within the family is reached in *Ambrosina*, from the Mediterranean, in which the spathe is divided into two halves, the one half containing a solitary female flower, the other a spadix of male flowers arranged in two rows.

A remarkable and very huge Aroid seen in larger Botanic gardens is *Amorphophallus titanum* Becc., a native of Sumatra.

The small family **Lemnaceae** is represented in Britain by both of the two known genera, *Lemna* and *Wolffia*. *Lemna* is a small genus of widely distributed tiny floating plants without distinct stems or real leaves. The small plant-bodies are frond-like and provided with roots, and occur either singly or two or three cohere by their edges. The minute flowers are borne on the margins of the plant-body, the male consisting of a

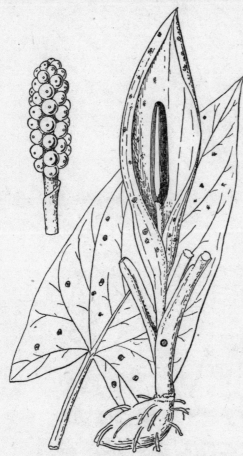

FIG. 139.—*Arum maculatum* L. is an advanced member of the family *Araceae*; there is no perianth, the flowers are unisexual, the females below, the males above, and the terminal part of the spadix is barren and serves to attract insects.

bract enclosing one to two stamens with two-locular anthers, and the female a single one-locular ovary with one or more ovules; the style is short.

There are four or five species in Britain, and they grow

on fresh-water ponds and still waters. One of the commonest species is *Lemna polyrhiza* Linn., with

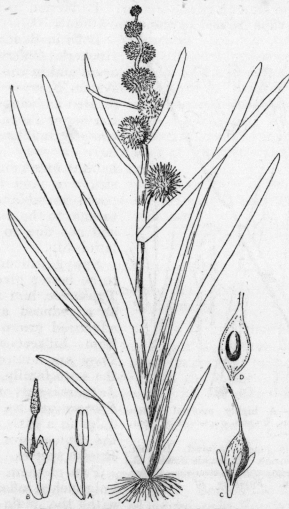

Fig. 140.—*Sparganium simplex* Huds.
(Sparganiaceae).
A, male perianth-segment and stamen.   B, female
flower. C, fruit. D, vertical section of fruit. (From
Hutchinson, *Families of Flowering* Plants).

numerous roots from each plant. The other British species have only one root.

s

even a *corona*, which is so common a feature in the more orthodox *Amaryllidaceae*.

As here delimited, therefore, *Amaryllidaceae* may have either a *superior or inferior ovary*. Except for *Agapantheae* the rootstock is a *corm* or *bulb*, which mark a climax habit with regard to the root and storage system.

I believe I may claim that this new conception of *Amaryllidaceae* has not been unfavourably received by some botanists and horticulturists." [1]

The genus *Allium* is represented in Britain by ten or eleven species, and is of great economic importance, providing us with the Leek (*A. ampeloprasum* Linn.) and the Onion (*A. cepa* Linn.). They are strong-smelling bulbous herbs, with an umbellate inflorescence subtended by one to two membranous bracts (spathes) as in typical *Amaryllidaceae*, but the ovary is superior.

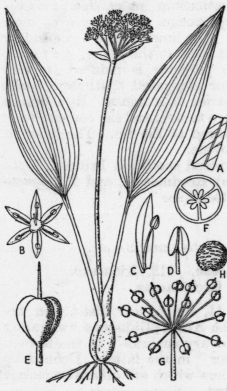

FIG. 142.—Not all botanists agree with the author's classification of the Alliums in the *Amaryllidaceae* instead of *Liliaceae*. This is *Allium ursinum* L., often to be found in abundance in woods and shady places.

A, part of lower surface of leaf. B, flower. C, perianth-segment and stamen. D, anther. E, pistil. F, cross-section of ovary. G, fruit. H, seed.

The " Snowdrop ", *Galanthus nivalis* Linn., a much loved little plant, is a herald of the spring and the forerunner of longer and warmer days. The inflorescence is

[1] It has been adopted by the Amaryllis Society of America.

AMARYLLIDACEAE TO ORCHIDACEAE

It would be futile even to guess how long a period elapsed from the dawn of the evolution of the AMARYLLIDACEAE to that of the ORCHIDACEAE. That AMARYLLIDACEAE are derived from the same stock as the LILIACEAE seems clear enough, and in the process have retained six stamens, but the ovary has become *inferior*, and the inflorescence reduced to an *umbel* subtended by a bract or bracts and sometimes even to a single flower as in the examples shown in the design (left, *Galanthus*, right, *Narcissus*). The next family, IRIDACEAE, has developed in a different way, economising in the number of stamens (3), and eventually some of its groups, such as *Gladiolus*, have evolved a *zygomorphic* flower (only *Iris* is shown). Intermediate stages to the most climax family of all in this line of development, i.e. ORCHIDACEAE, are found in the exotic APOSTASI-ACEAE, with three or two stamens, and with increasing zygomorphy of the flower. *Cypripedium* (top left) has still two stamens with normal powdery pollen, whilst the remainder of the British genera have only one stamen, some with waxy pollen (*Ophrys* is shown, top right).

The plants illustrated in the coloured plate are : Bottom, left, Galanthus nivalis *Linn.*; right, Narcissus pseudo-narcissus *Linn.* Middle, Iris pseudacorus *Linn.* Top, left, Cypripedium calceolus *Linn.*; right, Ophrys apifera *Huds.*

To face p. 268.

reduced to one flower and there is no corona. This plant is doubtfully native and is frequently naturalised.

Leucojum, the "Snowflake", is represented by two species, *L. aestivum* Linn., and *L. vernum* Linn., both of which are also doubtfully native.

Narcissus pseudo-narcissus Linn., the "Daffodil", is native. In this, of course, the flower is solitary (due to reduction), and there is a very well-developed corona.

The following diagram and key to genera will emphasise these points.

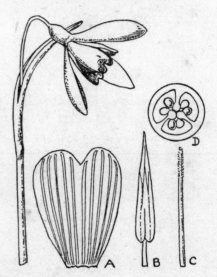

FIG. 143.—The common Snowdrop, *Galanthus nivalis* Linn., has a long phylogenetic history. Its bulbous root-system, inferior ovary, inflorescence reduced to a single flower, and anthers opening by a short terminal slit place it high in its family, *Amaryllidaceae*.

A, inner perianth-segment. B, stamen. C, style. D, cross-section of ovary.

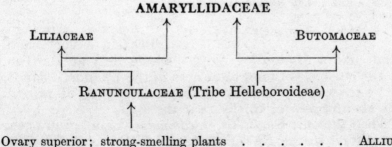

Ovary superior; strong-smelling plants . . . . . . ALLIUM
Ovary inferior :
 No corona :
  Outer perianth-segments larger than the inner . . GALANTHUS
  Perianth-segments equal . . . . LEUCOJUM
 Corona present . . . . NARCISSUS

Iridaceae is one of the most natural and homogeneous families. It is undoubtedly a climax group and occupies the end of a branch of our phylogenetic tree. The ovary is *inferior*,[1] and the stamens are reduced to *three*.

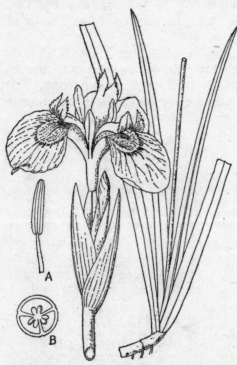

The flowers of the more primitive groups are actinomorphic (regular), but in some tribes, such as *Gladioleae* and *Antholyzeae*, mainly South African, the perianth becomes increasingly zygomorphic (irregular).

The distribution of some of the few British species is very interesting. *Sisyrinchium angustifolium* Mill. is very common in North America, and it occurs near Kerry and Galway in Ireland, where it is probably native.

FIG. 144.—*Iris pseudacorus* L. (Iridaceae), one of the most handsome of our wild flowers and widely distributed in Europe and Russian Asia.

A, stamen. B, cross-section of ovary.

Romulea parviflora Britten, a very small plant like a diminutive *Crocus*, occurs only at Dawlish, in Devon. It is found elsewhere in the Channel Islands, along the western coasts of Europe, and nearly all around the Mediterranean, chiefly near the sea.

Then the only *Gladiolus*, *G. communis* Linn., grows near Lyndhurst in the New Forest, and in the Isle of Wight. This, however, may have been introduced from Central and Southern Europe, where it is common.

[1] Except for one Tasmanian genus, *Isophysis*, included by me in the family.

Here is a key to the genera of *Iridaceae* :—

Perianth actinomorphic (regular), not oblique; flowers solitary or
  few :
  Perianth-segments equal or nearly so, horizontal :
    Rootstock a rhizome . . . . SISYRINCHIUM
    Rootstock a bulb :
      Perianth-tube very short. . . . . ROMULEA
      Perianth-tube very long . . . . CROCUS *
  Perianth-segments unequal, the inner narrower; stigmas petaloid,
    arching over the stamens . . . . IRIS
Perianth oblique, subzygomorphic; flowers in a secund spike
                                                  GLADIOLUS

It should be noted that the first-placed genus, *Sisy-rinchium*, has the most primitive type of rootstock, a rhizome, and the flowers resemble those of many *Liliaceae* —for example, *Lloydia*. But the ovary is inferior, of course, and the stamens *three*. The latter are *united*, which is a very advanced character. *Sisyrinchium angustifolium* occurs in Western Eire and is common throughout North America. Although formerly suspected to be introduced, Praeger regards it as native.[1] The remainder of the British genera have a bulbous or cormous rootstock, which is also an advanced character. *Romulea*, again, is very like *Liliaceae*, but with an inferior ovary, whilst in *Crocus* the perianth has a very long tube, and the ovary is below the soil. *Iris* and *Gladiolus* top the tree of the few genera found in Britain.

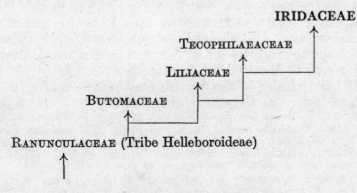

IRIDACEAE

TECOPHILAEACEAE

LILIACEAE

BUTOMACEAE

RANUNCULACEAE (Tribe Helleboroideae)

[1] Praeger, *The Botanist in Ireland* 159.

Iridaceae provide us with some of our most beautiful garden plants, many with delicately marked flowers (*Tigridia*, etc.).

We have now to deal with a very wonderful group of plants, the **Orchidaceae**. In most systems this family embraced also the *Apostasiaceae*, but these are not orchids in the true sense, although they may indicate the origin of the larger group.

In my *Families of Flowering Plants* I included the *Apostasiaceae* in the *Haemodorales*, showing that they were closely related to the *Hypoxidaceae*, especially the genus *Curculigo*. In *Apostasiaceae* the flowers are actinomorphic and there are either three or two perfect stamens, in the latter case the dorsal stamen having become modified into a linear staminode partly adnate to the style. This condition is found in the genus *Apostasia* (India to tropical Australia). In *Adactylus* (Indo-Malaya), the dorsal stamen is entirely suppressed, thus leaving only two fertile stamens as in the more primitive subfamily of the orchids, the *Diandreae*.

Orchidaceae are divided into two subfamilies, the *Diandreae*, with two stamens, and the *Monandreae*, with one stamen. Only one genus, *Cypripedium*, of the first subfamily, is found in Britain, the well-known " Lady's Slipper ", *Cypripedium calceolus* Linn., although it is now considered to be extinct or nearly so. Formerly it grew wild only in Durham, Yorkshire, and Westmorland. The species has a wide distribution, right from this north of England region as far south as the Pyrenees and Sicily, Caucasus and Himalayas, and eastward to Saghalien. There are several species in North America, from Hudson Bay south to Mexico, and in eastern Asia.

The remainder of the British *Orchidaceae* belong to the *Monandreae*, i.e., they have only one stamen. If we com-

---

Fig. 145.—*Neuwiedia lindleyi* Rolfe (Apostasiaceae); included here to show the gradual evolution of the *Orchidaceae*; this small exotic family was formerly included in *Orchidaceae*, of which it seems to be a primitive type, having retained three stamens, as shown on next page.

A, flower. B, outer perianth-segment. C, stamens and style. D, stigmas. E, cross-section of ovary.—After Bot. Mag. (From Hutchinson, *Families of Flowering Plants*).

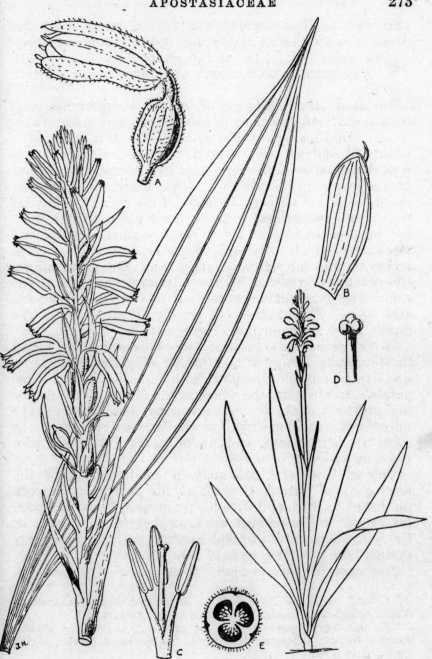

pare the floral structure of a typical member of the *Monandreae* with that of a typical flower of another Monocotyledonous family, let us say *Amaryllidaceae*, we shall find very great modifications and reduction of certain parts.

In most *Amaryllidaceae* there are six perianth segments, six fertile stamens in two whorls, and three ovaryloculi. In *Monandreae*, however, the flower is much more advanced and greatly reduced. There are three sepals (one dorsal, abaxial in origin, and two lateral), two lateral petals, and a lip (labellum), which is sometimes variously lobed, only one anther, the abaxial member of the outer whorl, and two lateral stigmas, the original third stigma having been transformed into the rostellum, a wonderful mechanism which by lying between the anther and stigmas serves to prevent self-pollination, and also often affixes the pollinia to visiting insects. In addition there is the column or gynostegium composed of the fused filaments and style. This make-up of the floral parts causes the flower to be zygomorphic (" irregular ").

A very primitive type of orchidaceous perianth is found in the genus *Thelymitra*, a native of Australia. It is quite actinomorphic (regular) with three sepals and three petals. In studying the whole of the Monocotyledons for my previous book, I was very much impressed by the number of " missing links " in the Monocotyledons of the southern hemisphere, and undoubtedly *Thelymitra* provides us with one of these.

Colonel Godfery [1] has made a careful study of the phylogeny of British Orchids in his monumental work published in 1933, and with his permission I have adapted his views [2] to the present work, as they coincide more or less with the general principles on which the evolutionary system here put forward is based.

Amongst British genera, then, after *Cypripedium*,

[1] Colonel M. J. Godfery, F.L.S., *Monograph and Iconograph of Native British Orchidaceae*, 1933. This author died in 1945.

[2] In this, as acknowledged in the preface, I have been greatly assisted by my colleague, Mr. V. S. Summerhayes, B.Sc., orchid specialist at Kew.

which, as already explained, takes first place on account of its two stamens and the pollen not particularly differentiated from the ordinary kind, *Cephalanthera* is probably the next most ancient and primitive genus. Godfery says of it, "It is the least differentiated from the monocotyledonous type of flower, for the anther is suspended from a filament, the pollen-grains do not cohere in tetrads, and there is no rostellum, in which points it differs from all other genera of the subfamily [suborder]." [1] Like *Cypripedium* it has a rhizome with numerous roots, which is presumably a primitive feature, and its antiquity is supported by the wide distribution of the genus, from Britain to the Himalayas and in North America. There are three species of *Cephalanthera* in Britain.

Epipactis follows next in order, differing from *Cephalanthera* in having a rostellum. This genus is even more widely spread, and there are six species in Britain.

In *Listera*, the "Twayblade", there are only two leaves, which are nearly opposite. *Listera ovata* (Linn.) R.Br. is the larger and commoner of the two species, with green flowers, and grows frequently in dense shade in woods and hedges. It ranges from Ireland to Siberia and the Caucasus Mountains and North West Himalaya. The lesser "Twayblade" is *Listera cordata* (Linn.) R.Br., with green flowers suffused with red. This grows in "mountain" woods (usually Pine woods) and under heather on moors. It ranges even farther afield than *L. ovata*, being also found in North America.

Neottia, the "Birds Nest Orchid", is a saprophytic plant without leaves and destitute of chlorophyll and resembling an *Orobanche*. It grows in deep shade, usually under beech trees. The stem is enclosed by the sheathing scale-like leaf-bases. "It shares with *Listera* an outstanding peculiarity—the development of the rostellum into a sensitive organ, ejecting two drops of viscid fluid on being touched" (Godfery). The single European species, *N. nidus-avis* (Linn.) Rich., extends eastward to Korea and Japan.

[1] Rarely the rostellum may be absent in other genera, as for instance in some species of *Epipactis*.

Goodyera, which belongs to a large group of orchids specially well represented in tropical Asia, is intermediate in some respects between *Epipactis* and *Spiranthes*. There is only one European species, *G. repens* (Linn.) R.Br., which is found in mossy pine woods of northern Britain, whence it ranges right across the north temperate zone to North America. It bears a superficial resemblance to the next genus *Spiranthes*, but is easily recognised even by its root system. In *Goodyera* there is a creeping rhizome with white slender runners, whilst in *Spiranthes* the roots are tuberous and carrot-like. In Britain *Spiranthes* frequents a different habitat from *Goodyera*, *S. spiralis* (L.) Koch. usually being found on chalk or limestone.

The distribution of *S. romanzoffiana* Chamisso [1] is of very great interest. It is found only in Ireland and in North America from the Atlantic to the Pacific and from Unalaska south to California.

The Monandrous genera we have considered so far belong to the tribe *Neottineae* of the *Acrotonae*.

We have now to deal with another tribe, the *Malaxidineae*. All of them have waxy pollinia and there are many exotic epiphytic genera. Only five are found in Europe and three are represented in Britain, namely *Hammarbya* (*Malaxis* of many British authors), *Liparis* and *Corallorhiza*. *Hammarbya* is a very small marsh plant with two small concave leaves, and the flowers are small and green, with the labellum pointing upwards. *Corallorhiza* is a leafless saprophyte with a coral-like rhizome and no roots, whilst *Liparis* is a small marsh plant, the stem with a bulb-like swelling at the base, and the flowers are green with slender sepals and petals and broader knee-like lip.

---

[1] There has been difference of opinion as to the identity of the Irish plant with the American. Colonel Godfery accepts it, following the opinions of Fernald and Oakes Ames, the former a noted critical botanist, the latter a well-known orchidologist. On the other hand, Wilmott, of the Natural History Museum, London, considered there were two species in Ireland, a northern one which he identified with the American *S. stricta* Rydberg, and a southern for which he retained the name *S. gemmifera* Smith. American botanists say that similar forms are found in North America.

All the genera mentioned so far are characterised by the absence of caudicles (stalks) at the base of the pollinia. The remainder of the British genera have the pollinia attached to viscid glands by caudicles.[1] Of these *Epipogium* has many points of resemblance with *Corallorhiza* and is possibly descended from the same stock. The flowers are showy, with a large inverted spur. The only British species, *E. aphyllum* (L.) Swartz, ranges from Europe to Siberia.

The other British genera all belong to the *Basitonae* and may be considered as representing a quite different line of evolution. The small honey-scented *Herminium* has slightly distant viscidia, which are specialised to fit on the joint of the leg of very small insects, one pollinium being removed at a time. There is only one species in Britain, *H. monorchis* R.Br., the Musk Orchid, and it is confined to eastern and southern England, but has a wide range eastward to Mongolia and Japan. *Coeloglossum* has more distant viscidia, with a ridge down the lip, compelling insects to enter on one side and remove one pollinium at a time. *C. viride* (L.) Hartman, (*Habenaria viridis* R.Br.), called the Frog Orchid because the side-view of the flower is sometimes faintly suggestive of a frog, has a wide range in Britain and in northern Eurasia generally.

From *Coeloglossum* we are led on to *Platanthera*, of which the British species are specialised for *Lepidoptera* by their long spurs with free honey at the apex, and lateral viscidia, which adhere to the sides of the insect's head. The white flowers and strong sweet scent emitted at night suggest that the larger moths are the insects responsible. The genus is represented by numerous species in North America and Eastern Asia.

In *Gymnadenia* and *Leucorchis* the stigmas are lateral and the viscidia central and linear for attachment to the proboscis of the visiting insect. These are *Lepidoptera* in the long-spurred *Gymnadenia conopsea* R. Br. (*Habenaria conopsea* L.) and in *Leucorchis*. *Gymnadenia* is widely

---

[1] These have no doubt been formed by sterilisation of part of the pollinia.

spread in Europe and Northern Asia, while *Leucorchis* is also found in Greenland and Iceland. In *Anacamptis* we have a genus with an extraordinary superficial resemblance to *Gymnadenia*, but with a single sticky disk and two remarkable vertical plates (lamellae) which probably serve to guide the insect to the centre of the flower and so make contact with the single disk, which wraps itself around the proboscis. This monotypic genus extends eastwards to the Caucasus and Persia and into North Africa.

Leucorchis leads on to *Neotinea*, a connecting link with *Orchis*. *Neotinea* in many respects resembles the former but has the sticky disk enclosed in a pouch as in *Orchis*. It is interesting as only occurring in South Eire outside the Mediterranean and Atlantic Islands.

Orchis is the largest European genus, and provides the family name. It is distributed throughout Europe, North Africa, and Central and Northern Asia. Although it shows considerable variations in gross flower structure, all the species have the common character of the two separate sticky disks being borne in a protective pouch. In *Orchis* no free nectar is secreted and the spur is dry, but there is a store of potable liquid in the walls, the inner skin of which is easily pierced. This acts as a powerful attraction to insects.

Aceras may be looked upon as an *Orchis* of the subsection *Militares*, but minus a spur, and it also shows marked resemblances to *Himantoglossum*, which, however, has a single sticky disk. *Aceras* is monotypic and is found in Central Europe and the Mediterranean region, whilst the British species of *Himantoglossum* is a Western European plant, but there are other closely allied species in South-East Europe and the Middle East.

In *Ophrys* evolution may be considered to have reached its peak, for in many of the species the lip resembles closely the females of various *Hymenoptera*. As a result of this and the complete absence of nectar, insect visitors are almost restricted to the males of the corresponding species. In *O. apifera*, the common bee-orchid, this restriction seems to have been so effective that the plant depends almost entirely on self-pollination. This is achieved by the pollinia dangling forwards so as to be brought in contact with the stigma below by any slight breeze. *Ophrys* embraces over thirty species which are characteristic of the Mediterranean, particularly the eastern parts.

Key to the British genera of *Orchidaceae*.[1] (In Bentham and Hooker's *British Flora* a wider conception was taken of some genera; *Himantoglossum* and *Anacamptis* were included in *Orchis*; *Platanthera*, *Gymnadenia*, *Neotinea*, *Leucorchis*, in *Habenaria*; by modern specialists the last mentioned is restricted to tropical species with more or less stalked stigmas.)

Stamens 2, separate (lateral members of the inner whorl), the third transformed into a large staminode more or less covering the anthers and style; stigmatic lobes 3, similar, all receptive .   CYPRIPEDIUM

Stamen 1 (median member of outer whorl), the others all reduced or represented by very small staminodes; lateral two lobes of the stigma receptive, the middle one transformed into a small rostellum placed in front of the anther-loculi and continued to form the sticky disk (viscidium) of the pollen masses (pollinia) :

Caudicles and sticky disks (viscidia) at the apex of the pollinia (*Acrotonae*); anther usually incumbent, rarely erect, attached by a usually narrow very short filament, usually caducous, rarely persistent :

Pollen masses granular, not well defined :

Anther incumbent :

Roots simple, fasciculate on a very short rhizome :

Labellum hollowed out in the lower half, semi-globose or spurred :

Flowers sessile or nearly so; fruits erect; column slender, with a small stigma; back of column higher than the rostellum
CEPHALANTHERA

Flowers stalked; fruits pendulous; column short, with a large stigma, shorter than the rostellum . . . .   EPIPACTIS

Labellum flat or nearly so :

Stem 2-leaved in the middle; column short . . . LISTERA

Stem leafless, pale; column medium-sized . . . NEOTTIA

Roots absent from the rhizome, the latter branched in a coral-like manner, fleshy; plants saprophytic, without chlorophyll
EPIPOGIUM

Anther erect or nearly so :

Roots fasciculate on a very short rhizome, fleshy; flowers in a more or less obvious spiral . . . . . .   SPIRANTHES

---

[1] Adapted from Schlechter's key in his " Monographie und Iconographie der Orchideen Europas und des Mittelmeergebietes " in *Fedde Repertorium*, Sonderbeih., A. **1**: 73–76 (1925).

Rhizome elongated, creeping; roots solitary at the nodes; flowers
not obviously spirally arranged . . . . . .   GOODYERA
Pollen masses waxy, well-defined (not granular) :
Stem thickened at the base into a fleshy pseudobulb, 1–2-leaved,
with simple flexuous more or less puberulous roots :
Flowers not resupinate, the lip above, rather concave; anther
persistent . . . .   HAMMARBYA
Flowers resupinate, the lip below, curved like a knee   .   LIPARIS
Stem simple, leafless, without a pseudobulb at the base; rhizome
much-branched, fleshy, without roots; saprophytic plants with-
out chlorophyll; flowers small . . . . .   CORALLORHIZA
Caudicles and sticky disks (viscidia) arising at the base of the pollinia
(*Basitonae*); anther erect or rarely slightly resupinate, closely
adnate at its base to the column, not deciduous after flowering;
pollinia always granular :
Stigmatic lobes forming 2 sessile knobs; lip 3-lobed; spur very
short; petals distinctly tapered to the apex . . .   HERMINIUM
Stigmatic lobes flat, borne in a concave stigmatic cavity :
Sticky disks of the pollinia naked (no pouch) :
Sticky disks nearly contiguous above the middle of the stigmatic
cavity, more or less surrounded by the stigmas :
Rostellum produced at the base into 2 distinct slightly divergent
somewhat vertical plates (lamellae) . . .   GYMNADENIA
Rostellum not produced at the base into a plate   .   LEUCORCHIS
Sticky disks divergent and situated above the side of the stigmatic
cavity; anther-loculi more or less divergent at the base :
Labellum 3-toothed at the apex, with 2 nectar-bearing pits at
the base; spur very short; rostellum with slightly incurved
margins . . . .   COELOGLOSSUM
Labellum tongue-like and entire, without a nectar-bearing pit;
spur long and slender, with an open mouth; rostellum with
flat margins . . . .   PLATANTHERA
Sticky disks of the pollinia immersed in a simple or bipartite pouch
(bursicule) :
Labellum distinctly spurred :
Pollinia attached to a single sticky disk :
Labellum without vertical plates (lamellae) at the base, the
middle lobe much larger than the lateral, usually several times
longer; petals hidden in the concave dorsal sepal, narrow,
adnate at the base to the sides of the anther
HIMANTOGLOSSUM
Labellum furnished at the base with 2 short rather high vertical
plates (lamellae), middle lobe generally smaller than the
laterals; petals free, as large as the intermediate sepal
ANACAMPTIS
Pollinia attached to 2 separate sticky disks (viscidia) :
Stigmatic lobes thickened; spur very short and conical
NEOTINEA
Stigmatic lobes not thickened; spur distinctly cylindric or
filiform . . . .   ORCHIS

Labellum not spurred :
Pouch entire (single); sticky disk 1; sepals and petals connivent into a helmet; labellum flat, the lateral lobes narrow, sticky forward; anther-connective obtuse . . . . . ACERAS
Pouch bipartite (double); sticky disks 2, separate; sepals and petals spreading or somewhat reflexed; labellum large, usually more or less convex . . . . OPHRYS

Glumiflorae.

JUNCALES and CYPERALES.

114. Juncaceae. 115. Cyperaceae.

There is a great resemblance between some species of *Juncus* and *Luzula* and certain *Cyperaceae*, and **Juncaceae** seems to be an intermediate stock between *Liliaceae* and *Cyperaceae*. The family is of worldwide distribution, but is most numerous in temperate and cold or montane regions, usually in wet or damp habitats. In South Africa and Australia their place is largely taken by a derived family *Restionaceae*, which have become almost entirely *dioecious*. In *Oreobolus* (see Fig. 147), a primitive genus of *Cyperaceae* found in the Antarctic and the Andes of South America,

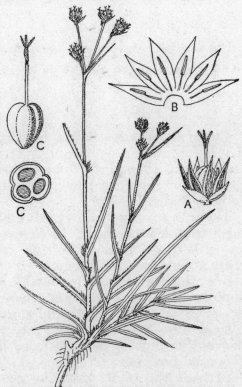

FIG. 146.—One of the commonest of the *Juncaceae, Luzula campestris* L.
A, flower. B, perianth laid open. C, pistil, and cross-section of the same.

T

there is a *distinct perianth of six segments*, just as in *Juncaceae*.

Juncus is very strongly represented by about fifteen species in Britain, and it is the more primitive genus, with a three-locular capsule. In some species the seeds are tailed at the ends as in *Narthecium* in *Liliaceae*. In *Luzlua* the capsule is one-locular and the seeds are reduced to three.

A striking *Luzula* is *L. nivea* Linn., naturalised in Britain, with grass-like spikelets.

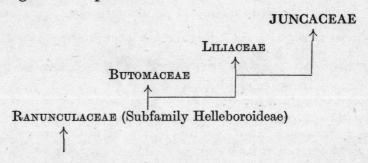

JUNCACEAE

LILIACEAE

BUTOMACEAE

RANUNCULACEAE (Subfamily Helleboroideae)

Cyperaceae, the Sedge family, is only slightly less reduced than the *Gramineae*. It is a very considerable family and abundantly distributed all over the earth, growing for the most part in moist places and near to or actually in fresh water.

There is a rough and ready method of distinguishing them from the Grasses. In *Cyperaceae* the sheath of the leaves is *closed* around the solid *triquetrous* stem, but in grasses the *cylindrical* stems are often *hollow*, except at the nodes, the leaf-sheath is usually split open on the side opposite the leaf-blade, and there is mostly a *ligule* at the junction of the blade and sheath.

Cyperaceae may be divided into two distinct groups, one the more primitive, with *bisexual* flowers, the other with *unisexual* flowers.

Perhaps the more primitive genera of the first group are those in which the glumes in each spikelet are imbricate all around the axis, and which have all the glumes except one containing flowers. These are *Eriophorum*,

Eleocharis, and *Scirpus,* and these in addition have
" hypogynous bristles," which are no doubt modified
perianth-segments. They are very conspicuous in the
first genus, which in consequence is known as " Cotton-
grass ".

In *Cladium* and
Rhynchospora several
of the lower glumes
of each spikelet are
smaller and empty,
the flowers having
been completely re-
duced. *Blysmus* is
distinguished by
having the spikelets
arranged in two op-
posite rows in a ter-
minal spike.

Fig. 147.—*Oreobolus pectinatus* Hk. f., the
most primitive member of the Cyperaceae,
and found in the Antarctic and the Andes
of South America.

E, shows the well-developed remains of the
perianth. A, leaf. B, flower and bracts.
C, stamen. D, ovary. F, vertical section
of fruit showing the seed. (From Hutchinson, *Families of Flowering Plants*).

Cyperus and *Scho-
enus* have the glumes
in each spikelet
arranged in two opposite rows ; and, finally, the unisexual
genera *Kobresia* and *Carex,* the latter being one of the
most highly evolved in the family, with the ovary enclosed
in a small bottle-shaped *utricle.* *Carex* is a very large
genus spread all over the world, with many aquatic
species, characteristics coinciding with its highly evolved
structure.

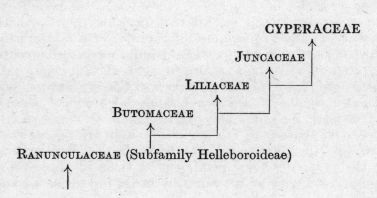

Key to genera of CYPERACEAE.

Flowers bisexual :
  Glumes in each spikelet imbricate all around the axis :
    Spikelets solitary or in heads, umbels or panicles :
      All the glumes of the spikelets, except the outermost, containing
        flowers :
        Hypogynous bristles shorter than the glumes or none :
          Spikelets usually clustered and lateral . . . . . SCIRPUS
          Spikelets solitary . . . . ELEOCHARIS
        Hypogynous bristles at length very long and conspicuous
                                                      ERIOPHORUM
      Several of the lower glumes of each spikelet empty :
        Spikelets very numerous in a compound panicle ; style-branches 3
                                                      CLADIUM
        Spikelets few ; style-branches 2 . . . . . RHYNCHOSPORA
      Spikelets in a terminal spike and arranged in two opposite rows
                                                      BLYSMUS
  Glumes in each spikelet arranged in two opposite rows :
    All the glumes, except the lowermost, fertile . . . . CYPERUS
    Several of the lower glumes infertile . . . . . . SCHOENUS
Flowers unisexual :
  Ovary partly enclosed in one or two glume-like scales open at the side
                                                      KOBRESIA
  Ovary partly enclosed in a small bottle-shaped utricle . . CAREX

Graminales.

116. Gramineae (by C. E. Hubbard).

The family **Gramineae** is a very distinctive and highly
successful group. It is found in all regions and in most
types of habitat in which Flowering Plants grow. Some
resemblance is apparent between it and certain other
families such as *Liliaceae, Juncaceae, Commelinaceae,*
and *Cyperaceae,* though apart from this there is little
definite evidence in support of theories of a relationship
with any one of them. The results of serodiagnostic
experiments, however, seem to suggest that there is a
closer affinity with the *Cyperaceae, Commelinaceae,* and
Liliaceae than with any other family of Monocotyledons.

That most classifications of the genera of grasses should
have been based on the structure and arrangement of
their spikelets appears perfectly logical. These organs,
by the great diversity displayed in their formation and
organisation, and by the amazing range in the shapes and

peculiar modifications of their separate parts, provide a far greater variety of distinguishing characters than do other portions of the grass-plant. There is no doubt, however, that little further progress can be made by these morphological studies alone towards that ideal natural classification which is the ambition of all interested in phylogeny. This has been widely recognised by specialists in other branches of botanical science, as is indicated by the vast amount of research on a wide range of problems connected with grasses which has been carried out between the two wars. Each has applied his special knowledge to some particular branch of the subject, such as anatomy, ecology, or cytology, in an attempt to elucidate the difficulties which had become obvious to, but impossible of final solution by the purely morphological methods of the systematic botanist. With the additional data provided we can, with greater confidence, group together genera and even tribes similar in a larger number of characters, and arrange them more or less in a sequence leading from those which appear to have primitive features to others which, judging by the same criteria, are more highly advanced. Even then, however, our knowledge is still insufficient to state with certainty which tribe or group of tribes should be regarded as the most ancient.

Fossil Grasses.

Palaeobotany, a source which in some families has yielded valuable evidence of the way evolution has proceeded through past geological ages, has provided very scanty data so far as the grasses are concerned. These plants must have been widespread in many parts of the world during the Tertiary period, but their vegetative and floral organs being, with few exceptions, relatively delicate, are not often preserved. It is true that fossil grass-like leaves and fruits have been referred to living genera such as *Panicum*, *Oryza*, *Poa*, and *Festuca*, but in the main they are not sufficiently complete for accurate determination. Apparently, the most reliable fossil grasses represented by vegetative remains are those considered to be species of *Phragmites* and *Arundo*; here the material consists of rhizomes, roots, culms, and leaves. In recent years, there have been discovered in late Tertiary formations in the Prairie Region of the United States, numerous grass fruits which have been preserved because of the indurated nature of the lemma and palea; these fruits belong to extinct genera of the *Stipeae* and to the living genera *Nassella*, *Panicum*, and *Setaria*.

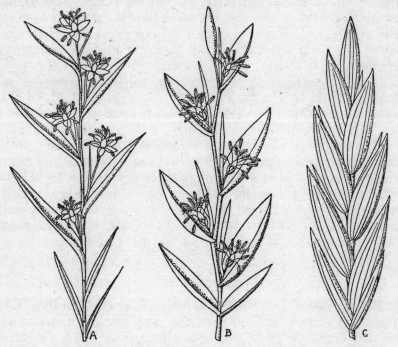

Fig. 148.—Theoretical stages in the evolution of the grass spikelet.

A, inflorescence of grass prototype. B, intermediate stage in the development of the spikelet. C, typical spikelet.

EVOLUTION OF THE SPIKELET.

Apart from a single tropical genus,[1] doubtfully included in the family, there seems no reason why the grasses should not have originated from a common stock. It is natural, therefore, in such reviews as these, for one to

[1] *Anomochloa.*

speculate on the kind of inflorescence and flower possessed by this grass prototype. We have only circumstantial evidence to guide us in our search, but from a consideration of theoretical evolutionary tendencies in the grass spikelet, and bearing in mind the homology of vegetative-leaf and lemma (flowering glume), we may assume that this ancient primary grass was provided with a leafy branched

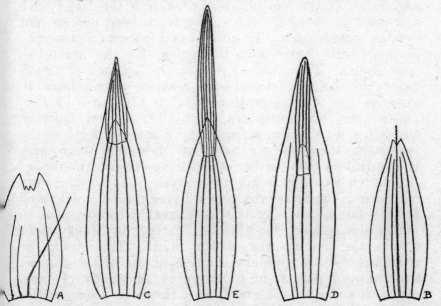

FIG. 149.—Lemmas from proliferating spikelets of *Deschampsia caespitosa* (L.) Beauv.

A, normal lemma. B, C, D, E, various transitions from lemma to miniature vegetative leaf.

flowering shoot. Each branch of this hypothetical inflorescence consisted of a several-noded axis (rhachilla), bearing singly at the nodes and alternately on opposite sides of the axis, a series of many-nerved herbaceous leaves, each with a sheathing base, much like the grass-like leaves of many other Monocotyledons. In each of the upper leaf-axils, a short branchlet bore a bracteole (prophyll) on the side adjacent to the axis and terminated in a solitary flower. The flower would be of the basic monocotyledonous type, in that it possessed six perianth leaves alternating in two whorls of three, two similar whorls of stamens, and a superior three-locular ovary with three styles.

A shortening of the axis-internodes and floral branchlets, brought about by drier habitat conditions, would permit the sheathing leaves to become contiguous or to overlap and envelop the flower, thus providing the latter with increased protection. Such may have been our ancient type of spikelet, with the glumes and lemmas represented by vegetative-leaves and the paleas by the bracteoles (prophylls). The conclusion that the lemmas are equivalent to the vegetative-leaves may be drawn from an examination of proliferating spikelets of species of *Poa*, *Dactylis*, or *Deschampsia*, in which all transitions between the two are to be found, and where some at least of the vegetative leaves bear a palea and flower in their axils. It is surmised that further stages in the transformation of this hypothetical spikelet to the type of spikelet usually regarded as the most primitive in living grasses, might well have been induced by the considerable compression to which the spikelet is subjected during its development within the leaf-sheaths of the plant. This would be responsible for a gradual reduction in size of the glumes, lemmas and paleas, in the number of whorls of both perianth and stamens, and from a three- to a one-locular ovary. Spikelets of this more advanced type, characterised by several many-nerved herbaceous awnless lemmas exserted from the glumes, each lemma enclosing a flower with one whorl of perianth leaves (lodicules), one or two whorls of stamens and a one-locular ovary with three styles, are to be found in some bamboos and in a few herbaceous grasses.

From a consideration of the numerous modifications of the parts of the spikelet, we can visualise the lines along which evolution may have proceeded from this relatively simple kind of spikelet to the highly specialised types such as occur in most of the larger tribes. Noteworthy evolutionary trends are those leading to increased protection for the seed, and the provision of elaborate devices to assure its widespread distribution. Associated with these progressive changes in the structure of the spikelet have been other developments—the outcome of growth under pressure. These have led to a further reduction in size or to a suppression of parts of the spikelet, in particular the loss of lodicules and stamens, and to a reduction in the number of florets from several to one per spikelet. A further stage in this retrogressive tendency is reached in many genera where certain florets of the spikelets have become male or sterile, and frequently represented only by the lemmas, whilst in other genera whole spikelets are similarly affected. Grasses possessing such deviations from the simple spiculate types are considered to be more highly evolved. Modifications for protection are noticeable in the increased development of the glumes whereby they almost envelop the lemmas, as in many of the *Aveneae*, or in the change of texture of the lemma from the herbaceous-membranous kind to one which has become hardened and leathery like that of *Milium*.

There are many adaptations to provide efficient methods for securing dispersal of the seed. The most important of these is the provision of an abscission layer in the spikelet-axis below each fertile floret or beneath the complete spikelet. This primary means of seed dispersal, which must have resulted directly from the imprisonment of the seed between the lemma and palea, has provided useful diagnostic characters which have been largely employed for purposes of classification. The furnishing of the spikelets with awns, barbs, hairs, and other dispersal-devices must be regarded as further evidence of advancement. To sum up in tabular form, those characters listed in the first column are generally regarded as more primitive features, whilst those contrasting characters in the second are considered more advanced.

Many-flowered spikelets. ⟶ One-flowered spikelets.

Florets all fertile. ⟶ Some florets fertile and others male or sterile.

Uppermost floret lateral on the spikelet-axis (rhachilla), with the axis produced. ⟶ Uppermost floret apparently terminal on the spikelet-axis, with the axis not produced.

Glumes persistent at maturity. ——→ Glumes deciduous with the rest of the spikelet.

Florets exserted from glumes. ——→ Florets enclosed by the glumes.

Lemmas many-nerved.——————→ Lemmas few-nerved or nerveless.

Lemmas herbaceous and leaf-like. —→ Lemmas indurated and rigid, or hyaline and delicate.

Lemmas awnless. ——————→ Lemmas awned.

Lodicules six or three. ————→ Lodicules two, one, or none.

Stamens in two whorls. ————→ Stamens in one whorl or further reduced.

Stigmas three. ——————→ Stigma one.

Examples of other evolutionary tendencies, both in the inflorescence and spikelet, will be given when the individual tribes are considered.

Parallel Development.

Although detailed investigations of the spikelets have yielded much valuable information and have drawn attention to marked similarities in their structure, it has not been possible at times to decide from such studies alone whether these resemblances point to a close relationship, and may therefore be used as evidence of evolutionary trends, or whether they are merely examples of parallel development. There are several cases of grasses superficially very much alike, and which at one time were considered congeneric or at least classified in the same tribe, but which by reason of our more complete knowledge of them are now referred to widely separated groups. The genera *Eragrostis* (*Eragrosteae*) and *Poa* (*Festuceae*) provide an illustration of the first type; here many species of the former were described originally as species of the latter genus, whilst in most classifications both are assigned to the same tribe—the *Festuceae*. This is an example of fortuitous parallelism, for although the spikelets of the two genera are built up on the same general plan, the genera must have developed independently on account of important anatomical and cytological distinctions. These differences are associated with morphological dissimilarities, previously considered of less significance. There are other instances of parallelism, such as the formation of the simple spicate inflorescence in *Lolium*, *Agropyron*, and *Parapholis*, which may be due to growth under somewhat similar conditions; these genera, often placed together in the *Hordeeae*, are preferably referred to different tribes. Thus it seems clear that parallel development has undoubtedly been the cause of some confusion in early attempts to provide a natural arrangement of grass genera.

THE FRUITS OF GRASSES.

The grass fruit, so often neglected in taxonomic studies, presents a number of characters of considerable systematic importance. It usually takes the form of a caryopsis, in which the pericarp is adnate to the seed. In closely related genera of the *Eragrosteae*, *Sporoboleae*, and *Chlorideae*, however, the pericarp is delicate and free from the seed, whilst in some of the bamboos the fruit is a nut or a berry.

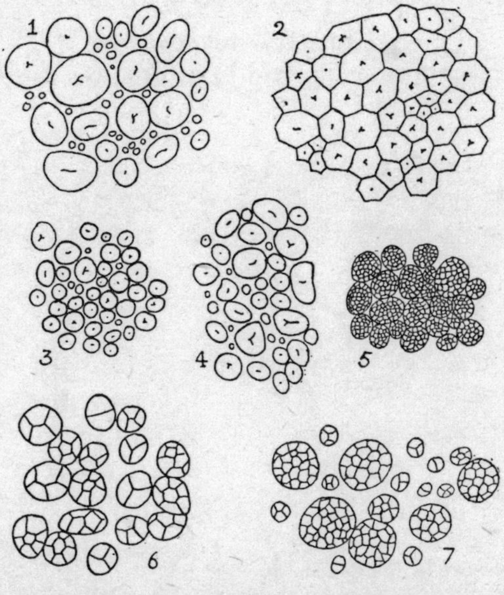

The hilum is usually uniform in shape for each genus and often for whole tribes. It has been noticed that in genera such as *Arundinaria*, *Festuca*, *Helictotrichon*, and *Agropyron*, which have retained features regarded as primitive,

FIG. 150.—Starch grains. Simple type : 1, *Triticum aestivum* L. (Hordeeae). 2, *Sorghum durra* (Forsk.) Stapf (Andropogoneae). 3, *Zea mays* L. (Maydeae). 4, *Bromus gussonii* Parl. (Festuceae). Compound type : 5, *Lolium perenne* L. (Festuceae). 6, *Bambusa longispiculata* Gamble (Bambuseae). 7, *Avena sativa* L. (Aveneae).

the hilum is very narrow and elongated, whereas in those genera and tribes showing advancement in spikelet structure, the hilum is basal and frequently dot-like.

The type of starch grain in the seeds of grasses has been found to be constant for whole tribes, and has proved of value in classifying a number of genera more accurately. For example, *Lolium*, *Nardus*, and *Parapholis*, having compound starch grains, are obviously out of place in the *Hordeeae*, typical genera of which possess simple grains. In the few bamboos—generally regarded as an ancient group—whose seeds have been examined, the starch grains are mainly compound.

VEGETATIVE CHARACTERISTICS.

The vegetative organs, in their external and internal morphology, provide important diagnostic features, several of which, on account of their prevalence in certain tribes or groups of tribes, and in view of their correlation with other distinctive characteristics, are of great value in phylogenetic studies.

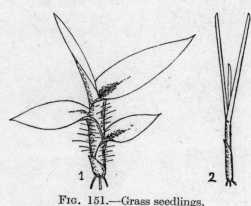

FIG. 151.—Grass seedlings.

1, *Panicum capillare* L. (Paniceae). 2, *Briza minor* L. (Festuceae).

The form of the first green leaf of the grass seedling has been found to be associated with other differences whereby the grasses may be divided into two groups. In the tribes *Festuceae*, *Aveneae*, *Hordeeae*, *Agrosteae*, and *Phalarideae*, forming the festucoid group, it is narrow, linear and erect; whereas in the tribes *Paniceae*, *Chlorideae*, *Andropogoneae*, etc., forming the panicoid group, it is relatively wide, lanceolate or elliptic and spreading.

Relatively broad adult leaf-blades, usually transversely veined, and sometimes with pseudo-petioles connecting them to the sheaths are typical of a few tribes. The *Bambuseae*, for example, have blades of this kind, which in addition are often articulated with the sheath. The usual type of leaf-sheath has free and overlapping margins, but in a number of genera the margins are connate. In a few cases, especially in *Bromus* and allied genera where such tubular sheaths occur, they appear to provide additional evidence of relationship.

The ligule, typically membranous in the majority of temperate grasses, is represented by a line of hairs in many tropical genera. In those examples where the latter type of ligule occurs in genera referred to essentially temperate tribes, it has usually been found that the particular genus has been wrongly classified (e.g., *Sieglingia* in *Aveneae* or *Festuceae*, and *Phragmites* and *Molinia* in *Festuceae*).

EPIDERMAL CELLS.

Intensive studies by continental botanists[1] have revealed that in the leaves certain types of epidermal cell exhibit a wide range in form, and moreover that cells of a particular kind are characteristic of genera of whole tribes or even larger groups. On the basis of these researches, the herbaceous grasses may be divided into two large and relatively well-defined groups. The first group, comprising genera referred to the *Festuceae*, *Aveneae*, *Hordeeae*, *Agrosteae*, and *Phalarideae*, possesses the festucoid type of epidermis. The second group includes the genera of the *Paniceae*, *Chlorideae*, *Eragrosteae*, *Andropogoneae*, etc., and has the panicoid type of epidermis. The cells, which provide the basis for this grouping, are of two types. Firstly those epidermal cells over the nerves which, by reason of their high silica content, are termed siliceous cells, and, secondly, minute hair-like outgrowths (cellules), not to be confused with the long hairs often found on grass leaves. In the first group, confined mainly to regions with a temperate climate, the siliceous cells are of a simple rounded or elongated type, and the minute hairs (cellules), if present, are never two-celled. The second

[1] Especially A. Grob and H. Prat.

group, mainly from tropical regions, possesses siliceous cells of a more complicated and varied structure, whilst the minute hairs are two-celled. This group, being more complex than the first, may be divided still further.   For

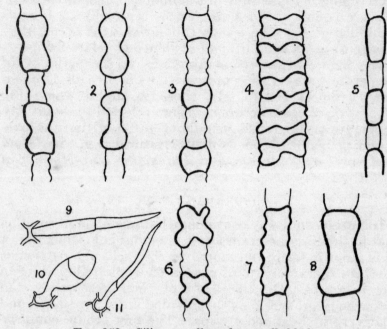

Fig. 152.—Siliceous cells and two-celled hairs.

Siliceous cells : 1, 2, 8, Longitudinal Dumb-bell type. 3, Saddle-type. 4, Transverse Dumb-bell type. 5, 7, Elongated simple type. 6, Cross-shaped type.   Two-celled hairs (9–11).—In part after Grob and Prat. 1, *Digitaria sanguinalis* (Paniceae).   2, *Trachypogon ligularis* (Andropogoneae).   3, *Dactyloctenium aegyptium* (Eragrosteae).   4, *Leersia hexandra* (Oryzeae).   5, *Phalaris arundinacea* (Phalarideae).   6, *Zea mays* (Maydeae).   7, *Agropyron repens* (Hordeeae).   8, 11, *Sieglingia decumbens* (Danthonieae).   9, *Nardus stricta* (Nardeae).   10, *Cynodon dactylon* (Chlorideae).

example, in the *Paniceae*, the two-celled hairs are relatively long and slender, and the siliceous cells are often dumb-bell- or cross-shaped, and in the former case arranged longitudinally to the axis of the leaf.   On the other hand, in the *Chlorideae* and related tribes the two-celled hairs are swollen, rounded at the apex and more or less club- or sphere-shaped, while the siliceous cells generally have the outline of a double-headed hatchet or a saddle. In a third subdivision, typified by *Oryza* and *Leersia* of the *Oryzeae*, the two-celled hairs are elongated and slender like those of the *Paniceae*, but the siliceous cells, although resembling small dumb-bells, are placed transversely to the axis of the leaf. The *Bambuseae* are stated to present a very diverse assemblage of cells. Their hair-like outgrowths are of the two-celled kind; usually they are slender, but sometimes they are swollen. In most genera the siliceous cells are of the saddle type like those of the *Chlorideae*, in a few they are of the kind characteristic of the *Oryzeae*, whilst in at least one genus they are of the rounded type as in some *Festuceae*. From a consideration of the epidermal cells, it has been suggested that the primary epidermal structure was similar to that of certain *Bambuseae* with bicellular hairs and siliceous cells of the saddle type, and that from grasses with this kind of epidermis there have been three principal lines of evolution, towards the epidermal types characteristic of the *Paniceae*, and *Oryzeae* (1), the *Chlorideae* (2), and the *Festuceae* (3).

Anatomical Characters.

In grasses, as in other plants, anatomy has proved a valuable source of evidence of relationships not obvious from purely floral studies. Leaves of herbaceous grasses may be roughly classified into two main types according to their anatomical structure. In the first, known as the festucoid type, the outer bundle sheath (parenchymatous sheath) is green or colourless and poorly differentiated, the inner bundle sheath (mestome sheath) is well developed and strongly thickened, whilst the chlorophyll tissue is not arranged in any special manner around the bundles, but disposed between them. This type is typical of the temperate group of tribes (*Festuceae*, etc.), but is also found in certain tribes (*Oryzeae*, etc.) from tropical regions; it is sometimes considered to be a rather primitive feature. The second, termed the panicoid type, usually has the inner sheath considerably reduced or absent, so that the xylem and phloem are more or less in contact with the outer sheath, the latter composed of rather large cells. In this type the chlorophyll tissue usually takes the form of a layer of cells radiating around the outer sheath. The panicoid type of leaf-anatomy is characteristic of the *Paniceae, Eragrosteae, Chlorideae* and

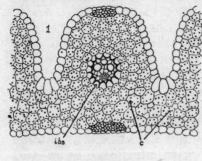

other tribes from tropical regions. The bamboos, in their leaf-anatomy, are said to present certain resemblances to each of these types, for both the outer and inner bundle sheaths are well developed. It has been suggested that evolution has proceeded in two directions from the bamboo ancestral stock, towards the panicoid type with its well-developed outer sheath and towards the festucoid type where the inner sheath is highly developed.

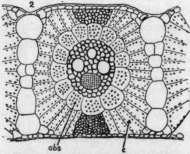

Fig. 153.—Transverse sections through portions of leaf-blades.

Festucoid type : 1, *Lolium perenne* L. (Festuceae). Panicoid type : 2, *Eleusine tristachya* Kunth (Eragrosteae). c, chlorophyll tissue. ibs, inner bundle sheath. obs, outer bundle sheath.

CYTOLOGY.

During the past twenty years considerable attention has been paid to the study of the chromosomes of grasses, in part on account of the economic importance of the group, but also because it was considered that an investigation of their morphology would have far-reaching effects in the clarification of taxonomic difficulties. After the chromosomes of many grasses from widely differing groups had been examined it became apparent that, with few exceptions, there existed a constant basic number for each genus, and that, in addition, this number occurred throughout whole groups of related genera demonstrating that it was a character of considerable systematic importance. Furthermore, it was noted that differences in the shape and size of the chromosomes were associated with particular basic numbers; for example, in most cases where the chromosomes occurred in multiples of seven, they were larger than those in multiples of ten or twelve.

On the basis of this combination of chromosome characteristics and basic number, correlated with other significant morphological and anatomical distinctions, a Russian cytologist[1] proposed a revolutionary change in the classification of grasses. He arranged the genera in three major groups. In the first, which includes the tribes *Bambuseae, Oryzeae, Arundineae,* and *Stipeae,* together with some isolated genera, the chromosomes are of the small type, often in multiples of twelve, and the chlorophyll tissue is of the festucoid type; in other respects, however, the group lacks uniformity. It was regarded as a collection of relicts, and on cytological and other grounds considered to be

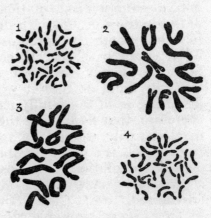

FIG. 154.—Chromosomes.

1, *Panicum miliaceum* L. (Paniceae), 2n = 36. 2, *Cynosurus echinatus* L. (Festuceae), 2n = 14. 3, *Lagurus ovatus* L. (Agrosteae), 2n = 14. 4, *Cynodon dactylon* (L.) Pers. (Chlorideae), 2n = 36. After Avdulov.

the oldest group amongst living grasses. The second group, comprising the temperate tribes *Festuceae, Aveneae, Agrosteae,* etc., is a much more natural one. It was distinguished by possessing relatively large chromosomes usually in multiples of seven, the festucoid type of chlorophyll tissue, erect narrow first green leaf-blades and by the absence of two-celled hairs in the epidermis. The last group included the tropical tribes *Chlorideae, Paniceae, Andropogoneae,* and *Maydeae* and various tropical genera from

---

[1] N. P. Avdulov.

U

other tribes. In this group the chromosomes are of the small type and usually in multiples of five, nine, ten, or twelve, the chlorophyll tissue usually takes the form of a sheath around the vascular bundles, two-celled hairs are present in the epidermis, and the first green leaf is lanceolate or elliptic and spreading.

This arrangement of the grasses was partly based on the assumption that twelve is the primary basic chromosome number in the family, and that this number has undergone a reduction as evolution has proceeded, to ten, nine, or five in those groups with small chromosomes, or to seven in tribes where the chromosomes have increased in size. This theory has been criticised on various grounds, one being that loss of chromosomes would lead to the death of the individual or that it would give rise to a life form deviating from the family circle. It has been suggested, therefore, that five, being the lowest basic number known in the family, should be regarded as the primary one from which the other numbers might have arisen in the course of evolution. This basic number occurs, however, in several genera which in other respects are highly specialised, e.g., *Coix*, *Sorghum*, and *Anthoxanthum*. It seems very probable that basic numbers have gone both up and down by increase or loss of whole chromosomes, and by splitting or fusion of chromosomes.

The position at present regarding the basic number for certain groups is not entirely satisfactory, for in those genera which possess other characteristics generally regarded as primitive, the chromosome numbers and consequently the basic numbers are relatively high. In such groups the species with lower chromosome numbers may have been eliminated, thus destroying the evidence of a lower basic number. This appears to have happened in the *Bambuseae*, where, in addition, the presence of two species with 54 ($2n$) chromosomes denotes a lower basic number than that (12) generally accepted for the tribe.

Although the evidence derived from cytological studies does not seem likely to provide us with sufficient data for a complete phylogenetic classification, it has indicated the way towards a vastly improved grouping of genera and tribes.

DISTRIBUTION AND HABITAT.

The distribution and habitat of grasses are worthy of special consideration in any treatment of their phylogeny. Where the grouping of genera is based on the greatest number of resemblances between them, it has been noted that such groups are usually centred in particular climatic regions. Thus the *Chlorideae* and *Paniceae* have their headquarters in the tropics, whence they have spread into cooler regions where the extremes are not too great. On the other hand, the *Festuceae* and related tribes, which are widespread in temperate regions, occur only at high altitudes in the tropics. Similarly, some tribes have special habitat preferences; for instance, the genera of the *Oryzeae* favour moist situations, whilst those of the *Stipeae* are more at home in relatively dry open grasslands. Where a genus, having been classified with other genera, disagrees with them in regard to its general distribution, it has usually been found that this divergence is associated with anatomical and cytological differences, and that some readjustment is needed. Those grasses which by reason of their retention of theoretically primitive types of structure are regarded as representatives of ancient groups, occupy moist or aquatic habitats or occur in regions of abundant rain where the conditions are most favourable for their preservation. On this account such habitats have been regarded as primitive for the *Gramineae*, as they have in the *Butomaceae* and *Alismataceae* (see p. 43).

THE TRIBES OF GRASSES.

After perusing the foregoing summary of some of the characters which have proved of value in indicating relationships, the reader will realise the extraordinary complexity of the subject and the difficulties encountered in attempting the preparation of a natural classification.

Our knowledge of many groups is still lamentably deficient in cytological, anatomical, and other data. The following arrangement must be regarded, therefore, as purely tentative.

The tribes occurring in Britain and represented by cultivated and wild grasses may be referred to four major groups. The first comprises several tribes, here collectively retained as the *Bambuseae*. It is a rather heterogeneous and isolated group of genera, well developed in the tropics, but also extending into warm temperate regions. Several features which appear to be primitive are retained in a number of genera, suggesting that its members are derivatives of an ancient group of grasses. The second group comprises several isolated tribes, the *Oryzeae*, *Stipeae*, *Arundineae*, and *Danthonieae*, resembling the bamboos and one another in possessing small chromosomes. In the third group are placed the chief tribes of temperate regions, the *Festuceae*, *Aveneae*, *Hordeeae*, *Phalarideae*, *Agrosteae*, *Monermeae*, and *Nardeae*, all with relatively large chromosomes and these frequently in multiples of seven. This group of tribes, except for the *Nardeae* and a few aberrant genera, appears to be a very natural one; it bears a closer resemblance to the earlier groups than to the fourth. The last group includes the *Chlorideae*, *Paniceae*, *Andropogoneae*, and *Maydeae*, all widespread in the tropics or warm regions and possessing the small type of chromosome. These tribes differ from those of the other groups in their leaf-anatomy, and appear to have diverged very early from the basic grass stock.

The relationships and possible lines of evolution of the above groups are shown in the diagram on p. 301.

I. BAMBUSEAE.

The *Bambuseae* are represented in the British Isles by the genera *Arundinaria* and *Phyllostachys*, which are often cultivated for ornament in parks and gardens. Although homogeneous in some respects, such as in the possession of woody culms, the group is very heterogeneous in others, particularly in the structure of the epidermis

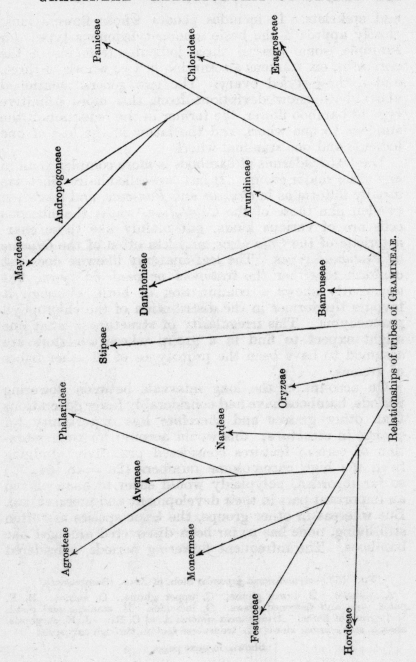

Relationships of tribes of GRAMINEAE.

in relation to the probable origin of these polyploids, seems to indicate a more remote ancestry for this group than any other tribe of grasses.

II. ORYZEAE.

It is a big step from the Bambuseae to the *Oryzeae*, the next tribe to be considered, but there are some connecting links amongst tropical grasses. It has often been regarded

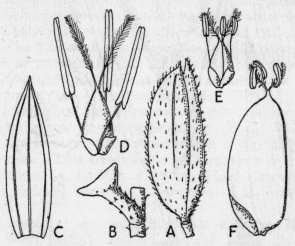

FIG. 156.—*Leersia oryzoides* (L.) Sw. (Oryzeae).
A, spikelet. B, pedicel with reduced glumes.
C, palea. D, normal flower. E, cleistogamous
flower. F, caryopsis, side view, with anthers.

as a rather primitive tribe, partly on account of the frequent retention of two whorls of stamens in the flower and also because its members favour moist or aquatic habitats. The spikelets in most respects, however, exhibit a considerable advancement in their structure, being reduced to the one-flowered condition, whilst in one section of the tribe there is a separation of the sexes into different parts of the same inflorescence or into different inflorescences.

The structure of the spikelets has been often misinterpreted due to the suppression or extreme reduction of the glumes and sterile florets.   The glumes, when present, are minute and frequently reduced to an obscure rim on the tip of the pedicel.   In *Oryza* (Rice), there are two small sterile lemmas at the base of the fertile floret, often erroneously regarded as glumes.   As these sterile lemmas fall at maturity with the rest of the spikelet, the tribe has frequently been classified near the *Paniceae* in which the spikelets fall entire, but to which tribe it bears no close relationship.   The spikelet of *Leersia* shows a further reduction in the suppression of the sterile lemmas, whilst in some species there is also a decrease in the number of stamens.   *Leersia oryzoides* (L.) Sw. (Cut Grass) is of rare occurrence in southern England in aquatic habitats. The genus, which is essentially tropical, seems to have reached its northern limit in western Europe, for it is only when we have exceptionally hot summers that normal (chasmogamous) flowering takes place in our species; then its three relatively long anthers become exserted from the floret.   With our usual summers, however, the inflorescences remain partly or wholly enclosed in the leaf-sheaths, whilst the anthers are very small and the flowers cleistogamous.

Amongst herbaceous grasses, the *Oryzeae* occupy a rather isolated position, not only on account of their spikelet structure, but because of the unusual combination of other characteristics.   Thus the foliage anatomy is of the festucoid type, the two-celled epidermal hairs are like those of the Paniceae, the siliceous cells are of a special type, the chromosomes are of the small kind and in multiples of twelve, the first green leaf-blade of the seedling is of the panicoid type, the caryopsis has a well-developed linear hilum and possesses compound starch grains.

III. Stipeae.

Stipa, the largest genus in the tribe *Stipeae*, and very well represented in the warm dry temperate regions of the northern and southern hemispheres, is briefly referred to here because one of its species—*S. pennata* L.—is frequently cultivated in gardens and at one time was included by error in our floras. Fossil fruits referable to the forerunners of this genus have been discovered in Tertiary beds in the Prairie Region of North America, an area in which the genus is still prominent. It retains a primitive feature in the possession of three lodicules in the flower, although the lemma has become so modified in providing for the protection and dispersal of the seed that it bears little resemblance to the theoretically ancient type of lemma. Cytologically the genus is very interesting in that it is one of the few genera of grasses with an aneuploid series of chromosome numbers. The chromosomes, which are of the small type, occur mainly in multiples of nine and eleven. The leaf-blades have the festucoid type of epidermis and anatomy. The *Stipeae* is a rather small isolated group of genera, without close relatives, unless there be some among the genera tentatively referred to the *Danthonieae*.

IV. ARUNDINEAE.

The *Arundineae* has been often treated as a subtribe of the *Festuceae*. The separation of these tribes, primarily on account of differences in spikelet morphology and general habit, has been fully justified by distinctions in the size and basic number of the chromosomes. The latter are of the small type and in multiples of twelve. The tribe diverges still further from the *Festuceae* in possessing either the *Chlorideae* or *Paniceae* type of leaf-epidermis, whilst in its leaf-anatomy it is stated to present some intermediate characters, partly panicoid and partly festucoid, although in most genera it is of the panicoid type. It comprises only a few genera of tall perennial grasses, occurring in both tropical and temperate regions, and with a preference for aquatic habitats. *Phragmites* (Reed), with an extremely wide area of distribution, is the only genus occurring naturally in the British Isles, although species of *Cortaderia* (Pampas Grass) and *Arundo* (Giant Reed) are frequently cultivated for ornament. *Phragmites communis* Trin., our tallest British grass, covers large areas of swamp, lake- and river-

margins. The genus *Phragmites* is believed to be of
relatively ancient origin, partly because of the discovery
of fossil vegetative remains and also by reason of its
prevalence in primitive types of habitat, a theory which
is supported by the high chromosome numbers ($2n =$
48, 96) reported for the genus. Its present representatives, however, display a considerable advancement in the
development of their spikelets.   The lowest floret is male
or barren, with a glabrous lemma; the following florets
are hermaphrodite and each provided with a basal beard
of long silky hairs, whilst the lemmas are thinly membranous and only three- or one-nerved.

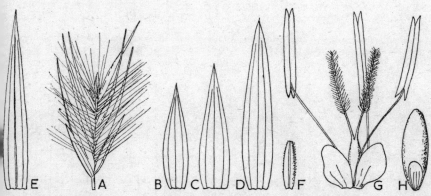

FIG. 157.—*Phragmites communis* Trin. (Arundineae).

A, spikelet. B, lower glume. C, upper glume. D, sterile lemma.
E, fertile lemma.   F, palea.   G, flower.   H, caryopsis, abaxial view.

V. DANTHONIEAE.

The *Danthonieae* has usually been regarded as a subtribe
of the *Aveneae*, but morphological, together with the cytological and anatomical distinctions so far recorded,
necessitate a different treatment of the group.   In typical
genera of the tribe, the lemma is divided at the apex into
three lobes and the middle lobe is often produced into a
geniculate awn, whereas in the *Aveneae* proper the awn
arises on the back of the lemma, the apex of which may
be entire or two-lobed.   Only three genera have been
examined cytologically, and these, with few exceptions,

have relatively small chromosomes with basic numbers of 6, 9, or 12.   The tribe has its greatest concentration in the southern hemisphere and favours a warmer and drier climate than the *Aveneae*.   It is represented in the northern hemisphere by the genera *Schismus*, *Sieglingia*, and *Danthonia*.   *Sieglingia*, with a single species, *S*.

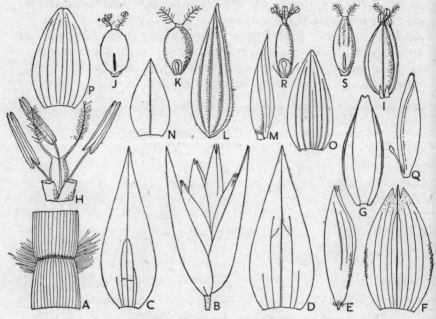

Fig. 158.—*Sieglingia decumbens* (L.) Bernh. (Danthonieae).

A, ligule. B, spikelet. C, lower glume. D, upper glume. E, floret. F, lemma. G, palea. H, chasmogamous flower. I, cleistogamous flower. J, caryopsis with detached anthers, adaxial view. K, caryopsis, abaxial view. L, basal axillary cleistogene. M, cleistogamous spikelet from cleistogene. N, lower glume. O, upper glume. P, lemma. Q, side view of palea. R, S, caryopsis, abaxial and adaxial views.

decumbens (L.) Bernh.[1] (Heath Grass), is the only genus occurring in the British Isles.   It is very closely related to, if not congeneric with, the large and widespread genus *Danthonia*.   Evidence of close affinity is provided by natural hybrids between *Sieglingia* and *Danthonia caly-cina* (Vill.) Reichb., which have been recorded from the Continent.   Not only does *Sieglingia* bear a close resem-

[1] *Triodia decumbens* (L.) Beauv.

blance to *Danthonia* in the structure of its spikelets, but also in the development of cleistogenes (modified cleistogamous spikelets) in the axils of the basal leaf-sheaths of the flowering culms. The spikelets of the terminal inflorescence of *Sieglingia* are usually cleistogamous also, and pollination takes place while the spikelets are enclosed in the leaf-sheaths. Chasmogamous inflorescences have been noted, however, in a few British plants; in these examples the panicle has spreading branches and the anthers are much longer than in the cleistogamous form. Because of certain similarities in structure, *Molinia*, which occupies an anomalous position in the *Festuceae* in many classifications, is here tentatively associated with *Sieglingia*. The two genera have the following characters in common :—the ligule is represented by a ciliate rim, the siliceous cells of the epidermis are of the dumb-bell type and the basic chromosome number is 9.

The third major group of tribes, under which the majority of the genera of British grasses are classified, includes the *Festuceae*, *Aveneae*, *Phalarideae*, *Hordeeae*, and *Agrosteae*. Its members, with few exceptions, are characterised by the possession of the festucoid type of epidermis and leaf-anatomy, erect narrow first leaf-blades in the seedlings, relatively large chromosomes usually with seven as the basic number, one- to many-flowered spikelets, mostly laterally compressed and typically articulated above the glumes so that they break up at maturity, and mostly five- or more-nerved lemmas. The genera of this group exhibit an increasing degree of modification or reduction of their spikelets, and/or inflorescences as one proceeds from the theoretically more primitive *Festuceae* to the *Hordeeae* and *Agrosteae*. They occupy a wide range of habitats in the temperate regions of both hemispheres, and are found in the tropics only at high altitudes. This tolerance of widely varying habitats is, in some genera, no doubt due to polyploidy, for the species with higher chromosome numbers (the tetraploids, etc.) are often able to persist in comparatively less favourable situations than their diploid relatives. Thus some species may be able to grow in progressively drier and others in wetter places.

For example, in our species of *Glyceria*, the diploid *G. declinata* Bréb. requires only a slightly moist habitat, whereas the tetraploid *G. fluitans* (L.) R.Br. (Manna Grass) grows best in shallow water, whilst the hexaploid *G. maxima* (Hartm.) Holmb. (Reed Grass) thrives in relatively deep water. On the other hand, a polyploid series may show an increasing capacity for withstanding greater heat or cold, those species with higher chromosome numbers spreading from the centre of origin of the genus, in some cases to warmer or in other to cooler regions.

VI. FESTUCEAE.

The *Festuceae* is generally considered to be the most ancient of those tribes referred to the third group, primarily on account of the relatively simple structure of its spikelets, which are less modified or reduced than those of the other tribes, and which, moreover, bear some resemblance to the spikelets of certain genera of the *Bambuseae*. In typical genera of the tribe the two- to many-flowered spikelets are mostly borne in loose or contracted panicles, the awnless or straight-awned and five- to many-nerved herbaceous lemmas project from the glumes, and the starch grains are compound. It is only in a few genera that sterility has affected the structure of the spikelets. In some cases the apical florets are sterile (*Melica*), but in other examples complete spikelets are barren (*Cynosurus*). Genera like *Catabrosa* show a reduction in the numbers of fertile florets in the spikelet and also in the number of nerves in the glumes and lemmas. Although many genera have been transferred to other tribes, the *Festuceae* still retains several anomalous ones, in particular *Melica*, *Glyceria*, *Bromus*, and *Brachypodium*, the positions of which are doubtful. The sixteen genera occurring in the British Isles are representative of the more important subtribes, although it should be noted that this secondary division of the tribe, based mainly on differences in spikelet and inflorescence structure, is unsatisfactory and now in need of revision.

In the genus *Festuca*, typical of the subtribe *Festucinae*

and often regarded as one of the most primitive of temperate herbaceous grass genera, the lemmas are rounded
on the back and frequently awned from the tip, while the
caryopsis has an elongated linear hilum, the latter a
feature also of the allied genera *Vulpia* and *Lolium*.
Festuca has a very wide area of distribution, occurring in
all temperate regions, and comprises a large number of
closely related perennial species. In Britain the most
prominent of these are the narrow-bladed species *F.*

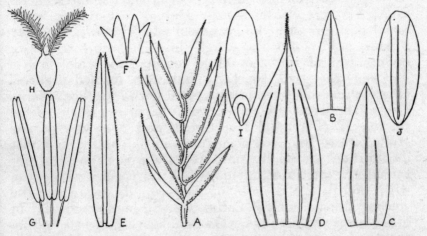

Fig. 159.—*Festuca ovina* L. (Festuceae).

A, spikelet. B, lower glume. C, upper glume. D, lemma. E, palea.
F, lodicules, G, stamens. H, pistil. I, J, caryopsis, abaxial and adaxial
views.

ovina L. (Sheep's Fescue) and *F. rubra* L. (Red Fescue),
and the broader-bladed *F. pratensis* Huds. (Meadow
Fescue) and *F. arundinacea* Schreb. (Tall Fescue).
Polyploidy is well developed in this genus, for in each of
the above sections the species may be arranged in a series
with chromosome numbers in multiples of fourteen (2*n*),
from fourteen to seventy.

Vulpia is a genus of slender annual species, considerably
fewer than in *Festuca*, of which it is frequently treated as
a section. Its greatest concentration is in the Mediterranean Region, but it is also represented in other areas

with a similar climate.   Several species extend to northern Europe, including the British Isles, where *V. myuros* (L.) Gmel. and *V. bromoides* (L.) S. F. Gray are often gregarious on sandy or stony soils.   The spikelets are more advanced than those of *Festuca*, in that the lower glume is much reduced or occasionally suppressed, the florets are often cleistogamous, and in some species the androecium is reduced to a single very small stamen, this being the front one of the outer staminal whorl.

Despite conspicuous differences in their inflorescences, *Lolium* is here classified near *Festuca* rather than in its usual position with the genera of the *Hordeeae*, not only because of its compound starch grains, but more especially on account of the very close relationship which exists between the two genera. Naturally formed hybrids (*Festulolium loliaceum* [Huds.] P. Fourn., *Festuca loliacea* Huds.) between the important pasture grass *Lolium perenne* L. (Perennial Rye Grass) and *Festuca pratensis* Huds. are of frequent occurrence in old pastures, whilst in addition artificially produced hybrids have been obtained by intercrossing many of the species of *Lolium* with the British species of *Festuca*. Disregarding the spicate inflorescence of *Lolium*, it will be noticed that in other respects there is a close similarity between *Lolium* and the broader-bladed species of *Festuca*, particularly in the structure of their spikelets, the former differing mainly in the suppression of the lower glume in all except the terminal spikelets.   The species of *Lolium* are all diploids with fourteen chromosomes.   They are mainly natives of the Mediterranean Region, where the climate and short growing season favour the annual species, whilst the single perennial, *L. perenne* L., has spread northwards into cooler and moister regions.

The genera *Puccinellia*, *Scleropoa*, and *Desmazeria* agree with *Festuca* in having the lemmas rounded on the back, but these organs are broader at the apex, five-nerved, and never awned, whilst the position of the hilum is indicated by a small dot at the base of the caryopsis. *Puccinellia* is often included in *Glyceria*, but in addition to differences in spikelet-structure and habitat-preferences, important cytological distinctions have recently been discovered. It is a world-wide temperate genus, restricted to maritime districts or inland situations with saline soils. *P. maritima* (Huds.) Parl. and *P. distans* (L.) Parl. are of common occurrence in salt marshes in the British Isles. *Scleropoa* and *Desmazeria*, represented in Britain by *S. rigida* (L.) Griseb. and *D. marina* (L.) Druce (*D. loliacea* [Huds.] Nym.), respectively, are both small genera of annual species with more or less specialised inflorescences, that of the latter

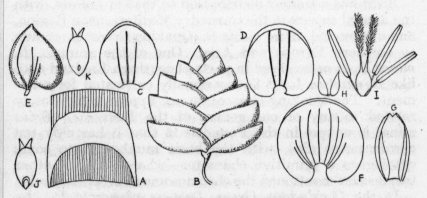

Fig. 160.—*Briza media* L. (Festuceae).

A, ligule. B, spikelet. C, lower glume. D, upper glume. E, floret. F, lemma. G, palea. H, lodicules. I, stamens and pistil. J, K, caryopsis, abaxial and adaxial views.

genus taking the form of a simple one-sided spike-like raceme. These grasses prefer relatively dry situations, the former often growing on walls, rocks, and in stony or sandy soils, and the latter on sandy sea-shores.

The subtribe *Poinae*, of which the largest genus *Poa* is well developed in all parts of the British Isles and indeed in all temperate climes, differs from the genera previously considered in possessing keeled and awnless lemmas. The absence of an awn is in *Poa* counterbalanced by the frequent provision of a tuft of woolly hairs at the base of the floret which assists in seed-disposal. *Poa*, like *Festuca*, may be regarded as a genus of ancient origin on account

x

In the morphology and number of its chromosomes, *Glyceria* does not conform to the festucoid type, for the chromosomes are much smaller than those of *Poa*, *Festuca* and other genera of the *Festuceae*, and moreover have 10 (?5)—not 7—as the basic number. Probably, and with good reason, some will see in this basic number and

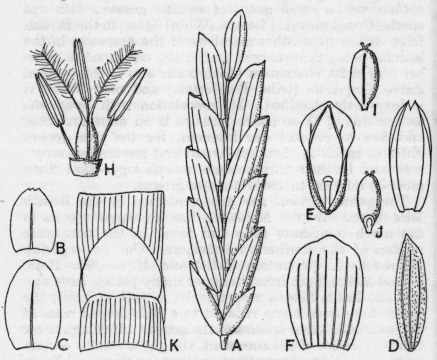

FIG. 161.—*Glyceria plicata* Fries (Festuceae).

A, spikelet. B, lower glume. C, upper glume. D, E, floret, side and front views. F, lemma. Above D, palea. H, flower. I, J, caryopsis, adaxial and abaxial views. K, ligule.

small type of chromosome, justification for regarding *Glyceria* as an ancient genus of grasses. This reasoning is further supported by its wide distribution in temperate regions, by the aquatic habitat of all the species, the relatively simple spikelet-structure, and the elongated linear hilum of the caryopsis.

It is with considerable doubt that *Bromus* and *Brachy-*

podium are included here, for both differ from other genera of the *Festuceae* in possessing simple starch grains, the outermost cell-layer of the nucellus developed into a thick-walled layer, whilst the ovary bears at its apex a hairy lobed appendage with the styles borne laterally on it. In recent years it has been discovered that *Bromus* contains a laevorotatory glycoside related to the triticin of *Agropyron* (*Hordeeae*), whereas *Festuca* possesses a different

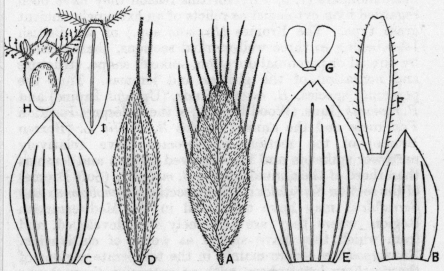

FIG. 162.—*Bromus mollis* L. (Festuceae).

A, spikelet. B, lower glume. C, upper glume. D, floret. E, lemma. F, palea. G, lodicules. H, pistil, with detached anthers. I, caryopsis, adaxial view.

glycoside (resembling phlein), which is also found in *Lolium*. Moreover, the species of *Bromus* and *Festuca* will not intercross as *Festuca* does with *Lolium*. On account of the simple starch grains, one or the other of these genera has been made the basis of distinct tribes, the *Bromeae* and *Brachypodieae*, or grouped with the *Hordeeae* where the ovary is also often hairy at the apex and the caryopsis has a similar elongated hilum. *Bromus*, a large genus of the temperate zones of both hemispheres and of some high mountains in the tropics, may be dis-

distinct generically as either *Trisetum* or *Arrhenatherum*.
It has a much wider area of distribution than *Avena*, with
numerous perennial species in the north temperate zone,
on the mountains of tropical Africa and Asia and in
southern Africa. *Helictotrichon pratense* (L.) Pilger
(*Avena pratensis* L.), " Perennial Oat Grass ", and *H.
pubescens* (Huds.) Pilger (*Avena pubescens* Huds.),
" Downy Oat Grass ", are of frequent occurrence in
British grasslands.   In both *Helictotrichon* and *Avena* the
spikelets are comparatively large, their lemmas many-
nerved and their caryopses each with an elongated linear
hilum, but the glumes of the former genus possess fewer
nerves and being relatively smaller afford less protection
to the remainder of the spikelet than do those of *Avena*.
The latter genus is limited to about a score of annual
species, most of which are natives of the Mediterranean
Region.   *Avena fatua* L. (Wild Oats) and *A. ludoviciana*
Dur. are often common weeds of arable land in England,
whilst *A. sativa* L. (Common Oats) is widely cultivated,
also *A. strigosa* Schreb. (Bristle-pointed Oats) but to a
less extent.   Attempts to produce hybrids between
Helictotrichon and *Avena* have so far proved unsuccessful.

In some respects, particularly in the development of the
awns, *Trisetum*, with one British species, *T. flavescens*
(L.) Beauv. (Golden or Yellow Oat Grass), is intermediate
between *Helictotrichon* and *Koeleria*.   *Trisetum* and *Koeleria* have numerous species in the temperate regions of
the northern hemisphere and several in the south temperate zone, whilst the latter genus is represented also on the
mountains of tropical Africa.   In both genera the fewer-
nerved thinner lemmas and the small basal hilum of the
caryopsis are considered more highly evolved than those of
Helictotrichon, whereas that genus shows a much greater
development of the awns.   The British species of *Koeleria*
(*K. gracilis* Pers. and *K. vallesiana* [Honck.] Bertol.) are
tufted perennials belonging to the subgenus *Airochloa*,
in which the few-flowered spikelets are crowded into a
dense spike-like inflorescence.   Their lemmas are awnless
or very short-awned, whereas those of *Trisetum* bear
awns differentiated into a column and bristle.   Although

Koeleria is often referred to the *Festuceae*, its annual species (subgenus *Lophochloa*) are obviously very closely related to the annual species of *Trisetum*.

In *Arrhenatherum* and *Holcus*, the number of florets in each spikelet is usually restricted to two, rarely three, but besides this reduction, the lower floret in the former genus is normally male, whilst in the latter genus it is the upper floret which is so affected. *Arrhenatherum*, a genus of few species in temperate Europe and Asia, with *A. elatius* (L.) J. et C. Presl (Tall Oat Grass) very abundant in Britain, appears to be derived from the same stock

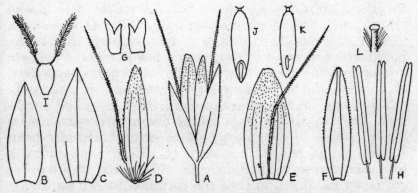

FIG. 164.—*Deschampsia flexuosa* (L.) Trin. (Aveneae).

A, spikelet. B, lower glume. C, upper glume. D, lower floret. E, lemma. F, palea. G, lodicules. H. stamens. I, pistil. J, K, caryopsis, abaxial and adaxial views. L, rhachilla-internode.

as *Helictotrichon*. On the other hand, *Holcus*, with a somewhat similar area of distribution, has no obvious near relatives in the *Aveneae*. Two species, *H. lanatus* L. (Yorkshire Fog) and *H. mollis* L. (Creeping Soft Grass), are common British grasses. In this genus, in which the two glumes envelop the florets, the dispersal of the seed is made possible by means of abscission layers beneath the glumes and florets, so that the spikelet may fall entire at maturity or the florets may be shed separately.

Two of the remaining three genera of the *Aveneae*, *Deschampsia* and *Corynephorus*, have often been included with the third, *Aira*, in British Floras, although both are sufficiently distinct to warrant separation. Judging from its wide distribution and numerous species in the temperate and cold regions of both hemispheres and at high altitudes in the tropics, *Deschampsia* must be regarded as an ancient genus, although so far as its spikelet structure is concerned, it shows considerable advancement. The spikelets are mostly only two-, rarely three- or four-flowered, and the glumes and lemmas of delicate texture, each with a few fine nerves. Most species are perennial, and of the four occurring in the British Isles, *D. caespitosa* (L.) Beauv. (Tufted Hair Grass) and *D. flexuosa* (L.) Trin. (Wavy Hair Grass) are those most frequently encountered. Proliferation of the spikelets is characteristic of *D. alpina* (L.) R. et S. and of some alpine variants of *D. caespitosa*. The small genus *Aira*, with its centre of distribution in the Mediterranean region, comprises a few species of delicate annual grasses, possessing strictly two-flowered spikelets. *A. caryophyllea* L. (Silvery Hair Grass) and *A. praecox* L. (Early Hair Grass) extend to the British Isles and northwest Europe, where they are of common occurrence on sandy soils. *Corynephorus* is another Mediterranean Region genus, with *C. canescens* (L.) Beauv. inhabiting a few sand-dunes in Britain. In this genus, the awn is curiously modified, in that the terminal bristle portion is club-shaped and bears at its base a circle of minute hairs.

VIII. PHALARIDEAE.

The tribe *Phalarideae* is in many respects similar to the *Aveneae*, especially to the genera *Arrhenatherum* and *Holcus*, but distinguished by the lower two florets of the three in each spikelet being male or barren. It is here restricted to *Hierochloë*, *Anthoxanthum*, and *Phalaris*, species of each being found in the British Isles and in most temperate regions. These genera form an instructive series illustrating various stages in the reduction of the lateral florets. Thus in *Hierochloë*, with a single British species *H. odorata* (L.) Beauv. (Holy Grass), the lower two florets are male or barren and as long as or longer than the third and the flower has two lodicules, whereas in the

closely allied *Anthoxanthum*, the lower two florets are
always barren and the lodicules suppressed. Although
the male flower of the lateral florets in *Hierochloë* is
triandrous, in this genus, as well as in *Anthoxanthum*,
the central fertile flower is diandrous. It is probable that
these two anthers belong to different whorls, the anterior
one between the lemma and ovary being all that remains
of the outer whorl, and the posterior stamen between the
ovary and palea, the surviving member of the inner whorl.

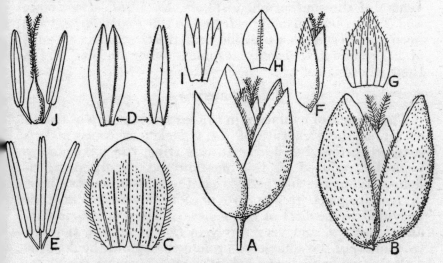

Fig. 165.—*Hierochloë odorata* (L.) Beauv. (Phalarideae).

A, spikelet. B, florets. C, lemma of lowest floret. D, palea of lowest
floret. E, stamens. F, uppermost floret. G, lemma of same. H, palea
of same. I, lodicules. J, stamens and pistil from uppermost floret.

It is worthy of note that the loss of lodicules and of male
organs in the lateral florets of *Anthoxanthum* occurs in
grasses with dense spike-like inflorescences in which the
crowded spikelets would be subjected to considerable compression during their development within the leaf-sheaths.
A further stage in reduction is reached in *Phalaris*,
where the two lateral florets are represented by very small
scales (vestigial lemmas) at the base of the fertile floret;
here, however, the flower retains three stamens and two
lodicules. *Anthoxanthum* differs from the other two

genera of the *Phalarideae* and from most of the genera possessing festucoid characters in that the basic chromosome number is 5.   In the Sweet Vernal Grass, *A. odoratum* L., cytologists have discovered two races, one with ten ($2n$) and the other with twenty ($2n$) chromosomes.   A few species of *Phalaris*, such as *P. canariensis* L. (Canary Grass), have the basic chromosome number of 6, but in most species, including *P. arundinacea* L. (Reed Canary Grass) (*Digraphis arundinacea* Trin.), it is 7.   The three genera of the southern hemisphere, *Ehrharta*, *Microlaena*, and *Tetrarrhena*, usually referred to the *Phalarideae*, have been transferred to a position near the *Oryzeae* on account of differences in their chromosome number and size, and in their siliceous cells.

IX. AGROSTEAE.

The climax of evolution in the festucoid group of tribes, so far as the structure of the spikelets is concerned, is reached in the *Agrosteae*.   In this tribe, the spikelets are typically reduced to the one-flowered condition.   Evidence favouring the theory that the *Agrosteae* have been derived from genera with two- or more-flowered spikelets is provided by several of our genera.   Thus in *Ammophila* and *Deyeuxia*, and very rarely in *Calamagrostis*, the axis (rhachilla) of the spikelet is prolonged beyond the floret as a fine hairy or glabrous bristle.   Such a structure is also found in *Gastridium*, as well as in *Lagurus*, where it occasionally terminates in the vestige of a second floret. In *Agrostis* and *Apera* the axis is minutely produced, in the former genus sometimes bearing a second vestigial or very rarely a complete floret, whilst in the latter a few examples have been discovered in British material of *Apera interrupta* (L.) Beauv., in which the axis bears a second and sometimes a third fertile floret.   Associated with this reduction in the number of florets is a decrease in the number of nerves (usually three to five) in the lemma.   It might be expected that a classification of genera based on such characters would result in a very artificial grouping;   this is true, particularly of those arrangements in which anatomical, cytological, and

distributional distinctions have not received due consideration. For example, some genera with relatively
firm terminally awned lemmas exserted from the glumes
resemble genera of the *Festuceae,* whereas others, on
account of their shorter dorsally awned and more delicate
lemmas and relatively longer firmer glumes, might equally
well be placed with the genera of the *Aveneae.* Certain
tropical genera, such as *Sporobolus* and *Aristida,* together
with *Stipa* and its allies, have already been segregated

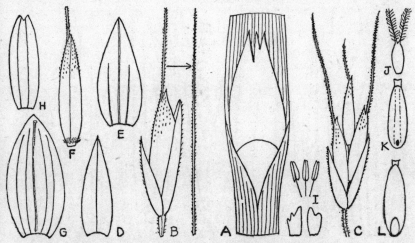

FIG. 166.—*Apera interrupta* (L.) Beauv. (Agrosteae).

A, ligule. B, spikelet. C, spikelet with three florets. D, lower glume.
E, upper glume. F, floret. G, lemma. H, palea. I, lodicules and
stamens. J, pistil. K, L, caryopsis, adaxial and abaxial views.

into different tribes. Our knowledge of this group of
grasses is too incomplete, however, for all the genera to
be disposed of satisfactorily.

Except for the anomalous genus *Milium,* the other
British genera here included in the *Agrosteae* agree in all
important morphological, cytological, and anatomical
characters. *Milium,* a small genus of the north temperate zone, has a strongly indurated lemma and palea, and
on this account has been referred to the *Stipeae.* It disagrees with the genera of that tribe in having dorsally
compressed florets, and above all, in possessing the large

kind of chromosome. *Milium effusum* L. (Spreading Millet) is common in damp woodland.

In the eleven British genera of the *Agrosteae* now to be considered, there is great diversity in the form of the inflorescence, ranging from the much-branched lax panicles of several species of *Agrostis* to the more specialised types seen in the cylindrical false spikes of *Phleum* and *Alopecurus* and the solitary one-sided spike-like racemes of *Mibora*. There is also a wide range in the texture of

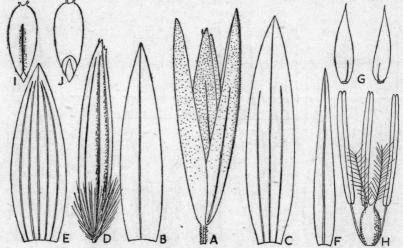

FIG. 167.—*Ammophila arenaria* (L.) Link (Agrosteae).

A, spikelet.   B, lower glume.   C, upper glume.   D, floret.   E, lemma.
F, palea.   G, lodicules.   H, stamens and pistil.   I, J, caryopsis, adaxial and abaxial views.

the lemmas from the indurated ones of *Ammophila* to the thinly membraneous kind characteristic of *Calamagrostis* and *Agrostis*. Adaptations and devices, such as the provision of awns and hairs ensuring wider seed-dispersal, are also prominent. It is such obvious distinctive features which have been largely employed in the delimitation of the genera of the *Agrosteae*.

The genera *Ammophila*, *Calamagrostis*, and *Deyeuxia* form a very natural group at least so far as the European species are concerned, agreeing in bearing a well-developed pappus-like ring of hairs at the base of the floret. The lemmas of these three genera have developed in a different manner, influenced no doubt by habitat and by the degree of protection afforded by the glumes, those of *Ammophila* being indurated and about as long as the glumes, of *Deyeuxia* somewhat less indurated, whilst those of *Calamagrostis* are delicately membranous and much shorter than the glumes. *Ammophila* (*Psamma*) comprises three species on the shores of the North Atlantic and Mediterranean, of which the very important sand-binder, *A. arenaria* (L.) Link (Marram Grass), is often dominant on the sand-dunes of western Europe. It is obviously closely related to *Calamagrostis*, in particular *C. epigejos* (L.) Roth (Wood Small Reed), with which it has formed two sterile hybrids, one *Ammocalamagrostis baltica* (Flügge) P. Fourn. (*Ammophila baltica* Link) occurring on the shores of East Norfolk, Northumberland, and Handa Island. Putative hybrids have also been recorded between species of *Calamagrostis* and *Deyeuxia*, although up to the present none has been discovered in the British Isles. *Calamagrostis* is more widespread than *Ammophila*, favouring damp habitats throughout the northern temperate zone and extending via the high mountains of East Africa to South Africa. Two species, *C. epigejos* (L.) Roth and *C. canescens* (Web.) Roth (*C. lanceolata* Roth), are natives of the British Isles. *Deyeuxia* is the largest of these genera, equally well represented in all temperate regions and with a few species on the mountains of tropical Asia and America. Some species, especially several from South America, closely resemble species of *Deschampsia*, whilst others in Asia are very similar to *Trisetum*. *Deyeuxia neglecta* (Ehrh.) Kunth is of rare occurrence in the British Isles.

Agrostis and *Polypogon* are grouped together, for although they show prominent structural differences, yet there exists a close affinity between them, *Polypogon monspeliensis* (L.) Desf. (Annual Beard Grass) forming natural hybrids with one or more species of *Agrostis*. The British hybrid, *Agropogon littoralis* (Sm.) C. E. Hubbard (*Polypogon littoralis* Sm.), originally discovered near Cley in Norfolk, has on several occasions been seen growing with its reputed parents, *Polypogon monspeliensis* and *Agrostis stolonifera* L. (Creeping Bent). Both *Agrostis* and *Polypogon* are widespread in temperate regions and in the tropics at high altitudes, although the former has by far the greater number of species. In *Agrostis*, distribution of the seed is first brought about by the spikelets breaking up, the axis being articulated between the upper glume and lemma so that the floret is freed at maturity. On the other hand, in *Polypogon* there is also a zone of articulation in the pedicel, thus permitting the complete spikelet to fall entire at maturity. This additional means of seed-shedding is connected with the presence of awns and minute rough points on the glumes, those of *Agrostis* being awnless. The British species of *Agrostis* fall into two sections, one comprising *A. stolonifera* L., *A. gigantea* Roth (Black Bent) and *A. tenuis* Sibth. (Fine Bent), having a palea one-third or more the length of the floret and normally awnless lemmas, and the second with *A. canina* L. (Brown Bent) and *A. setacea* Curt. (Bristle Bent), in which the palea is reduced to a very minute scale and the lemmas usually each provided with a dorsal awn.

Two species of the small European and Asiatic genus *Apera* were very early introduced into the British Isles, *A. spica-venti* (L.) Beauv. (Silky Bent Grass) occurring as a weed of arable land, and *A. interrupta* (L.) Beauv. principally in the Breckland of East Anglia. In these grasses the lemma, which is awned from just below the tip, becomes slightly indurated and rigid at maturity when it tightly envelops the grain. The elongated straight or flexuous awn (never geniculate as in *Agrostis*) and the rare development of two- to three-flowered spikelets with the florets exserted from the glumes, may be regarded as evidence that this genus is more closely related to the genera of the *Festuceae*, rather than to those of the *Aveneae*.

Gastridium, Lagurus, and *Mibora* are typical Mediterranean Region genera, all being annuals, with specialised inflorescences or spikelets. In *Gastridium ventricosum* (Gouan) Schinz et Thell. (Nit Grass), the spikelets, which are borne in spiciform panicles, frequently occur in two forms in the same inflorescence, some possessing awned hairy lemmas and others with these organs awnless and hairless.

Lagurus ovatus L. (Hare's Tail Grass) is frequently cultivated for ornament and has become naturalised in the Channel Islands. In this genus the spikelets are crowded into dense ovoid or oblong panicles, the loosely plumose glumes gradually attenuated into a fine bristle tip, and the lemma, in addition to being awned on the back, bears two fine bristles from its apex. Judging by their geniculate

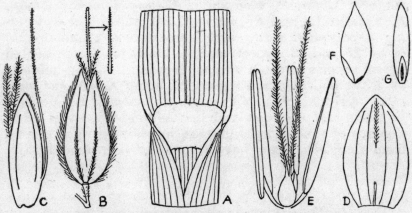

FIG. 168.—*Alopecurus pratensis* L. (Agrosteae).

A, ligule. B, spikelet. C, floret. D, lemma. E, stamens and pistil. F, G, caryopsis, side and abaxial views.

and twisted awns, both *Gastridium* and *Lagurus* are derivatives of avenaceous-like ancestors. *Mibora minima* (L.) Desv. (*Chamagrostis minima* Bork.), one of the smallest of our grasses, is found in sandy places in the Channel Islands and on Anglesey. It does not appear to have any close relatives amongst our genera of the *Agrosteae*.

Phleum and *Alopecurus* are often classified together in the subtribe *Phleinae* on account of the dense cylindrical spike-like inflorescences and apical projection of the stigmas from the florets, but this association is only one of convenience, for the two genera differ much in spikelet structure and the above similarities are no doubt due to

Y

parallel development. In *Phleum*, the glumes persist after the rest of the spikelet has fallen, whereas in *Alopecurus*, the spikelets fall entire at maturity due to an articulation at the tip of the pedicel. Furthermore, in *Alopecurus* the glumes are usually connate towards the base and likewise the margins of the lemmas, the lodicules are suppressed and the flower is protogynous. *Phleum* is limited in its distribution to the northern hemisphere, but *Alopecurus* is also present in the southern hemisphere. Five species of *Phleum* are native in the British Isles, three of them, *P. nodosum* L. (Lesser Timothy Grass), *P. alpinum* L., and *P. pratense* L. (Timothy Grass) forming a polyploid series with chromosome numbers $(2n)$ of 14, 28 and 42 respectively. *Alopecurus* is represented by six species in these islands, growing in damp habitats or heavy soils, the most common being *Alopecurus myosuroides* Huds. (Slender Foxtail), *A. pratensis* L. (Meadow Foxtail), and *A. geniculatus* L. As might be expected in a genus of protogynous grasses, hybrids between species from similar habitats have frequently been recorded.

X. HORDEEAE.

The *Hordeeae* might well have followed immediately after the *Festuceae* on account of their resemblance to *Brachypodium* and *Bromus*, all having simple starch grains, and somewhat similar caryopses, each with an elongated linear hilum. Economically it is one of the most important tribes of grasses, including such cereals as the Wheats, Barleys, and Rye. The tribe is here limited to the subtribes *Triticinae* and *Elyminae*, the genera *Nardus*, *Lolium*, and *Parapholis* (*Lepturus* of British Floras) being referred, respectively, to the tribes *Nardeae*, *Festuceae*, and *Monermeae*. The genera of the *Hordeeae*, thus restricted, have their spikelets arranged on opposite sides of the continuous or fragile axis of simple spikes or spike-like racemes, each spikelet with one to many florets and five- or more-nerved awnless or terminally awned lemmas. In Britain, the *Triticinae* comprise the genera *Agropyron*, *Triticum*, and *Secale*, in which the spikelets are solitary at each node of the inflorescence-axis, whereas in the *Elyminae*, represented by *Hordeum* and *Elymus*, two or three or more spikelets are clustered at each node. Reduction in the number of florets in each spikelet is greatest in *Hordeum* where the median spikelets of each cluster are one-flowered, and the lateral male or barren except in some cultivated barleys.

The close relationship which exists between most of the

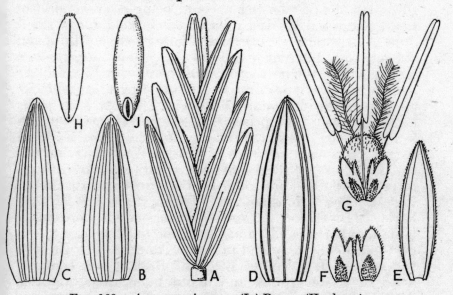

FIG. 169.—*Agropyron junceum* (L.) Beauv. (Hordeeae).

A, spikelet. B, lower glume. C, upper glume. D, lemma. E, palea.
F, lodicules. G, flower. H & J, caryopsis, adaxial and abaxial views.

genera of the *Hordeeae* has been demonstrated by the production of artificial hybrids, particularly between *Agropyron* and *Triticum*, *Triticum* and *Secale*, *Agropyron* and *Elymus*, and by the discovery of putative natural hybrids between *Agropyron* and *Elymus* (= *Agroëlymus*), and *Agropyron* and *Hordeum* (= *Agrohordeum*). The hybridisation of species of *Triticum* (Wheat) and *Agropyron* has been carried out largely in Russia and Canada, the aim of the plant-breeder being the production of perennial, hardy winter and early annual, drought- and disease-resistant wheats, besides forage grasses with large seeds. These researches, which are being continued, have already attained a fair measure of success.

Agropyron is by far the largest of all the genera of the *Hordeeae*, with numerous species in the temperate zones. In the British Isles, *A. repens* (L.) Beauv. (Couch Grass), *A. pungens* (Pers.) Roem. et Schult., and *A. junceum* (L.) Beauv. are provided with extensively creeping rhizomes, the first on this account being a serious pest of arable land and the last a valuable consolidator of sand-dunes. *A. caninum* (L.) Beauv. forms compact tufts and belongs to a different section of the genus. *Elymus* is a large genus of the northern hemisphere, with *E. arenarius* L. (Lyme Grass) serving as an important sand-binder on the shores of western Europe. *Triticum* and *Secale* have relatively few species with a smaller area of distribution, being restricted mainly to the Mediterranean region. *Triticum aestivum* L. (Bread Wheat), *T. turgidum* L. (Cone or Rivet Wheat), and *Secale cereale* L. (Rye) are all well-known cereals which are cultivated in the British Isles. *Hordeum*, in addition to the cultivated barleys (*H. vulgare* L. and *H. distichon* L.), includes a large number of wild annual and perennial species in the northern hemisphere and in South America. In Britain, the annual *H. murinum* L. (Wall Barley) is a common weed of waste ground and about habitations, and the perennial, *H. nodosum* L. (Meadow Barley), a frequent constituent of grassland on moist, heavy soils.

XI. Monermeae.[1]

In British Floras and Plant Lists, a small coastal species commonly known as " Hard Grass " has been usually described or listed as *Lepturus filiformis* (Roth) Trin. In recent years this grass and *L. incurvus* (L.) Druce, an addition to our flora, have been included in the genus *Pholiurus*, but a comprehensive study has shown that

---

[1] *Hordeae* subtribe *Leptureae* Hack. in Engl. u. Prantl, *Nat. Pflanzenf.* ii. Abt. 2, **78** : 1887 (excl. *Scribneria*). *Rottboellieae* Rouy, Fl. France, xiv. 337 (1913).

they are generically distinct from both *Lepturus* and *Pholiurus*. The two species have been referred therefore to a new genus, *Parapholis*, as *P. strigosus* (Dum.) C. E. Hubbard and *P. incurvus* (L.) C. E. Hubbard respectively. These species and a few other grasses belonging to the genera *Monerma* and *Pholiurus*, have usually been treated

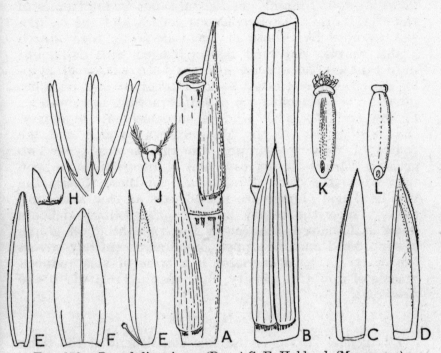

FIG. 170.—*Parapholis strigosus* (Dum.) C. E. Hubbard. (Monermeae).

A, portion of spike, side view. B, the same, front view. C, lower glume. D, upper glume. E, (right) floret. E, (left), palea. F, lemma. H, lodicules and stamens. J, pistil. K, L, caryopsis, adaxial and abaxial views.

as part of the *Hordeeae* on account of their spicate inflorescences, although in recent years some have seen fit to segregate them from that tribe and classify them with *Lepturus* in the *Leptureae*. Unfortunately, neither of these arrangements has proved satisfactory. From the *Hordeeae*, these grasses may be readily distinguished by their compound starch grains, one- to three-nerved membranous lemmas, and by their spikelets being more or less sunken in depressions in the axis of slender spikes. They do bear, however, a very close resemblance in general structure to species of the genus *Lepturus*. Nevertheless, it seems very probable that we have here another example of parallel development. True species of *Lepturus* are found mainly on coastal sands in the tropics of the Old World. Their siliceous cells are of the saddle-shaped type like those of the *Chlorideae*, their starch grains simple, and their ligules fringed with hairs, but unfortunately no species has yet been examined cytologically. On the other hand, *Parapholis* and its allies possess the festucoid type of leaf-structure, membranous ligules, and the large kind of chromosome; moreover, they are natives of the Mediterranean region and the coasts of western Europe. On this account our two grasses, *Parapholis strigosus* and *P. incurvus*, have been referred to the tribe *Monermeae*. In these species the two hardened glumes are placed side by side and completely cover the cavity in which the solitary delicate floret is immersed, whereas in *Monerma* the lower glume is suppressed and the upper glume alone entirely covers the cavity. The *Monermeae* is a tribe of very reduced grasses of doubtful affinity, but possibly related to the *Festuceae*.

XII. NARDEAE.

The genus *Nardus* is the sole constituent of the tribe *Nardeae*. Its single species, *N. stricta* L. (Mat Grass or White Bent), has a wide geographical distribution, extending from western Asia through Europe to north-west Africa and the Azores, and to Newfoundland and Greenland. In the British Isles it is frequently abundant on acid peaty soils from the lowlands to quite high altitudes. It has usually been grouped with the genera of the *Hordeeae*, no doubt on account of its spicate inflorescence, although striking differences in spikelet structure alone should have been sufficient to warrant its separation as a distinct tribe. *Nardus* presents a unique combination of characters, strongly suggesting that it is a relict of a very

ancient group of grasses from which both the festucoid
and panicoid groups of tribes have been derived. Although
the solitary one-sided spike-like inflorescences and the
three-nerved lemmas recall those of several genera of the
Chlorideae, yet it has to be kept apart on account of
important anatomical and cytological differences. The
epidermis is provided with slender two-celled hairs of the

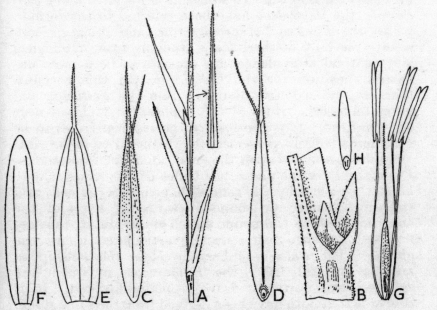

Fig. 171.—*Nardus stricta* L. (Nardeae).

A, apical part of spike. B, rhachis, with glumes of terminal spikelet.
C, D, floret, back and front views. E, lemma. F, palea. G, stamens
and young grain. H, caryopsis, abaxial view.

type found in the *Paniceae*, but the siliceous cells are not
of one kind, being apparently saddle-, or dumb-bell-shaped,
rounded or elongated. The leaf-anatomy of *Nardus* is
similar to that of the festucoid group of tribes. Cytologically it resembles this group also in having relatively
large chromosomes, but the basic number is 13 instead of
the usual 7. The one-flowered spikelets are characterised
by extreme reduction or suppression of the glumes,
absence of lodicules and by the solitary papillose stigma.

It should be noted that absence of lodicules is here associated with protogyny, which also occurs in *Anthoxanthum* and *Alopecurus*, two more genera deficient in lodicules.

XIII. CHLORIDEAE.

In those classifications in which the *Gramineae* have been divided into the two subfamilies *Pooideae* and *Panicoideae*, the *Chlorideae* have been referred to the former, whilst the *Paniceae*, *Andropogoneae*, and *Maydeae* constitute the bulk of the latter. Judging from cytological and anatomical evidence this appears to be a most unnatural position for the *Chlorideae*. In this account, therefore, it has been divorced from the *Festuceae* and other temperate tribes of the *Pooideae* and placed near the *Paniceae*. It is the first of the tropical tribes to be considered which possesses the panicoid type of leaf anatomy associated with the small kind of chromosomes. From the *Paniceae* and other tribes of this series it may be distinguished by the saddle-shaped siliceous cells and the short swollen or rounded two-celled hairs of the epidermis, by the compound starch grains and by the one-flowered spikelets being usually articulated above the glumes. The *Chlorideae* bears a close relationship to another tropical tribe—the *Eragrosteae*, in which the spikelets are normally two- to many-flowered. It is probable that both have been derived from the same stock. In the case of the *Chlorideae* evolution has proceeded from several-flowered spikelets in panicles to the one-flowered condition of the spikelets and their arrangement in one-sided spikes and spike-like racemes.

The two genera *Cynodon* and *Spartina*, found in the British Isles, belong to very distinct subtribes of the *Chlorideae*. *Cynodon* is a typical member of the tribe with the chromosomes in multiples of nine, whereas *Spartina* occupies a somewhat isolated position, its chromosomes being in multiples of seven. *Cynodon dactylon* (L.) Pers. is a creeping perennial with slender digitately arranged spikes, widespread in tropical and warm temperate regions and established on sandy seashores in south-west England.

The species of *Spartina* are mostly maritime, inhabiting salt-marshes and mud-flats on both sides of the Atlantic, but the majority of species are natives of North America. On account of the high proportion of polyploid species and the absence of diploids it is considered that the genus must have been for a long time established, so that its centre of origin is not known. Up to 1870, only two species, *S. maritima* (Curt.) Fernald (*S. stricta* Roth) and *S. alterniflora* Lois., were known from the British Isles, but a third, *S. townsendi* H. et J. Groves, was then dis-

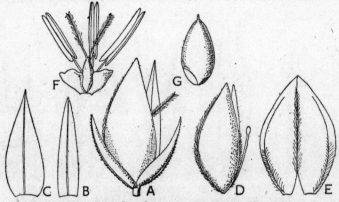

FIG. 172.—*Cynodon dactylon* (L.) Pers. (Chlorideae).
A, spikelet. B, lower glume. C, upper glume. D, fertile floret and vestige of second floret. E, lemma. F, flower. G, caryopsis, side view.

covered in the salt-marshes of Southampton Water. The last species, which has the very high chromosome number of 126, is presumed to be the product of hybridisation between *S. maritima* and *S. alterniflora*. It has spread rapidly in the tidal mud of estuaries and harbours of southern England, at times becoming a menace to navigation, but more often proving of great benefit to mankind by consolidating and protecting foreshores from erosion. The species of *Spartina* differ from other genera of the *Chlorideae* in the spikelets being articulated below the glumes, the absence of lodicules, the rounded siliceous cells and the specialised type of two-celled hair which is sunken in the epidermis.

The *Paniceae, Andropogoneae,* and *Maydeae* are essentially tribes of tropical regions, where they form the greater part of the grass flora. The few species belonging to them and occurring in the British Isles are weeds—sometimes relicts of earlier cultivations—or are cultivated for food or ornament. The three tribes resemble one another in many respects and appear to be closely related, especially the *Andropogoneae* and *Maydeae.* The group may be recognised by the following combination of cytological, anatomical, and morphological characters. The chromosomes are of the small type, mainly with basic

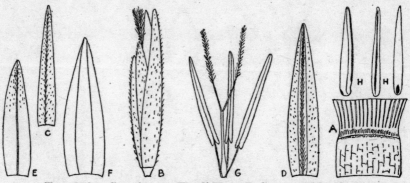

FIG. 173.—*Spartina townsendi* H. et J. Groves (Chlorideae).

A, ligule. B, spikelet. C, lower glume. D, upper glume. E, lemma. F, palea. G, stamens and pistil. H, caryopsis, side, adaxial and abaxial views.

numbers of 5, 9, 10, or 12; the leaf-anatomy is of the panicoid type; the epidermis is provided with filiform two-celled hairs and usually cross- or dumb-bell-shaped siliceous cells; the first green leaf-blade of the seedling is relatively wide and spreading; the caryopses contain simple starch grains, and the hilum is usually small and basal; the spikelets are reduced to two florets, and being articulated below the glumes fall entire at maturity; the lower floret is mostly male or barren and the upper hermaphrodite in fertile spikelets.

XIV. PANICEAE.

The *Paniceae* are represented in the British Isles by annual weedy species of the genera *Setaria, Echinochloa,* and *Digitaria*, whilst species of *Panicum*, especially *P. miliaceum* L. (Common or Broomcorn Millet), are occasionally found on rubbish-tips. In this tribe, protection of the grain is effected by the awnless upper lemma and palea becoming indurated at maturity, whilst the glumes and lower lemma remain membranous. The simplest form of inflorescence is found in the genus *Panicum*, where the spikelets are pedicelled on the branches of open or contracted panicles. In our species of *Setaria*, the inflorescence is densely spicate and bristly; many of the

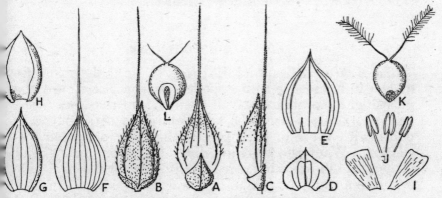

FIG. 174.—*Echinochloa crus-galli* (L.) Beauv. (Paniceae).

A, B, C, spikelet, front, back and side views. D, lower glume. E, upper glume. F, lemma of lower floret. G, lemma of upper floret. H, palea of upper floret. I, lodicules. J, stamens. K, pistil. L, caryopsis, abaxial view.

branchlets being sterile and reduced to barbed bristles. Occasionally some of these bristle-like branchlets may be found bearing spikelets at their tips, especially in *Setaria italica* (L.) Beauv. (Italian or Foxtail Millet). In *S. verticillata* (L.) Beauv., the bristles are retrorsely barbed, so that the inflorescence may become attached to the fur of animals, thus assisting in the dispersal of the seeds. The inflorescences of *Echinochloa* and *Digitaria* provide an excellent example of the way in which the arrangement of the spikelets has been modified so that during development they may fully occupy the limited spaces within the leaf-sheath. Here the spikelets are borne in pairs on the

lower side of the branches, with one of each pair short-
and the other longer-pedicelled, so that the naked backs
of the branches may fit tightly against the main axis of
the inflorescence or against one another.   In *Echinochloa*
the spike-like branches are scattered or in clusters along
the main axis, whereas in *Digitaria* they are digitately
arranged at the apex of the culm.   Amongst our *Paniceae*,
Digitaria exhibits the greatest reduction in the structure
of the spikelets, for the lower glume is minute or suppressed and the lower floret is barren with the palea very
small and with two minute lodicules.

XV. ANDROPOGONEAE.

The *Andropogoneae* and *Maydeae*, so far as the structure
of the inflorescence and spikelets is concerned, are the
most highly specialised of all the tribes of the *Gramineae*.
In the *Andropogoneae* the spikelets are mostly borne in
pairs, with those of each pair similar or more often dissimilar.   When the pairs are dissimilar, then one spikelet
is hermaphrodite and often sessile and the other male
or barren and pedicelled.   These distinctions in sex
are correlated with differences in shape, size, and
structure; thus while the fertile spikelets are mostly
awned, the male or barren spikelets are awnless.   The
glumes of the fertile spikelets in the *Andropogoneae* both
exceed the florets, and being rigid and indurated protect
the delicate lemmas and paleas and the grain.   Few
genera of this tribe, so abundant in the tropics, are met
with in the British Isles, but species of *Sorghum* are
occasionally encountered on rubbish-tips, whilst species of
Miscanthus, especially forms with variegated leaves, are
cultivated for ornament in gardens.   The *Andropogoneae* includes the important cereals known as Durra,
Milo, Kafir Corn, etc. (*Sorghum* spp.), Sugarcane (*Sac-
charum* spp.), and the essential-oil grasses (*Cymbopogon*
and *Vetiveria* spp.).

XVI. Maydeae.

The *Maydeae* represents the climax of evolution in the panicoid group of tribes. The basic structure of the spikelets is essentially like that of the *Andropogoneae*, but the spikelets are all unisexual and awnless; those of each sex being different in appearance. The sexes are either borne in different inflorescences or in different parts of the same inflorescence. *Zea mays* L. (Maize or Indian Corn), the most important member of the tribe, is frequently cultivated in the warmer parts of these islands, either as fodder, or for the young " cobs " which are used as a vegetable. In this genus the female inflorescence, commonly known as the " cob ", is borne in the axils of the lower leaves and is closely enveloped by sheaths. The spikelets are arranged in longitudinal rows on a fleshy, thickened axis, and their elongated styles project from the apex of the sheaths. The male spikelets are to be found in spike-like racemes clustered at the apex of the culm and forming the " tassel ". *Coix lacryma-jobi* L. (Job's tears), occasionally cultivated for ornament, has the female spikelets enclosed in a globose or ovoid ivory-like sheath, from the apex of which emerges the male raceme.

Key to the tribes and genera of the Gramineae.

(The tribes and genera represented by cultivated species only are enclosed in square brackets.)

Tree-like or shrubby; culms woody, persistent; leaf-blades flat, broad, usually with a petiole-like base (pseudo-petiole) and frequently articulated with the sheath; lemmas 5- to many-nerved
[I. BAMBUSEAE]

Perennial or annual herbs, with herbaceous, very rarely somewhat woody culms; leaf-blades usually sessile and rarely articulated with the sheath :

*Spikelets with one to many florets, usually breaking up at maturity, rarely falling entire; lowest floret hermaphrodite, rarely male or barren and then the spikelets with more than two florets, or with the rhachilla prolonged beyond the uppermost floret :

Palea 3- or more-nerved; stamens 6 or less; spikelets with one to three florets but in the latter case with the lower two reduced to the lemmas; glumes minute or suppressed; grain with an elongated linear hilum . . . . II. ORYZEAE

Palea 2-nerved or nerveless, rarely 1-nerved; stamens 3 or less; glumes usually well developed, at least the upper, rarely with one or both much reduced or suppressed :

Florets enveloped by long silky hairs from the rhachilla or the lower part of the lemma; tall grasses with stout culms, long flat leaf-blades and usually large panicles; spikelets 2–10-flowered; lemmas 1–7-nerved. . . . . . . IV. ARUNDINEAE

Florets usually not enveloped by long hairs, but if so then the spikelets only 1-flowered :

†Spikelets borne in open or contracted or spike-like panicles, rarely in racemes or spikes and then with both glumes developed and the lemmas 5-nerved if on one side of the axis, or with the lower glume suppressed if on opposite sides of a continuous axis :

Spikelets typically with two or more florets, but not always all fertile :

Ligule represented by a line of hairs   . V. DANTHONIEAE

Ligule membranous :

Glumes usually shorter than the lowest floret and with the upper florets distinctly exserted, rarely longer and then often with dull firm margins like those of the lemmas; lemmas awnless, or with a straight or flexuous awn from the entire or bifid apex, or up to 5-awned or -toothed VI. FESTUCEAE

Glumes usually as long as or longer than the lowest floret, often as long as the spikelet and enclosing the florets; lemmas awnless or more often awned from the back, the awn frequently geniculate; glumes frequently with thin shining margins :

Spikelets mostly with two or more hermaphrodite florets, never with two male or sterile florets beneath a terminal hermaphrodite one . . . . . . VII. AVENEAE

Spikelets with three florets, the lower two male or barren, and the terminal floret hermaphrodite and awnless

VIII. PHALARIDEAE

Spikelets typically with only one floret :

Lemma indurated and rigid at maturity, more or less terete, with involute or convolute margins, awned from the entire or minutely 2-lobed tip . . . . . . [III. STIPEAE]

Lemma hyaline or membranous at maturity, awnless or often awned from the back, rarely indurated and then dorsally compressed and awnless . . . . . IX. AGROSTEAE

††Spikelets sessile or shortly pedicelled along one side of the axis of spikes or spike-like racemes, or on opposite sides of the axis of solitary spikes or racemes :

Spikelets on opposite sides of the axis of solitary spikes or spike-like racemes :

Lemmas 5- to 9-nerved, at length indurated; spikelets 1- to many-flowered, solitary or in clusters, not sunken in hollows in the axis, the latter continuous or articulated; starch grains simple . . . . X. HORDEEAE

Lemmas 1- to 3-nerved, hyaline or membranous; spikelets 1-
to 2-flowered, solitary, more or less sunken in hollows in the
usually articulate axis; starch grains compound
IX. MONERMEAE
Spikelets in one or two rows on one side of the usually continuous axis of solitary, digitate or scattered spikes or spike-
like racemes; lemmas 1- to 3-nerved :
Glumes extremely small, the upper usually suppressed;
rhachilla not produced beyond the single floret; stigma 1;
lodicules suppressed; spikes solitary. . XII. NARDEAE
Glumes usually well developed, or the lower reduced; rhachilla
produced; stigmas 2; lodicules 2 or rarely suppressed.
XIII. CHLORIDEAE
**Spikelets with two florets, mostly falling entire at maturity, usually
with the upper floret hermaphrodite (or male or female in a few
cases), and the lower male or barren, all alike or differing in size,
shape and structure; rhachilla not produced beyond the upper
floret; starch grains simple :
Glumes usually membranous, the lower frequently smaller or sometimes suppressed; lower lemma mostly resembling the upper
glume in texture; upper lemma papery to tough and rigid, usually
awnless; spikelets more or less similar . . XIV. PANICEAE
Glumes as long as the spikelets and enclosing the florets, more or
less rigid and firmer than the lemmas, which are both hyaline or
thinly membranous; spikelets often in pairs, with one sessile
and the other pedicelled, those of each pair similar or often
dissimilar :
Spikelets all hermaphrodite, or with male or barren and hermaphrodite spikelets mixed in the same inflorescence and so arranged
that a male or barren spikelet is near a hermaphrodite spikelet;
upper lemma frequently awned in hermaphrodite spikelets
[XV. ANDROPOGONEAE]
Male and female spikelets in separate inflorescences, or in different
parts of the same inflorescence and of different appearance;
upper lemma awnless . . . . [XVI. MAYDEAE]

[I. BAMBUSEAE.]

Culms usually circular in transverse section . . [ARUNDINARIA]
Culms with the internodes more or less flattened on one side
[PHYLLOSTACHYS]

II. ORYZEAE.

Spikelets 1-flowered, strongly laterally compressed; lemmas papery
when dry; glumes reduced to a very obscure rim at the tip of the
pedicel . . . . LEERSIA

[III. STIPEAE.]

Lemmas 5- to 7-nerved; awn bent or geniculate, often twisted below
the bend; lodicules usually 3; hilum linear, almost as long as the
grain . . . . [STIPA]

IV. ARUNDINEAE.

Spikelets bisexual; leaf-blades more or less evenly distributed along the many-noded culms; rhizomatous grasses :

Lowest floret male or barren; fertile lemmas glabrous, but enveloped by silky hairs arising on the basal callus . . . . PHRAGMITES

Lowest floret hermaphrodite; lemmas long-hairy in the lower part
[ARUNDO]

Spikelets unisexual, the sexes on different plants; leaf-blades crowded at the base; forming dense tussocks . . . . [CORTADERIA]

V. DANTHONIEAE.

Glumes exceeding the lemmas, the latter three-toothed and 7-nerved; florets usually cleistogamous . . . . SIEGLINGIA

Glumes shorter than the lemmas, the latter obtuse or acute, entire and 3-nerved; florets not cleistogamous . . . . MOLINIA

VI. FESTUCEAE.

*Lemmas awnless, or awned from the usually entire or two-toothed tip; stigmas usually laterally exserted from the florets, mostly short and plumose :

†Spikelets without a club-shaped mass of sterile lemmas at the apex; lemmas usually exserted from the glumes; glumes membranous to coriaceous :

‡Spikelets all alike in the same inflorescence :

§Lemmas 5- to many-nerved :

¶Lemmas longer than broad, not cordate at the base, erect or spreading obliquely :

Ovary with a hairy 2- to 3-lobed appendage at the apex, with the styles lateral on the appendage; hilum linear, long; starch grains simple; spikelets 5- to many-flowered; lemmas usually awned or mucronate :

Spikelets borne in loose or contracted panicles . . BROMUS

Spikelets very short-pedicelled on opposite sides of the axis of solitary racemes . . . . BRACHYPODIUM

Ovary without an appendage at the apex; starch grains compound :

α Lemmas rounded on the back, at least below the middle :

Lemmas usually narrowed towards the apex, awnless, awned or mucronate, with the nerves more or less converging in the upper part :

Spikelets pedicelled in open or contracted panicles :

Perennials, tufted or rhizomatous; lemmas lanceolate, acute, awnless or awned; glumes usually not markedly unequal; hilum linear, long . . . . FESTUCA

Annual grasses :

Lemmas subulate-lanceolate, gradually tapering into a slender straight awn; glumes usually very unequal; panicle contracted and rather dense; hilum linear, long
VULPIA

Lemmas oblong, obtuse, awnless; glumes slightly unequal; panicle rigid; hilum basal, punctiform. . Scleropoa
Spikelets sessile or short-pedicelled on opposite sides of the axis of a solitary spike or raceme :
  Spikelets sessile; lower glume suppressed in all except the terminal spikelet; hilum linear, long . . . Lolium
  Spikelets very shortly pedicelled; both glumes developed; hilum basal, punctiform . . . . . . Desmazeria
Lemmas rather broad, awnless, obtuse and hyaline at the apex, with the nerves more or less parallel :
  Nerves of lemma not prominent; hilum basal, punctiform; grasses of saline soil . . . . . . Puccinellia
  Nerves of lemma prominent; hilum linear, as long as the grain; fresh water grasses . . . . . Glyceria
ααLemmas keeled; hilum punctiform, basal :
  Spikelets in loose or contracted, not one-sided, panicles; lemmas awnless . . . . Poa
  Spikelets in dense one-sided clusters, arranged in contracted panicles; lemmas mucronate or short-awned . Dactylis
¶¶Lemmas about as long as broad, closely imbricate, awnless, cordate at the base, spreading horizontally; spikelets many-flowered
                                                 Briza
§§Lemmas 3-nerved, awnless, truncate; spikelets up to 4-flowered; plants stoloniferous . . . . Catabrosa
‡‡Spikelets of two kinds, clustered, the terminal spikelet of each cluster fertile, the lateral barren and composed of numerous bracts, persistent; panicle dense, spike-like, one-sided
                                          Cynosurus
††Spikelets with a club-shaped mass of sterile lemmas at the apex; glumes membranous and shining, more or less equalling the lemmas; hilum linear, as long as the grain . . . . . . Melica
**Lemmas up to 5-toothed, the teeth awned or awnless; stigmas rather long, pubescent, projecting from the apices of the florets; inflorescence very dense and spike-like. . . . . . . Sesleria

VII. AVENEAE.

Lemmas awnless, or with a mucro or short awn from or near the tip, 3- to 5-nerved; spikelets 2- or more-flowered; rhachilla glabrous or finely hairy; panicles dense and spike-like, often cylindrical
                                       Koeleria
Lemmas usually awned, or if awnless, then with different panicles from those above :
Spikelets breaking up at maturity leaving the persistent glumes, when 2- or more-flowered then with the second floret hermaphrodite :
Lowest floret hermaphrodite :
  Awns not articulated, the bristle part finely pointed :
    Spikelets relatively large, 1 cm. or more long; ovary hairy from the middle upwards or all over; lemmas 5- to 11-nerved; hilum linear, elongated :

z

Perennials; spikelets erect or spreading; glumes 1- to 7-nerved
                                                          HELICTOTRICHON
Annuals; spikelets pendulous; glumes 7- to 11-nerved. AVENA
Spikelets smaller, less than 1 cm. long; ovary glabrous; lemmas
    3- to 5-nerved :
  Lemmas awned from the back above the middle, 2-toothed,
      keeled; spikelets 2- to 6-flowered; glumes 1- to 3-nerved;
      rhachilla ciliate or long-haired . . . . . TRISETUM
  Lemmas usually awned from below the middle, rarely above or
      awnless, rounded on the back :
    Lemmas 2-lobed, truncate or toothed at the apex; upper
        glume 3-nerved; spikelets 2- to 4-flowered; mostly perennials
                                                          DESCHAMPSIA
    Lemmas acute, usually minutely 2-toothed at the apex; upper
        glume 1-nerved; spikelets strictly 2-flowered; annuals
                                                          AIRA
Awns articulated, and with a circle of minute hairs at the point of
    articulation, the bristle part club-shaped; spikelets 2- to 3-
    flowered; lemmas acute, awned from near the base
                                                          CORYNEPHORUS
Lowest floret usually male; spikelets 2- to 3-flowered; lowest
    lemma awned from near the base, the second awned from the tip
    or awnless; ovary hairy . . . . . . ARRHENATHERUM
Spikelets articulated below the glumes, strongly laterally compressed,
    strictly 2-flowered; lower floret awnless; upper floret awned,
    usually male . . . . HOLCUS

VIII. PHALARIDEAE.

Lower two florets male or barren, their lemmas awned or awnless and
    longer than the terminal lemma :
  Glumes equal or nearly so; lower florets male or barren; spikelets
      brownish; panicle open or closed; lodicules 2. . . HIEROCHLOË
  Glumes unequal; lower florets barren; spikelets greenish, yellowish
      or tinged with purple; panicle spike-like; lodicules 0
                                                          ANTHOXANTHUM
Lower two florets barren, their lemmas reduced to very small awnless
    scales much shorter than the terminal lemma . . . PHALARIS

IX. AGROSTEAE.

*Lemma thinly membranous, often hyaline, very rarely indurated, but
    then with strongly laterally compressed spikelets :
  †Inflorescence a loose or contracted or spike-like panicle, with spikelets
      all round the axis :
    ‡Spikelets in loose or contracted or sometimes spike-like panicles;
        stigmas laterally exserted :
      §Glumes glabrous, or at least not conspicuously hairy; lemmas
          truncate, entire, or 2-toothed at the apex but the lobes awnless :
        Floret with a tuft of hairs from the basal callus, the hairs from
            one-fourth the length of to much longer than the lemma :

Panicles loose or dense, but not spike-like :
Lemma much shorter than the glumes, hyaline or delicately membranous ; callus long-bearded, the hairs as long as or much longer than the lemma ; rhachilla not produced or only as a very short bristle ; glumes very narrowly lanceolate
CALAMAGROSTIS
Lemma nearly as long or as long as the glumes, becoming indurated at maturity ; callus usually short-bearded ; rhachilla produced, plumose ; glumes broader . DEYEUXIA
Panicles dense, spike-like, more or less cylindrical ; lemma about as long as the glumes, becoming indurated and coriaceous
AMMOPHILA
Florets glabrous on the basal callus or only slightly hairy there :
Glumes not swollen and bulging at the base ; panicles open or contracted :
Spikelets breaking up at maturity, leaving the more or less persistent glumes ; glumes awnless :
Lemma as long as the glumes or slightly longer, awned from the back just below the entire tip with the awn straight and relatively long ; lemma becoming slightly hardened and rigid, with involute margins . . . . APERA
Lemma shorter than the glumes, awned from the back, rarely from the tip, with the awn short, or awnless, membranous and often hyaline . . . . AGROSTIS
Spikelets articulated below the glumes and more or less falling entire at maturity ; glumes awned . . . . POLYPOGON
Glumes swollen and shining near the base ; lemma much shorter than the glumes, awned or awnless ; panicle spike-like
GASTRIDIUM
§§Glumes closely plumose with fine spreading hairs, tapering into a fine bristle ; lemma much shorter than the glumes, 2-toothed at the apex, with each tooth produced into a fine bristle, awned from the back ; panicle spike-like . . . . . . LAGURUS
‡‡Spikelets in narrowly cylindrical and densely spike-like panicles ; stigmas terminally exserted from the spikelet :
Spikelets breaking up at maturity ; glumes mucronate or short-awned ; lemma awnless . . . . PHLEUM
Spikelets articulated below the glumes and deciduous as a whole at maturity ; glumes awnless ; lemmas awned. . ALOPECURUS
††Inflorescence a solitary one-sided spike-like raceme ; lemmas awnless ; low tufted annual with very slender hair-like culms . . MIBORA
**Lemmas indurated and coriaceous, smooth and shining, awnless ; floret dorsally compressed ; panicles loose or contracted . . MILIUM

X. HORDEEAE.

Spikelets solitary at each node of the axis of the spike :
Perennials, rhizomatous or tufted ; glumes and lemmas lanceolate to oblong ; grain adhering to the palea . . . . . AGROPYRON

Annuals; grain free from the palea :
Glumes broad, ventricose, 3- or more-nerved; spikelets 2- to 5-flowered . . . . [TRITICUM]
Glumes very narrow, linear-subulate, 1-nerved; spikelets usually 2-flowered . . . . [SECALE]
Spikelets paired or clustered at each node of the axis :
Spikelets three at each node, 1-flowered, the lateral spikelets of each cluster usually much reduced and barren (except in some cultivated races) . . . . HORDEUM
Spikelets usually paired at each node, 2- to 6-flowered . . ELYMUS

XI. MONERMEAE.

Spikes very slender, cylindrical, articulated; spikelets 1-flowered; glumes placed side by side; annuals . . . . . PARAPHOLIS

XII. NARDEAE.

Spikelets 1-flowered, awned; stigma elongated, minutely hairy; densely tufted perennial, with setaceous leaf-blades . . NARDUS

XIII. CHLORIDEAE.

Spikes borne along the main axis of an elongated inflorescence; spikelets articulated below the glumes, hence falling entire at maturity; lemma as long as or shorter than the glumes, 1-nerved . SPARTINA
Spikes digitately arranged at the apex of the culm; spikelets breaking up at maturity; lemmas exceeding the glumes, 3-nerved . CYNODON

XIV. PANICEAE.

Spikelets pedicelled in lax or contracted panicles . . . [PANICUM]
Spikelets variously arranged, in spike-like bristly panicles or in one-sided spike-like racemes :
Spikelets subtended by one or several bristles (modified branchlets), often borne in spike-like panicles . . . . SETARIA
Spikelets not subtended by bristles, borne in one-sided spike-like racemes :
Spikelets cuspidate or awned, borne in dense scattered or clustered spike-like racemes . . . . ECHINOCHLOA
Spikelets awnless, borne in slender spike-like racemes which are usually more or less digitately arranged . . . . DIGITARIA

[XV. ANDROPOGONEAE.]

Spikelets in pairs, all alike, unequally pedicelled, borne in large panicles of slender hairy racemes . . . . [MISCANTHUS]
Spikelets of each pair dissimilar, one sessile and hermaphrodite, the other pedicelled and male or barren, borne in panicles [SORGHUM]

[XVI. MAYDEAE.]

Male spikelets borne in large terminal panicles; female spikelets in stout axillary sheathed spikes . . . . [ZEA]

ARTIFICIAL KEY TO THE FAMILIES OF BRITISH FLOWERING PLANTS.

THE following key to the DICOTYLEDONES and MONO-COTYLEDONES is entirely artificial and is provided to enable the student to ascertain the family of any indigenous plant in the British Isles. It is adapted from the key published in my *Families of Flowering Plants*, but in this case the more easily observed characters are placed first, such as the presence or absence of petals or whether they are free from one another or united, and whether the ovary is superior or inferior. These features can be seen in most cases even without a lens, but a sharp penknife or razor-blade and lens or small dissecting microscope is necessary to find out if the ovules are attached to the walls (parietal) or to the central axis (axile). Wherever there seems likely to be any doubt as to the position of the ovules, the family has been put in more than one group.

Groups III and VII contain the largest number of families, and in both of these the ovules are attached to the central axis or top or bottom of the ovary, this being a climax type of placentation and characteristic of the larger families such as *Umbelliferae, Rubiaceae, Compositae, Scrophulariaceae, Boraginaceae*, and *Labiatae*, which are also climax groups judged by other standards. The most advanced type of ovary is, of course, that characteristic of *Compositae*, which is inferior, reduced to one loculus, and with a single ovule. Another very advanced but different type is found in *Labiatae*, in which it is vertically divided into four uniovulate lobes with the style arising from within their base (gynobasic).

Leaves usually with a net-like venation; embryo in the seed and the seedling with two seed-leaves; vascular bundles in the stem arranged in a ring or rings . . . . DICOTYLEDONES
Leaves usually with parallel nerves and often narrow leaves; embryo in the seed and the seedling with only one seed-leaf; vascular bundles in the stem scattered . . . . . MONOCOTYLEDONES (p. 358)

Key to the artificial groups of Dicotyledones

Carpels free from one another, more than 1; styles free .   *Group* 1
Carpels united, or carpel 1, or if carpels free below, then with styles
    united :
    Petals present, free from one another :
      Ovary superior :
        Ovules attached to the walls of the ovary   .   .   .   *Group* 2
        Ovules attached to the middle, top or bottom of the ovary
                                               Group 3
      Ovary inferior :
        Ovules attached to the walls of the ovary   .   .   .   *Group* 4
        Ovules attached to the middle, top or bottom of the ovary   *Group* 5
    Petals present, united into a tube :
      Ovary superior :
        Ovules attached to the walls of the ovary .   .   .   .   *Group* 6
        Ovules attached to the middle, top or bottom of the ovary   *Group* 7
      Ovary inferior :
        Ovules attached to the walls of the ovary   .   .   .   *Group* 8
        Ovules attached to the middle, top or bottom of the ovary   *Group* 9
    Petals absent :
      Ovary superior :
        Ovules attached to the walls of the ovary .   .   .   .   *Group* 10
        Ovules attached to the middle, top or bottom of the ovary   *Group* 11
      Ovary inferior :
        Ovules attached to the walls of the ovary .   .   .   .   *Group* 12
        Ovules attached to the middle, top or bottom of the ovary   *Group* 13

Group 1.

Leaves alternate or all radical :
   Leaves stipulate, sometimes the stipules on the leaf-stalk   *Rosaceae*
   Leaves not stipulate :
     Flowers actinomorphic (regular) :
       Petals free or absent :
         Carpels not sunk in the torus   .   .   .   .   .   *Ranunculaceae*
         Carpels sunk in the torus   .   .   .   .   .   *Nymphaeaceae*
         Petals united ; flowers in racemes   .   .   .   .   *Crassulaceae*
       Flowers zygomorphic (irregular), blue   .   .   .   *Ranunculaceae*
   Leaves opposite :
     Carpels more than 2, completely free ; corolla not tubular or absent
       and sepals more or less petaloid   .   .   .   .   *Ranunculaceae*
     Carpels 2, free only at the base ; corolla tubular   .   *Apocynaceae*

Group 2.

Leaves alternate or all radical :
   Stamens numerous (more than 12) :
     Flowers actinomorphic (regular) :
       Sepals more than 3, more or less persistent :
         Not aquatic ; carpel 1   .   .   .   .   .   .   *Ranunculaceae*

Aquatic; carpels more than 1 . . . . *Nymphaeaceae*
Sepals 2 or 3, soon falling off . . . . . . *Papaveraceae*
Flowers zygomorphic (irregular) :
  Ovary of 1 carpel :
    Petals considerably modified; seeds with endosperm
                                                 Ranunculaceae
    Petals not particularly modified, composed of standard, wing and
      keel; seeds without endosperm . . . . . *Papilionaceae*
  Ovary of more than 1 carpel; petals divided . . . *Resedaceae*
Stamens 12 or fewer :
  Stamens tetradynamous (four long and two short); sepals and
    petals 4 each; ovary of 2 carpels, often divided by a false septum
                                                 Cruciferae

Stamens and other organs not as above :
Flowers actinomorphic (regular) :
  Shrubs :
    Fruit a berry; branches with leaf-thorns . . *Berberidaceae*
    Fruit a capsule; branches not thorny . . . *Tamaricaceae*
  Herbs :
    Stamens free :
      Sepals, petals and stamens hypogynous . . . *Resedaceae*
      Sepals, petals and stamens perigynous :
        Leaves covered with viscid gland-tipped hairs . *Droseraceae*
        Leaves not as above. . . . . *Saxifragaceae*
    Stamens 6, connate into two bundles . . . *Fumariaceae*
Flowers zygomorphic (irregular) :
  Stamens 4 or 6, opposite the petals, more or less united into 2
    bundles; inflorescence often leaf-opposed . . *Fumariaceae*
  Stamens with at least one row alternate with the petals :
    Placentas more than 1 :
      Anther with produced connective; leaves stipulate . *Violaceae*
      Anther connective not produced; no stipules . . *Resedaceae*
    Placenta 1; connective not produced; corolla consisting of
      standard, wings and keel . . . . . *Papilionaceae*
Leaves opposite (never all radical) :
Stamens more than double the number of the petals. . . *Cistaceae*
Stamens the same number or double the number of the petals :
  Stamens and petals hypogynous . . . . . . *Frankeniaceae*
  Stamens and petals perigynous . . . . . . *Crassulaceae*

Group 3.

Perfect stamens the same number as the petals and opposite to them :
  Calyx imbricate; no disk :
    Petals biglandular at the base; shrub with prickly leaves and thorny
      branches; sepals 3 or more. . . . . . . *Berberidaceae*
    Petals not glandular at the base; sepals 2 . . . *Portulacaceae*
  Calyx valvate; disk present; shrubs . . . . . . *Rhamnaceae*
Perfect stamens the same number as the petals and alternate with
  them, or more numerous or rarely fewer :

Flowers zygomorphic (irregular) :
  Lower sepals not spurred :
    Stamens 8, united into two bundles . . . .   *Polygalaceae*
    Stamens 3, free from each other . . . . .   *Portulacaceae*
  Lower sepal spurred ; stamens 5 . . . . . .   *Balsaminaceae*
Flowers actinomorphic :
  Stamens united into more than one bundle :
  Leaves alternate or radical :
    Sepals valvate . . . .   *Tiliaceae*
    Sepals imbricate . . . .   *Geraniaceae*
  Leaves opposite, often gland-dotted . . . .   *Hyperiacceae*
  Stamens free or not in separate bundles, sometimes in 1 bundle
    (monadelphous) :
  Leaves opposite (not all radical) :
    Trees, shrubs or small woody shrublets :
      Trees with lobed leaves . . . .   *Aceraceae*
      Shrubs with undivided leaves . . . . .   *Celastraceae*
      Shrublets with small ericoid leaves . . . .   *Frankeniaceae*
    Herbs :
      Ovary incompletely septate, with free central or basal placenta-
        tion :
      Ovary with several ovules ; styles more than 1   *Caryophyllaceae*
      Ovary with 1 ovule ; styles or stigmas 2–3 .   *Illecebraceae*
      Ovary with several ovules ; style 1 . . . .   *Lythraceae*
      Ovary completely septate :
      Leaves stipulate :
        Stipules paired :
        Minute aquatic or marsh annuals with small entire leaves
                                              Elatinaceae
        Herbs with much divided or compound leaves .   *Geraniaceae*
        Stipules solitary, sometimes minute ; stamens with small teeth
          between them ; petals twisted in bud . . . .   *Linaceae*
      Leaves not stipulate :
        Petals and stamens hypogynous . . . . . .   *Linaceae*
        Petals and stamens perigynous :
          Style single . . . .   *Lythraceae*
          Styles 2 or more . . . .   *Saxifragaceae*
  Leaves alternate or all radical :
    Stamens more than twice as many as the sepals or petals :
    Sepals valvate in bud :
      Anthers 2-locular ; stamens not monadelphous :
        Flower hypogynous ; trees . . . .   *Tiliaceae*
        Flower perigynous ; herbs . . . . . .   *Lythraceae*
      Anthers 1-locular ; stamens monadelphous . .   *Malvaceae*
    Sepals imbricate :
      Petals and stamens perigynous ; seeds without endosperm
                                       Rosaceae
      Petals and stamens more or less hypogynous :
        Carpels not sunk in the torus ; not aquatic .   *Ranunculaceae*

Carpels sunk in the torus; aquatic . . . *Nymphaeaceae*
Stamens twice as many as the petals or fewer than twice as many :
Anthers opening by transverse slits . . . . *Monotropaceae*
Anthers opening by apical pores :
Flowers zygomorphic (irregular). . . . . *Polygalaceae*
Flowers actinomorphic (regular) . . . . . *Pyrolaceae*
Anthers opening by slits lengthwise :
Shrubs or trees :
Leaves stipulate . . . . *Rosaceae*
Leaves not stipulate :
Small shrublets with small ericoid leaves . . *Empetraceae*
Shrubs or trees with broad prickly leaves . . *Aquifoliaceae*
Herbs :
Leaves stipulate :
Sepals, petals and stamens more or less perigynous. *Rosaceae*
Sepals, petals and stamens hypogynous :
Fruit dehiscent :
Fruits with a central axis; leaves divided . *Geraniaceae*
Fruits without a central axis; leaves entire . . *Linaceae*
Fruit nut-like and indehiscent . . . . . *Illecebraceae*
Leaves not stipulate :
Flower hypogynous :
Leaves simple . . . . *Linaceae*
Leaves digitately 3-foliolate . . . . . . *Oxalidaceae*
Flower perigynous . . . . *Saxifragaceae*

Group 4.

Aquatic herbs with usually floating leaves and handsome flowers;
water lilies . . . . *Nymphaeaceae*
Not aquatic :
Shrubs with alternate palmately lobed and nerved leaves; no stipules;
flowers racemose or solitary . . . . . . *Grossulariaceae*
Herbs :
Flowers hermaphrodite; not climbers :
Sepals and petals imbricate . . . . . . *Saxifragaceae*
Sepals valvate; petals contorted . . . . . *Onagraceae*
Flowers unisexual; herbaceous climbers . . . *Cucurbitaceae*

Group 5.

Leaves opposite or whorled; stipules absent :
Not parasitic :
Shrubs with bractless cymes or small herbs with a head of flowers
surrounded by white bracts; leaves entire . . . *Cornaceae*
Herbs with toothed leaves; style simple or divided at the top
Onagraceae
Aquatic herbs with very small flowers; styles or stigmas separate
Halorragaceae
Parasitic on trees; small shrubs; berries white; stamens 4, opposite
the petals . . . . *Loranthaceae*

Leaves alternate or all radical :
  Flowers umbellate :
    Herbs with usually compound umbels ; leaves usually much divided
                                                        Umbelliferae
    Shrubs or climbers with simple umbels; leaves broad and at most
      shortly lobed . . . .   *Araliaceae*
  Flowers not umbellate :
    Stamens numerous :
      Aquatic and with floating leaves ; petals numerous *Nymphaeaceae*
      Not aquatic ; petals not numerous . . . . . .   *Rosaceae*
    Stamens definite in number :
      Trees or shrubs . . . .   *Rosaceae*
      Herbs :
        Ovules more than one in each loculus. . . . . *Onagraceae*
        Ovules solitary in each loculus :
          Terrestrial . . . .   *Rosaceae*
          Aquatics with very small flowers . . . . *Halorrhagaceae*

Group 6.

Stamens free from the corolla-tube :
  Stamens free among themselves . . . . . .   *Tamaricaceae*
  Stamens united into bundles :
    Stamens, more than 6, united into 2 unequal bundles *Papilionaceae*
    Stamens 6, united into 2 equal bundles . . . .   *Fumariaceae*
Stamens inserted on the corolla-tube :
  Stamens double the number of the corolla–lobes or petals
                                                        Polygalaceae
  Stamens the same number as the corolla-lobes :
    Leaves opposite ; corolla-lobes imbricate or contorted
                                                        Gentianaceae
    Leaves alternate or radical ; corolla-lobes valvate . *Menyanthaceae*
  Stamens fewer than the corolla-lobes ; parasites on the roots of other
    plants . . . .   *Orobanchaceae*

Group 7.

Stamens the same number as and opposite to the corolla-lobes
                                                        Primulaceae
Stamens the same number as and alternate with the corolla-lobes or
  more numerous or fewer :
  Stamens as many as or more than the corolla-lobes (to p. 356) :
    Flowers zygomorphic (irregular) :
      Ovary deeply 4-lobed ; style gynobasic :
        Leaves alternate or radical, stem not quadrangular *Boraginaceae*
        Leaves opposite ; stem quadrangular . . . . .   *Labiatae*
      Ovary not 4-lobed ; style not gynobasic :
        Lower sepal elongated into a tubular spur ; ovary 5-locular
                                                        Balsaminaceae
        Lower sepal not spurred ; ovary usually 2-locular :
          Ovules numerous . . . .   *Scrophulariaceae*

Ovules few :
  Anthers opening by slits lengthwise . . .   *Verbenaceae*
  Anthers opening by a terminal pore . . .   *Polygalaceae*
Flowers actinomorphic (regular) :
  Leaves opposite or verticillate (not all radical) :
    Anthers opening by terminal pores . . . .   *Ericaceae*
    Anthers opening by slits lengthwise :
      Ovary deeply vertically lobed :
        Leaves alternate ; stem not quadrangular . .   *Boraginaceae*
        Leaves opposite ; stem quadrangular . . . . *Labiatae*
      Ovary not lobed :
        Corolla dry and scarious . . . . . . *Plantaginaceae*
        Corolla not dry or scarious :
          Style with one capitate stigma :
            Ovules several in each loculus of the ovary :
              Corolla-lobes contorted . . . . . . *Apocynaceae*
              Corolla-lobes imbricate . . . . *Scrophulariaceae*
              Ovules solitary in each loculus . . . . *Verbenaceae*
          Style with more than one separate stigmas :
            Style gynobasic . . . . *Boraginaceae*
            Style not gynobasic . . . . . . *Gentianaceae*
  Leaves alternate or radical or reduced to scales :
    Not parasitic ; leaves normally developed and more or less green :
      Stamens free from the corolla :
        Woody plants ; anthers opening by pores . . .   *Ericaceae*
        Herbs ; anthers opening by slits lengthwise . *Plantaginaceae*
      Stamens inserted on the corolla tube :
        Style gynobasic . . . . *Boraginaceae*
        Style not gynobasic :
          Corolla valvate or plaited in bud :
            Ovary with not more than 2 ovules in each loculus
                            Convolvulaceae
            Ovary with more than 2 ovules in each loculus *Solanaceae*
          Corolla imbricate or contorted in bud :
            Corolla contorted ; leaves pinnate . . . *Polemoniaceae*
            Corolla imbricate :
              Flowers in dense or elongated spikes ; herbs with a rosette
                of radical leaves :
                Corolla scarious . . . . *Plantaginaceae*
                Corolla not scarious . . . . . . *Scrophulariaceae*
             Flowers not as above, but sometimes in a globose head :
              Herbs :
                Ovary with 1 cell and 1 ovule . . . *Plumbaginaceae*
                Ovary with more than 1 cell and more than 1 ovule in each
                            Solanaceae
              Shrubs or trees with leathery sharply toothed leaves, small
                white flowers, and red berries . . . *Aquifoliaceae*
    Parasitic plants ; leaves reduced to scales :
      Ovules numerous in each loculus ; not twining . *Monotropaceae*

Ovules 1–2 in each loculus; twining plants with thread-like
stems . . . . *Convolvulaceae*
Stamens fewer than the corolla-lobes; leaves mostly opposite :
Ovary 1-locular with free basal placentation . *Lentibulariaceae*
Ovary 1 locular with free central placentation . . *Portulacaceae*
Ovary with axile placentation (with more than 1 loculus) :
Herbs :
Ovules numerous in each loculus; sometimes semi-parasites
Scrophulariaceae
Ovules solitary in each loculus :
Ovary not lobed, with terminal style . . . *Verbenaceae*
Ovary deeply 4-lobed, with gynobasic style . . . . *Labiatae*
Shrubs or trees; stamens 2 . . . . *Oleaceae*

Group 8.

Flowers unisexual; herbaceous climbers with tendrils . *Cucurbitaceae*

Group 9.

Anthers not united around the style :
Leaves alternate or radical :
Anthers straight (not flexuous) :
Anthers opening by slits lengthwise :
Stamens opposite the corolla-lobes . . . . . *Primulaceae*
Stamens alternate with the corolla-lobes :
Ovary more than 1-locular, with several ovules in each loculus
Campanulaceae
Ovary 1-locular, with a single pendulous ovule . *Valerianaceae*
Anthers opening by terminal pores . . . . . *Vacciniaceae*
Anthers flexuous . . . . *Cucurbitaceae*
Leaves opposite or whorled (apparently) :
Leaves stipulate, sometimes the stipules leafy and forming a whorl
with the leaves :
Leaves simple . . . . *Rubiaceae*
Leaves pinnate . . . . *Caprifoliaceae*
Leaves not stipulate:
Shrubs, climbers or trailers . . . . . . *Caprifoliaceae*
Herbs :
Flowers or flower-heads without an involucre of bracts :
Ovary more than 1-locular :
Ovules more than 1 in each loculus . . . . *Campanulaceae*
Ovule 1 in each loculus . . . . *Adoxaceae*
Ovary 1-locular, with 1 pendulous ovule . . . *Valerianaceae*
Flowers in heads surrounded by an involucre of bracts *Dipsacaceae*
Anthers united into a tube around the style :
Flowers not in heads and not surrounded by an involucre
Lobeliaceae
Flowers in heads surrounded by an involucre of bracts; flowers all
tubular or the rays ligulate or all ligulate :
Anthers united their full length; ovary with 1 ovule . *Compositae*

Anthers united only at the base; ovary with several ovules
Campanulaceae

Group 10.

Trees, shrubs or subherbaceous; flowers unisexual, in catkins; willows and poplars . . . . *Salicaceae*

Group 11.

Flowers enclosed in an involucre (cyathium) composed of united bracts with variously shaped glands on the margin (see Fig. 44); male composed of 1 stamen, surrounding the female composed of one usually stalked ovary; juice milky . . . . . *Euphorbiaceae*
Flowers not arranged as above :
Leaves opposite or verticillate (not all radical) :
Leaves stipulate :
Ovary with free central placentation . . . *Caryophyllaceae*
Ovary with axile, basal or apical placentation :
Flowers bisexual, very small . . . . . . *Illecebraceae*
Flowers unisexual :
Twining habit; embryo spirally coiled . . . *Cannabinaceae*
Not twining; embryo not coiled :
Ovary with only 1 ovule . . . . *Urticaceae*
Ovary with more than 1 ovule . . . . . *Euphorbiaceae*
Leaves not stipulate :
Ovary 1-locular :
Stamens the same number as the sepals and alternate with them
Primulaceae
Stamens if the same number as the sepals then opposite to them
Caryophyllaceae
Stamens 10–20, crowded on a flat torus; leaves verticillate; aquatic . . . . *Ceratophyllaceae*
Ovary 2- or more-locular :
Leaves pinnate; trees; stamens 2. . . . . . *Oleaceae*
Leaves not pinnate; stamens more than 2 :
Ovules 2 or more in each loculus of the ovary :
Flowers bisexual; herbs . . . . *Lythraceae*
Flowers unisexual; hard wooded shrubs with leathery leaves
Buxaceae
Ovule solitary; herbs :
Flowers bisexual . . . . *Chenopodiaceae*
Flowers unisexual . . . . *Callitrichaceae*
Leaves alternate or all radical :
Leaves stipulate :
Ovary 2- or more-locular :
Trees :
Flowers in catkins . . . . *Betulaceae*
Flowers in clusters . . . . *Ulmaceae*
Herbs with often milky juice . . . . . . *Euphorbiaceae*
Ovary 1-locular :

Flowers axillary, solitary or in small cymes; stamens often solitary :
Carpels 2 or more; ovule pendulous . . . . *Zannichelliaceae*
Carpel solitary; ovule erect . . . . *Najadaceae*
Marine or salt marsh plants :
Flowers spicate :
Flowers hermaphrodite . . . . *Ruppiaceae*
Flowers monoecious or dioecious, arranged on one side of a flattened
axis . . . . *Zosteraceae*
Flowers axillary or cymose . . . . . . *Zannichelliaceae*

Group 2.

Branches modified into cladodes and bearing the flowers on their
surface; true leaves reduced to scales . . . . . *Ruscaceae*
Small herbs with spike-like racemes of small flowers *Juncaginaceae*
Perennial aquatic or marsh plants with tufted linear leaves; flowers in
heads . . . . *Eriocaulaceae*

Group 3.

Flowers (or flower) arranged in a scapose umbel subtended by more or
less membranous spathaceous bracts or bract; rootstock a bulb;
leaves radical, linear . . . . *Amaryllidaceae*
Flowers and bracts not as above :
Flowers arranged in a spadix subtended by or enclosed in a spathe,
small and inconspicuous and often unisexual . . . . *Araceae*
Flowers not arranged in a spadix and without a spathe :
Branches modified and leaf-like (cladodes) and bearing flowers on
their surface, the true leaves reduced to scales; woody plants;
fruit a berry . . . . *Ruscaceae*
Branches not as above :
Leaves alternate or all radical :
Ovary composed of 6 carpels; flowers ebracteate *Juncaginaceae*
Ovary composed of 3 carpels; flowers bracteate . . . *Liliaceae*
Leaves in a whorl of 4 subtending a single terminal flower
Trilliaceae

Group 4.

Inflorescence subtended by a spathaceous bract :
Terrestrial plants with precocious spikes of flowers, the leaves develop-
ing later . . . . *Araceae*
Aquatic plants; plant body minute, not differentiated into stem and
leaves; flowers very minute . . . . *Lemnaceae*
Tall herbaceous aquatic plants :
Flowers in globose clusters . . . . *Sparganiaceae*
Flowers in dense cylindric spikes . . . . . . *Typhaceae*
Inflorescence not subtended by a spathaceous bract . . *Juncaceae*

Group 5.

Stems mostly solid and triquetrous; leaves usually with closed sheaths; flowers in the axil of a single bract and collected into spikelets, the latter variously arranged . . . . . *Cyperaceae*

Stems mostly with hollow internodes, usually terete; leaves usually with open sheaths; flowers enclosed in a bract and bracteole (lemma and palea), arranged in spikelets . . . . . . *Gramineae*

Group 6.

Stamens 3 or more; flowers actinomorphic :

Aquatics; ovules inserted on the walls of the ovary or on the intrusive placentas . . . . *Hydrocharitaceae*

Terrestrial plants; ovules inserted at the inner angles of the loculi of the ovary . . . . *Iridaceae*

Stamens 2 or 1; ovary spirally twisted; flowers zygomorphic
Orchidaceae

Group 7.

Ovules spread all over the inner walls of the carpels or on the intrusive septa . . . . *Hydrocharitaceae*

Ovules borne on placentas at the inner angles of the loculi or at the base or apex of the ovary :

Inflorescence scapose, umbellate, subtended by an involucre of one or more spathaceous bracts, sometimes reduced to one flower; stamens 6 . . . . *Amaryllidaceae*

Inflorescence not as above :

Stamens 6; climbers; flowers unisexual, small, in racemes
Dioscoreaceae

Stamens 3; herbs; flowers hermaphrodite, showy . . *Iridaceae*

Stamen 1: ovary spirally twisted . . . . . . *Orchidaceae*

GLOSSARY

abaxial : away from the axis.

abscission layer : a layer of separation causing an organ to fall off.

achene : a small, dry seed-like fruit.

actinomorphic : flowers capable of division into similar halves in two or more planes.

adaxial : towards or against the axis.

adhesion : union of dissimilar parts.

adnate : attached the whole length to another organ.

aestivation : arrangement of parts of flower in the bud (sepals, petals).

aggregate : collected together.

alae : wing petals of pea family.

Algae : chlorophyll-containing Thallophytes, usually in marine or fresh water.

alternate : the reverse of opposite.

anatomy : internal structure.

anemophilous : borne by the wind.

aneuploid : having an odd multiple of basic number of chromosomes.

androecium : collective name for stamens.

angiosperm : plants with ovules enclosed in an ovary.

annual : lasting one year.

anterior : in front.

anther : portion of stamen bearing the pollen.

anticous : in front.

apetalous : without petals.

apocarpous : carpels free from one another.

apomictic : asexually reproduced fertile seed.

aquatic : living in water.

arboreal : tree-like.

aril : outgrowth (sometimes brightly coloured) from seed stalk.

aristate : awned.

articulated : jointed.

austral : southern.

awn : bristle-like appendage.

awned : provided with a bristle-like appendage.

axile : on the central axis.

baccate : berry-like.

berry : fleshy fruit with seeds immersed in the pulp.

bicarpellate : two carpels.

bicellular : two-celled.

bicollateral : applied to a vascular bundle with two groups of phloem lying on opposite sides of the xylem.

bifid : shortly two-lobed.

bilabiate : two-lipped.

bilobed : two-lobed.

bisexual : two sexes.

bract : modified (usually small) leaf at the base of the flower-stalk; sometimes collected to form an involucre as in *Compositae*.

362

bracteole : small bract on the flower-stalk or below the calyx.
bulb : modified bud (usually underground).

calcareous : chalk-like or of the substance of chalk.
callus : thickened part.
Calyciferae : calyx bearers.
calyx : outermost, usually green, floral envelope.
cambium : zone of meristimatic tissue giving rise to secondary thickening
of stem and root.
campanulate : bell-shaped.
capitulum : head of flowers.
capsule : dry fruit which opens.
carina : keel petals of pea family.
carpel : ovule- and seed-bearing part of flower.
caryopsis : one-seeded fruit with pericarp united to seed.
catkin : slender pendulous inflorescence (as in nut-tree).
caudicle : cartilaginous strap connecting certain pollen-masses to the
stigma, as in some orchids.
chasmogamous : flowers which open normally.
chlorophyll : green colouring matter of plants.
ciliate : fringed with hairs.
circinnate : coiled like a watch-spring.
cleistogamous : flowers which are fertilised without opening.
cleistogene : cleistogamous spikelet in axil of leaf-sheath.
climax : complete.
cohesion : union of similar parts.
cohort : group of families.
collateral : xylem and phloem side by side.
column : united stamens and styles into a central body, as in orchids.
compound : formed of many similar parts.
concrescent : growing together.
conduplicate : folded together lengthwise.
cone : collection of scales bearing naked seeds.
connate : united similar parts.
connective : part of stamen between anther-lobes.
connivent : clinging or converging together.
contorted : twisted.
convolute : rolled around.
corm : bulb-like fleshy base of stem.
corolla : collective name for the petals.
Corolliferae : corolla bearers.
corona : crown-like production (as in Daffodil).
corymb : more or less flat-topped collection of flowers.
corymbose : arranged in a corymb.
cotyledon : seed-leaf.
culm : the stem or " straw " of grasses.
cuticle : outer skin.
cyathium : cupular involucre of *Euphorbia*.
cyme : an inflorescence repeatedly divided with usually the oldest flower
in the middle of each fork.
cymose : see cyme.
cystoliths : mineral concretions as found in the nettle family.
cytology : life history, nuclear division and development of the cell.

declinate : bent or curved downwards.
dehiscent : opening naturally.

dentate : toothed.
diadelphous : in two bundles.
diandrous : with two stamens.
dicotyledon : two seed-leaves.
didymous : divided into two lobes; in pairs.
digitate : arranged like fingers.
dioecious : unisexual flowers on different plants.
diphyletic : branched into two phyla.
diploid : organism having two genomes.
diplostemonous : stamens in two whorls.
disk : fleshy portion of the floral axis, often secreting nectar.
divaricate : spreading.
drupaceous : stone-like.
drupe : stone fruit such as a plum.

ecology : study of plant life mainly in relation to its environment.
embryo : rudimentary plant formed in the seed.
endosperm : reserve food material in the seed.
entire : neither toothed nor divided.
entomophilous : borne by insects.
epicalyx : one or more bracteoles subtending the real calyx.
epidermis : outer skin.
epigynous : above the ovary.
epiphyte : living in the air (either on trees or dry rocks).
exotic : from abroad.
exserted : protruded.
exstipulate : without stipules.

filament : stalk of stamen.
filiform : thread-like.
floral axis : central part of flower supporting its various parts.
floret : little flower such as that of a grass or composite.
follicle : free carpel which opens automatically.
foveolate : pitted.
free basal : arrangement of ovules on an axile placenta not reaching to the top of a one-locular ovary.
free central : arrangement of ovules on an axile placenta in a one-locular ovary.
frutescent : shrubby.

geniculate : bent like a knee.
genome : minimum group or set of chromosomes derived from a zygote or gamete.
glume : chaffy outer scales of inflorescence of grasses and sedges.
Glumiflorae : flowers with small dry perianth or glumes.
glycoside : condensation product of a sugar and other substances.
gregarious : growing in company or association.
Gymnosperm : plant with naked ovules and seeds.
gynobasic : from base of ovary.
gynoecium : collective name for carpels or pistil.
gynostegium : covering of a gynoecium.

Herbaceae : group of fundamentally herbaceous plants.
herbaceous : not woody.
hermaphrodite : stamens and pistil in same flower.
heterogeneous : mixed.

hexaploid : six times basic number of chromosomes.
hilum : scar of attachment of seed.
homogeneous : uniform.
hyaline : thin and translucent.
hydathode : water-pore.
hydrophilous : pollinated by water agency.
hypogynous : below the ovary.
hypothetical : based on a theory; conjectural.

idioblast : isolated cell differing in structure from its neighbours.
imbricate : overlapping, with one part wholly outside.
imparipinnate : pinnate with an odd terminal leaflet.
incumbent : resting or leaning on.
indehiscent : not opening.
indigenous : original or native in a country (not introduced).
indumentum : hairy covering.
induplicate-valvate : margins bent inwards and not overlapping.
indurated : hardened.
inferior : below (such as ovary below calyx).
inflorescence : collection of flowers.
interfascicular : between the vascular bundles.
internode : between the nodes.
interpetiolar : between the petioles.
intrapetiolar : within the petioles.
intraxylary : within the xylem.
inulin : a body like starch as found in some *Compositae*.
involucel : a little involucre.
involucre : a ring or series of bracts surrounding one or more flowers.

labellum : lip (of orchid).
laevorotatory : rotating the plane of polarisation of polarised light to the
    left.
latex : milk-like juice.
laticiferous : latex bearing.
legume : dehiscent fruit of *Papilionaceae*.
lemma : outer bract of grass floret.
lepidote : scaly.
ligneous : woody.
Lignosae : group of fundamentally woody plants.
ligulate : strap-shaped.
ligule : thin projection from the top of the leaf-sheath of grasses; strap-
    shaped limb of ray flower of *Compositae*.
limb : expanded part of corolla or calyx.
linear : long and narrow.
locular : chambered.
loculus : chamber of ovary, fruit or anther.
lodicule : a scale-like perianth-segment.
lomentum : a fruit contracted or divided between the seeds.
Lusitanian : Portuguese and/or Spanish.

medullary : relating to the pith.
mericarp : portion of fruit splitting away as a single perfect fruit.
meristematic : capable of dividing.
merous : denotes parts or numbers.
mesophyll : green tissue of leaf.
micropyle : aperture in skin of seed.

mobile : capable of movement.
monadelphous : in one bundle.
monandrous : with one stamen.
monocotyledon : plant with one seed-leaf.
monoecious : flowers of each sex on the same plant.
monotypic : of one kind.
morphology : study of form and shape.
mucilage : gelatinous vegetable secretion.
mucilaginous : slimy.
multiseriate : many-rowed.
myrosin : glucoside found in the seeds of many *Cruciferae*.

node : joint or " knot " in stems and branches.
nutlet : little nut.

ochrea : a large sheathing stipule.
opposite : inserted in pairs at same level, as leaves on a shoot.
ovary : basal part of pistil containing the ovule or ovules.

palaeobotany : study of plants in a fossil state.
palea : inner bract of grass floret.
palisade : mesophyll cells arranged like a paling.
palmate : divided like the palm of the hand.
panicle : branched raceme or spike.
paniculate : flowers arranged in a branched raceme or spike.
papillae : small projections from a plant cell.
pappus : modified calyx (as in *Compositae*).
parasite : an organism which derives its nourishment from another.
parenchyma : spony, porous tissue (pith).
parietal (placentation) : on the walls.
paripinnate : pinnate without an odd terminal leaflet.
pedicel : stalk of an individual flower.
pedunculate : stalked inflorescence.
peltate : attached in the middle (like a mushroom).
pentamerous : consisting of five parts.
perennial : lasting more than two years.
perianth : floral envelope.
pericarp : wall of fruit.
perigynous : around the ovary.
petaloid : petal-like.
phloem : cortical tissue.
phylogeny : ancestral history deduced from development.
phylum : a major line of descent.
phytogeographical : pertaining to the distribution of plants (plant geography).
pinnate : completely divided laterally like a feather.
pinnatipartite : deeply divided like a feather.
placenta : organ bearing the ovules in an ovary or seeds in a fruit.
plicate : folded.
plumose : like a feather.
pollinia : pollen-masses.
polygamo-dioecious : with bisexual flowers and either male or female on separate plants.
polygamous : with bisexual and unisexual flowers on the same plants.
polymorphic : of several kinds or shapes.
polyploid : reduplication of chromosome number, as triploid, tetraploid, etc.

pome : inferior fruit of several loculi (such as an Apple).
posterior : behind.
precocious : flowers before the leaves.
proangiosperm : ancient type of flowering plant.
proliferation : bearing progeny as offshoots.
prosenchyma : lengthened cells with tapering ends which overlap.
protandrous : anthers maturing before the stigma.
protogyny : pistil receptive before pollen is ripe or released.
pseudobulb : thickened and often bulb-like node of some orchids.
Pteridosperm : seed fern.
pulvinus : swollen base of leaf or leaflet.
punctiform : in the form of a dot or point.
pungent : sharp-pointed.
putative : considered to be of hybrid origin but not proven.

quadrangular : with four angles or sides.

raceme : unbranched inflorescence with individual flowers stalked.
racemose : arranged in an unbranched inflorescence with individual
flowers stalked.
radical : from the root.
ranalean : pertaining to the family *Ranunculaceae.*
raphides : needle-shaped crystals in the cells of plants.
receptacle : same as floral axis.
reflexed : bent back.
Reihe : German term for cohort.
resupinate : upside down.
rhachilla : axis of grass spikelet.
rhachis : axis of compound leaf or of an inflorescence.
rhizome : rootstock, often underground.
rostellum : narrow extention of upper edge of stigma of certain orchids.
rotate : wheel-shaped.
ruminate : intrusive.

saccate : bag-shaped.
saprophyte : plant which lives on dead organic matter.
scalariform : ladder-like.
schizogenous : development by splitting.
secund : to one side.
semilunar : half-moon-shaped.
septum : division of a chamber (ovary or fruit).
serodiagnostic : a testing by injection into animals of plant extract.
sessile : not stalked.
setae : bristles.
sieve tubes : elongated cells in the phloem in which elaborated foods are
transported.
silicified : impregnated with silica.
simple : consisting of one part.
spathaceous : spathe-like or spathe-bearing.
spathulate : spoon-shaped.
Spermaphyta : seed plants.
Spermatozoid : a male ciliated mobile gamete.
spicate : like racemose but with flowers sessile.
spiciform : like a spike.
spike : stiff imbranched inflorescence with the flowers not stalked.
spikelet : little spike.

sporophyll : leaf which bears spores.
staminode : modified or barren stamen.
standard : vexillum, back petal of leguminous plant.
stellate : star-like.
stigma : part of ovary or style which receives the pollen.
stipule : small appendage at base of leaf or its stalk.
stomata : breathing pores.
strobilus : a cone.
style : portion of pistil between ovary and stigma.
sub : partially.
subphylum : a minor line of descent.
subsidiary : additional or supplementary.
subulate : awl-shaped.
succulent : fleshy.
superior : above (such as ovary above calyx).
sympetalous : united or partly united petals.
syncarpous : united or partly united carpels.

taxonomist : one who deals with classification.
taxonomy : classification.
tendril : a thread-like climbing organ.
terrestrial : living on land.
tetrad : a set or group of four cells.
tetradynamous : having four long and two short stamens.
tetramerous : consisting of four parts.
torus : central axis of a flower.
tracheids : elongated pitted cells in the xylem which transport food.
translucent : more or less transparent.
triandrous : with three stamens.
trifoliolate : three leafleted.
trimerous : three-parted.
triquetrous : three-sided.
truncate : abruptly cut off.

umbel : inflorescence branched like the ribs of an umbrella.
umbellate : umbrella-like arrangement of flower stalks.
unicellular : one-celled.
unifoliolate : one-leafleted.
uniseriate : one-rowed.
unisexual : one sex.
utricle : structure enclosing the fruit in some *Cyperaceae*.

valvate : not overlapping.
valve : opening of fruit or anther.
vascular bundles : strands of specialized tissue.
vernation : arrangement of shoots or leaves in the bud.
versatile : turning freely on its support (like some anthers).
vexillum : standard (adaxial) petal of pea family.
vittae : aromatic oil tubes in the fruits of many *Umbelliferae*.

whorl : a circle.
whorled : arranged in a circle.

xerophilous : growing in arid places.
xylem : wood.

zygomorphic : flowers capable of division into similar halves in only one
    plane.

INDEX to ORDERS, FAMILIES, and GENERA

(Family names and principal page position of family and genus in blacker type.)

369